Elementary
Solid State
Physics:

a short course

Elementary Solid State Physics:

a short course

CHARLES KITTEL, Professor of Physics
University of California, Berkeley, California

John Wiley & Sons, Inc., New York · London

LIBRARY OF CONGRESS CATALOG CARD NUMBER: 62-17462

PRINTED IN THE UNITED STATES OF AMERICA

8/63

Preface

This book is a short and elementary version of the text *Introduction to Solid State Physics*. The present version is written for use in one semester undergraduate courses by students of engineering, chemistry, and physics. It draws freely on the background provided by the usual semester course in atomic physics. I have sought to develop here in a simple form an account of the basic physical processes which occur in solids, with emphasis on semiconductors and on metals. This is not a book on solid state devices, but it is concerned with explaining in fundamental terms how such applications arise.

A note to engineering students: In some areas of solid state physics one can obtain fairly accurate quantitative results or engineering approximations. In other areas one can only make order of magnitude estimates; although lacking in precision, these are valuable as a guide to research and development, and I have tried constantly in the text to encourage facility in this type of thinking.

Both MKS and gaussian cgs units are used in parallel at appropriate points, as in the treatment of the interaction of electromagnetic fields with solids.

The names of the numerous persons who have assisted me with advice, photographs, and tabulations are given in the preface to the longer edition; Dr. Bernard Cooper kindly read the manuscript of the present version; Mrs. Eleanor Thornhill and Miss Kaye Wells were of constant assistance.

C. KITTEL

Berkeley, California
June, 1962

Contents

1. CRYSTAL STRUCTURE   1

    Miller indices. Simple crystal structures. Hexagonal close-packed structure (hcp). Diamond structure. Zinc blende structure. Sodium chloride structure. Cesium chloride structure. Calcium fluoride (fluorite) structure. Collections of crystal structure data. Empirical classification of crystal binding. Ionic crystals. Covalent crystals. Metal crystals. Molecular crystals. Hydrogen-bonded crystals. Ionic radii.

2. DIFFRACTION OF WAVES BY CRYSTALS   29

    Bragg's law. Laue diffraction equations. Interference conditions and the reciprocal lattice. Atomic scattering factor. Geometrical structure factor. Experimental x-ray diffraction methods. Laue method. Rotating-crystal method. Powder method.

3. THERMAL PROPERTIES OF SOLIDS   45

    Harmonic oscillator model—classical mechanics. Einstein model of the lattice heat capacity. Debye model of the lattice heat capacity. Heat capacity of conduction electrons in metals. Phonons. Thermal conductivity of solids. Thermal expansion.

4. DIELECTRIC PROPERTIES   69

    Local electric field. Depolarization field. Lorentz field. Field of dipoles inside cavity. Field in dielectric between condenser plates. Dielectric constant and polarizability. Measurement of dielectric constants. Electronic polarizabilities. Classical theory of electronic polarizability. Ionic polarizabilities. Orientational polarizabilities. Dipole orientation in solids. Dipole relaxation and dielectric losses. Debye relaxation time. Relaxation in solids. Complex dielectric constants and the loss angle. Ferroelectric crystals. Electrets. Classification of ferroelectric crystals. Theory of barium titanate. The polarization catastrophe in ferro-electrics. Local field in the perovskite structure. Ferroelectric domains.

5. FREE ELECTRON MODEL OF METALS   106

Electrical conductivity and Ohm's law. Wiedemann-Franz ratio. Heat capacity of conduction electrons. Paramagnetic suscepti-bility of conduction electrons. Quantum theory of free particles in a box. Fermi-Dirac distribution law. Absolute zero. Quan-tum theory of the heat capacity of the electron gas. Quantum theory of spin paramagnetism. Effect of Fermi-Dirac distribution on the electrical conductivity. Plasma frequency. Transparency of alkali metals in the ultraviolet. Thermionic emission equation.

6. BAND THEORY OF SOLIDS: BRILLOUIN ZONES   143

Brillouin zone in one dimension. Wave functions in a periodic lat-tice. Wave functions for zero wave vector. Effective mass of electrons in crystals. Physical basis of effective masses. Holes: positive charge carriers. Motion of holes. Hall effect. Electrical conductivity of metals. Residual resistance. Brillouin zones. Face-centered cubic lattice. Hexagonal close-packed structure. Band structure of metals. Alkali metals. Noble metals. Diva-lent metals. Trivalent metals. Binary alloys. Hume-Rothery rules for alloy phases. Transition elements. Order-disorder transformation.

7. SEMICONDUCTORS: PHYSICS AND DEVICES   199

Intrinsic conductivity. Mobility in the intrinsic region. Impurity or extrinsic conductivity. Impurity states. Thermal ionization of impurities. Mobility in the presence of impurity atoms. Anal-ysis of experimental results. Lifetime and recombination. Minor-ity carrier transport and hole injection. Cyclotron resonance experiments. Radiation damage in semiconductors. Barrier rectification. p-n junction rectification. Tunnel diodes. Point contact transistors. Junction transistors.

8. MAGNETISM AND MAGNETIC RESONANCE   251

Diamagnetism. Derivation of the Langevin diamagnetism equa-tion. Paramagnetism. Langevin theory of paramagnetism. Cooling by adiabatic demagnetization of a paramagnetic salt. Magnetic resonance. Ferromagnetic resonance absorption. Fer-romagnetism. Temperature dependence of the spontaneous mag-

netization. Spontaneous magnetization at absolute zero. Ferromagnetic domains. Origin of domains. Coercive force and
hysteresis. Reversible permeability. Anisotropy energy. Magnetostriction. The Bloch wall. Domain dimensions. Antiferromagnetism. Two-sublattice model. Antiferromagnetic resonance.
Determination of spin lattices by neutron diffraction. Ferrites.
Spin waves.

9. DISLOCATIONS: STRENGTH OF SOLIDS   305

Shear strength of single crystals. Dislocations. Stress fields of
edge dislocations. Low-angle grain boundaries. Dislocation densities. Dislocation multiplication and slip. Strength of alloys.
Dislocations and crystal growth.

APPENDIX

A. Perturbation of nearly free electrons by a periodic potential.
Three dimensions. B. Tight binding approximation for metallic
electrons. C. Important conversion factors. D. Values of general physical constants.

INDEX   337

General References

CRYSTALLOGRAPHY

F. C. Phillips, *An introduction to crystallography*, Longmans, London, 1946.
M. J. Buerger, *Elementary crystallography*, John Wiley and Sons, New York, 1956.

ATOMIC PHYSICS BACKGROUND

Max Born, *Atomic physics*, Hafner, New York, 5th ed., 1951.
F. K. Richtmyer and E. H. Kennard, *Introduction to modern physics*, McGraw-Hill Book Co., New York, 4th ed., 1947.

ELEMENTARY TEXTS

F. O. Rice and E. Teller, *Structure of matter*, John Wiley and Sons, New York, 1949.
J. C. Slater, *Introduction to chemical physics*, McGraw-Hill Book Co., New York, 1939.
J. C. Slater, *Quantum theory of matter*, McGraw-Hill Book Co., New York, 1951.

GENERAL TEXTS

A. J. Dekker, *Solid state physics*, Prentice-Hall, Englewood Cliffs, New Jersey, 1957.
J. E. Goldman, Ed., *Science of engineering materials*, John Wiley and Sons, New York, 1957.
C. Kittel, *Introduction to solid state physics*, John Wiley and Sons, New York, 1956.
N. F. Mott and H. Jones, *Theory of the properties of metals and alloys*, Clarendon Press, Oxford, 1936; Dover, New York, 1958 (reprint).
F. Seitz, *Modern theory of solids*, McGraw-Hill Book Co., New York, 1940.
F. Seitz and D. Turnbull, *Solid state physics, advances in research and applications*, Academic Press, New York.

A. H. Wilson, *Theory of metals*, Cambridge University Press, Cambridge, 2nd ed., 1953.

R. E. Peierls, *Quantum theory of solids*, Clarendon Press, Oxford, 1955.

G. H. Wannier, *Elements of solid state theory*, University Press, Cambridge, 1959.

Handbuch der Physik, Springer, numerous volumes.

DATA COLLECTIONS AND BIBLIOGRAPHICAL AIDS

Chemical Abstracts (especially the decennial indices).

Gmelins *Handbuch der anorganischen Chemie*.

Landolt-Börnstein *Physikalisch-chemische Tabellen*, J. Springer, Berlin, 5th ed., 1935; 6th ed., 1952.

1 Crystal structure

Crystals are formed from atoms, sometimes in simple and sometimes in complicated ways. It is fairly accurate to think of a few crystals as built up of neutral atoms only weakly deformed by the crystalline binding—crystals of the rare gas atoms are like this. Many crystals may be thought of as built up of ions bearing positive and negative charges: rock salt is composed of Na^+ and Cl^- ions. Crystals of the alkali metals are made up of small positive ion cores immersed in a negatively charged sea of conduction electrons. Some crystals are made up of neutral atoms having slightly overlapping electron clouds forming electron bridges or covalent bands between neighboring atoms; we may think of diamond and silicon in this way. Other crystals consist of neutral molecules bound together in the solid by weak interactions: many crystals of organic molecules are of this type.

The differences among these varieties of crystalline binding forces (Fig. 1.1) are closely connected with differences in the mechanical, electrical, and magnetic properties of crystals. Yet in all crystals the actual interaction which causes the binding is almost entirely the ordinary Coulomb electrostatic interaction between charges—the attraction between the negative charges of the electrons and the positive charges of the nuclei. The differences in the types of crystalline binding thus are not differences in the nature of the interaction, but are qualitative differences in the distribution of electronic charge. The distribution of charge is determined in principle by the theory of quantum mechanics. Although exact solutions of crystalline problems are not attainable, it is often possible to use the theory guided by experiment to obtain helpful insight. One of the questions we should always ask ourselves, and on which we should seek experimental enlightenment when possible, is "Where are the nuclei and the electrons in the solid?" This problem is called the determination of the structure of the solid.

The principal purpose of the first two chapters is to explain the

1

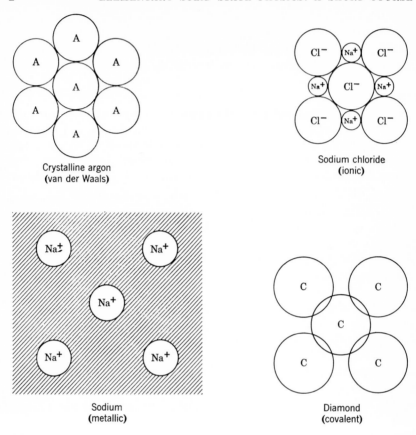

Crystalline argon
(van der Waals)

Sodium chloride
(ionic)

Sodium
(metallic)

Diamond
(covalent)

FIG. 1.1.   Schematic models of several of the principal types of crystalline binding forces.

single most important and direct method for structure determination—x-ray diffraction. In certain problems electron diffraction and neutron diffraction are important. In particle diffraction the de Broglie waves associated with the particles are diffracted by the atoms of the crystal exactly as x-rays are diffracted. Neutron diffraction experiments are particularly informative with magnetic crystals. The scattering cross section of a neutron by a magnetic atom depends on the orientation of the magnetic moment of the atom, so that neutron diffraction experiments can give us the magnetic structure of the crystal.

The characteristic dimensions of the atomic structure of crystals are very small compared to anything we can resolve with our eye or with optical microscopes. Usually we do not expect to resolve a feature which is smaller than some fraction, say $\frac{1}{4}$, of the wavelength of the radiation or illumination with which the feature is viewed; thus with optical instruments 10^{-5} cm is about as small a feature as we can expect to resolve, except in quite special circumstances. The criteria for resolution are discussed in most books on physical optics.

We can easily estimate the order of magnitude of the dimensions of concern in crystals. Consider metallic iron: the density is 7.86 grams per cubic centimeter and the atomic mass is about 55.85 grams per mole. Thus 1 cm^3 of iron contains $7.86/55.85 = 0.14$ mole. The Avogadro number gives the number of atoms in a mole of an element: 6.03×10^{23} atoms per mole. Thus 1 cm^3 of iron contains

$$0.14 \times 6.03 \times 10^{23} = 0.85 \times 10^{23} \text{ atoms/cm}^3.$$

If we associate with each atom a cube of side a and of volume a^3, then

$$0.85 \times 10^{23} a^3 = 1 \text{ cm},$$

so that

$$a^3 = \frac{1}{0.85 \times 10^{23}} \cong 12 \times 10^{-24} \text{ cm}^3,$$

or

$$a \cong 2.3 \times 10^{-8} \text{ cm}.$$

We see that 10^{-8} cm is a good unit of length for interatomic spacing in a crystal. Now 10^{-8} cm or 10^{-10} meter is called the angstrom unit, denoted by A, so our result may be expressed as $a \cong 2.5$ A. In MKS units the density of iron is 7.8×10^{-3} kg/meter^3 and $a \cong 2.5 \times 10^{-10}$ meter.

We are then faced with the problem of looking for interatomic spacings of ~ 1 A with an instrument, the optical microscope, which can resolve down to the order of 1000 A. This will not work. We need much shorter waves. It is not difficult to get a source of electromagnetic radiation having a wavelength of 1 A. The short wavelength limit of the x-rays produced when electrons accelerated by a voltage V strike a target can be found by equating the photon energy

$$(1.1) \quad h\nu = \frac{hc}{\lambda} \cong 6.6 \times 10^{-27} \text{ erg-sec} \frac{3 \times 10^{10} \text{ cm/sec}}{\lambda} \cong$$

$$\frac{2.0 \times 10^{-17}}{\lambda} \text{ erg}$$

to the kinetic energy

$$(1.2) \qquad eV \cong (4.8 \times 10^{-10}) \frac{V}{300} \cong 1.6 \times 10^{-12} V \text{ erg.}$$

Above h is Planck's constant; λ is the wavelength in centimeters; and V is the accelerating voltage in volts.   Thus

$$(1.3) \qquad \lambda = \left(\frac{2 \times 10^{-17}}{1.6 \times 10^{-2}}\right) V^{-1} = \frac{1.2 \times 10^{-5}}{V} \text{ cm;}$$

for $V = 10 \text{ kev} = 10^4$ volts,

$$(1.4) \qquad\qquad\qquad \lambda = 0.12 \text{ A.}$$

This wavelength is sufficiently short for our purpose.

The Language of Crystals.   A body of language has been built up to describe crystal structures.   A person trained in this symbolic language can reconstruct for himself, in whole or in part, a crystal structure from another person's account of it.   We give here a few elementary ideas about the crystallographic language, with reference to the geometry of simple crystal structures.

An ideal crystal is constructed by the infinite regular repetition in space of identical structural units or building blocks.   For the very simplest of the monatomic crystals the building block is a single atom, but in most crystals the building block contains several atoms or molecules, where several may mean a number between 2 and 100,000 or more.

We define an ideal crystal as a body composed of atoms arranged in a lattice such that there exist three fundamental translation vectors **a, b, c**, with the property that the atomic arrangement looks the same in every respect when viewed from any point **r** as when viewed from the point

$$(1.5) \qquad\qquad \mathbf{r'} = \mathbf{r} + n_1\mathbf{a} + n_2\mathbf{b} + n_3\mathbf{c},$$

where n_1, n_2, n_3 are arbitrary integers.   The fundamental translation vectors are *primitive* if any two points **r, r'** from which the atomic arrangement looks the same always satisfy (1.5) with a suitable choice of the integers n_1, n_2, n_3.   We shall consider frequently the primitive translation vectors as defining the *crystal axes* **a, b, c**, although other (nonprimitive) choices of crystal axes will be employed also.

The operation of displacing a crystal parallel to itself by

$$(1.6) \qquad\qquad \mathbf{T} = n_1\mathbf{a} + n_2\mathbf{b} + n_3\mathbf{c}$$

is called a *translation operation*.   The totality of such operations, for all values of the integers n_1, n_2, n_3, is known as the *translation group* of the crystal. The most important descriptive characteristics of crystal structures are the symmetry operations which carry the crystal into itself. The translation operations **T** are not the only symmetry operations which a crystal may have: about various points within a building block we may be able to apply rotation and reflection operations that also carry the crystal into itself. Such operations are called point operations; and there may be still other symmetry operations.

We speak of a crystal lattice. This is a mathematical abstraction. A *lattice* is a parallel, netlike arrangement of points with the special property that the environment about any particular point is in every way the same as about any other point of the lattice. In the very simplest crystal structures there is a single atom associated with each lattice point, and all we have to do here to classify the structure completely is to give the crystal axes **a**, **b**, **c**. To go beyond these happy structures we have to associate with every lattice point a unit assembly, or *basis*, of atoms; every basis must be identical in composition, arrangement, and orientation. The formation of a crystal structure by the addition of a basis to every point of a lattice is shown in Fig. 1.2.

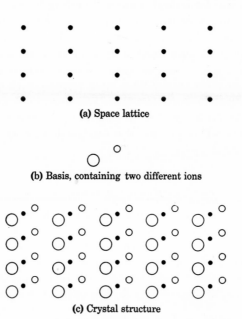

(a) Space lattice

(b) Basis, containing two different ions

(c) Crystal structure

FIG. 1.2.   The crystal structure (c) is formed by the addition of the basis (b) to every lattice point of the space lattice (a).

The parallelepiped defined by primitive axes **a**, **b**, **c** is said to be a *primitive cell*. A primitive cell is a type of *unit cell*. A unit cell is any cell that will cover all space under the action of the crystal translation operations. A primitive cell is a minimum-volume unit cell, and the primitive cell can be chosen such that it contains lattice points only at its corners. The volume V_c of a cell is

$$(1.7) \qquad\qquad V_c = \mathbf{a} \times \mathbf{b} \cdot \mathbf{c},$$

by elementary vector analysis.

Crystal lattices and crystal structures are carried into themselves not only by the operations **T**, but also by various other operations. Typical operations include rotation about an axis through a lattice point. Lattices can be found such that one-, two-, three-, four-, and six-fold rotation axes are permissible, corresponding to rotations by 360°, 180°, 120°, 90°, and 60°. The rotation axes are denoted by the symbols 1, 2, 3, 4, and 6. The axes 2, 3, 4, and 6 are often referred to as diad, triad, tetrad, and hexad axes, respectively. We cannot find a lattice that goes into itself under other rotations, such as by $2\pi/173$ or even by $2\pi/5$. Indeed, it can be proved mathematically that the only allowed rotations are those just given. Other symmetry operations for a lattice having a cubic primitive cell are shown in Fig. 1.3.

The various permissible combinations of point symmetry operations (rotation, reflection, inversion, and rotation followed by inversion) require fourteen different kinds of space lattices, each kind defined by special conditions on the axial ratios and angles. Each set of conditions defines what is called a *Bravais lattice*. The fourteen Bravais lattices are shown in Fig. 1.4. For further details the student should consult specialized works.

TABLE 1.1
CHARACTERISTICS OF CUBIC LATTICES

	Simple	Body-Centered	Face-Centered
Unit cell volume	a^3	a^3	a^3
Lattice points per cell	1	2	4
Lattice points per unit volume	$1/a^3$	$2/a^3$	$4/a^3$
Nearest neighbor distance	a	$3^{1/2}a/2$	$a/2^{1/2}$
Number of nearest neighbors	6	8	12
Second neighbor distance	$2^{1/2}a$	a	a
Number of second neighbors	12	6	6

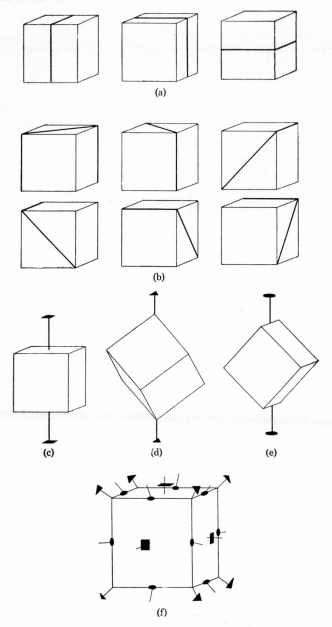

FIG. 1.3. (a) The three planes of symmetry parallel to the faces of a cube. (b) The six diagonal planes of symmetry in a cube. (c) One of the tetrad axes of a cube. (d) One of the triad axes of a cube. (e) One of the diad axes of a cube. (f) The thirteen axes of symmetry shown by a cube. (After Phillips.)

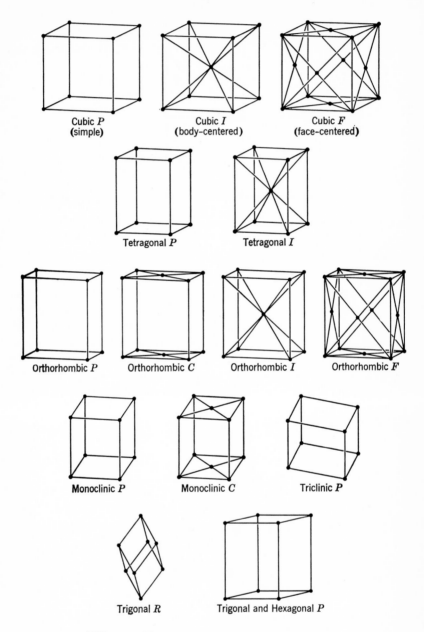

FIG. 1.4. The fourteen Bravais or space lattices.

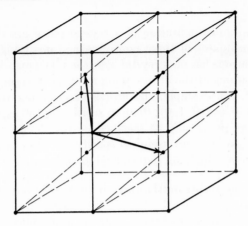

FIG. 1.5.   Primitive translation vectors of the body-centered cubic lattice; the primitive cell is obtained on completing the rhombohedron.

In the cubic system there are three space lattices: the simple cubic P lattice which is primitive; the body-centered I lattice; and the face-centered F lattice.   The characteristics of the three cubic space lattices are summarized in Table 1.1.   The primitive translation vectors of the body-centered cubic (bcc) lattice are shown in Fig. 1.5, and of the face-centered lattice in Fig. 1.6.   The primitive cells contain only one lattice point per cell, whereas the conventional cubic unit cells of Table 1.1 contain two points per cell for the bcc lattice and four points per cell for the fcc lattice.

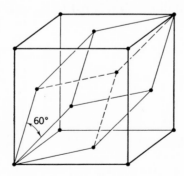

FIG. 1.6.   The rhombohedral primitive cell of the face-centered cubic F lattice.

MILLER INDICES

The position and orientation of a crystal plane are determined by giving the coordinates of three noncolinear atoms lying in the plane. If each of the atoms lies on a crystal axis, the plane may be specified by giving the positions of the atoms along the axes in terms of the lattice constants. If, for example, the atoms determining the plane have coordinates $(4, 0, 0)$; $(0, 1, 0)$; $(0, 0, 2)$ relative to the axis vectors from some origin, the plane may be specified by the three numbers 4, 1, 2.

It turns out to be more useful to specify the orientation of a plane by *Miller indices*, which are determined as follows:

1. Find the intercepts on the three basis axes in terms of the lattice constants.

2. Take the reciprocals of these numbers and reduce to the smallest three integers having the same ratio. The result is enclosed in parentheses: (hkl).

For the plane whose intercepts are 4, 1, 2 the reciprocals are $\frac{1}{4}$, 1 $\frac{1}{2}$, and the Miller indices are (142). If an intercept is at infinity, the corresponding index is zero. The Miller indices of some important planes in a cubic crystal are illustrated by Fig. 1.7.

The indices (hkl) denote a single plane or a set of parallel planes. If a plane cuts an axis on the negative side of the origin, the corresponding index is negative and is indicated by placing a minus sign above the index: $(h\bar{k}l)$. The cube faces of a cubic crystal are (100); (010); (001); $(\bar{1}00)$; $(0\bar{1}0)$; and $(00\bar{1})$. Planes equivalent by symmetry are denoted by curly brackets (braces) around Miller indices; the cube faces are $\{100\}$.

The indices of a direction in a crystal are expressed as the set of the smallest integers which have the same ratios as the components of a vector in the desired direction referred to the axis vectors. The inte-

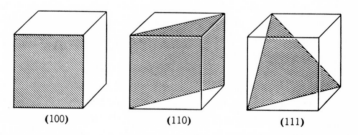

      (100)   **(110)**   **(111)**

FIG. 1.7.   Miller indices of some important planes in a cubic crystal.

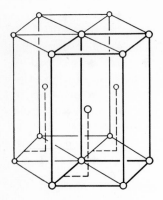

FIG. 1.8. The hexagonal close-packed structure. The atom positions in this structure do not constitute a space lattice. The space lattice is *simple hexagonal* with two atoms $(000; \frac{2}{3} \frac{1}{3} \frac{1}{2})$ associated with each lattice point. (By permission from *Structure of metals*, by C. S. Barrett. Copyright 1943. McGraw-Hill Book Co.)

gers are written between square brackets, $[uvw]$. The x axis is the $[100]$ direction; the $-y$ axis is the $[0\bar{1}0]$ direction. A full set of equivalent directions is denoted this way: $\langle uvw \rangle$. In cubic crystals a direction $[uvw]$ is perpendicular to a plane (uvw) having the same indices, but this is not generally true in other crystal systems.

The positions of points in a unit cell are specified in terms of lattice coordinates, in which each coordinate is a fraction of the axial length, a, b, or c, in the direction of the coordinate, with the origin taken at the corner of a unit cell. Thus the coordinates of the central point of a cell are $\frac{1}{2} \frac{1}{2} \frac{1}{2}$, and the face-center positions are $\frac{1}{2} \frac{1}{2} 0$; $0 \frac{1}{2} \frac{1}{2}$; $\frac{1}{2} 0 \frac{1}{2}$.

SIMPLE CRYSTAL STRUCTURES

We discuss briefly a small number of simple crystal structures of general interest, including the hexagonal close-packed, diamond, cubic zinc sulfide, sodium chloride, cesium chloride, and fluorite structures.

HEXAGONAL CLOSE-PACKED STRUCTURE (hcp)

There are two regular ways of arranging equivalent spheres to minimize the interstitial volume. One way leads to a structure with cubic symmetry and is the face-centered cubic (cubic close-packed) structure; the other has hexagonal symmetry and is called the *hexagonal close-packed structure* (Fig. 1.8). Spheres may be arranged in a single closest-packed layer by placing each sphere in contact with six others. A second similar layer may be packed on top of this by placing each sphere in contact with three spheres of the bottom layer. A third layer can be added in two ways: in the cubic structure the spheres in the third layer are placed over the holes in the first layer not occupied by the second layer; in the hexagonal structure the spheres in the third layer are placed directly over the spheres of the first layer. The two possibilities are illustrated in Fig. 1.9. The c/a ratio for hexagonal closest-packing of spheres is $(\frac{8}{3})^{\frac{1}{2}} = 1.633$. By convention we refer to

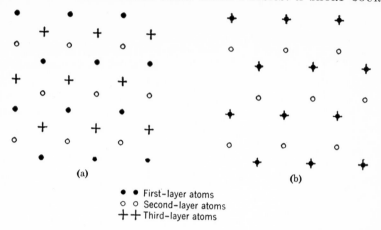

(a)   (b)

• • First-layer atoms
○ ○ Second-layer atoms
+ + Third-layer atoms

FIG. 1.9.   Modes of superposition of close-packed layers of spheres in (a) cubic
close-packing and (b) hexagonal close-packing.

crystals as hcp even if the actual c/a ratio departs somewhat from the
theoretical value.   Thus zinc with $c/a = 1.85$ ($a = 2.66$ A; $c = 4.94$ A)
is referred to commonly as hcp, although the interatomic bond angles
are quite different from the ideal hcp structure.   The unit cell of the
hcp structure is the hexagonal primitive cell; the basis contains two
atoms, as shown in Fig. 1.8.

DIAMOND STRUCTURE

The space lattice of diamond is face-centered cubic with a basis of
two atoms at 000; $\frac{1}{4} \frac{1}{4} \frac{1}{4}$ is associated with each lattice point, as shown
in Fig. 1.10.   The tetrahedral bonding of the diamond structure is pre-
sented in Fig. 1.11.   Each atom has four nearest neighbors and twelve
next nearest neighbors.   There are eight atoms in a unit cube.   The
diamond lattice is relatively empty; the maximum proportion of the
available volume which may be filled by hard spheres is only 0.34,
or about 46 percent of the filling factor for a closest-packed structure.   Carbon, silicon, germanium, and gray tin crystallize in the diamond structure, with lattice constants 3.56, 5.43, 5.65, and 6.46 A,
respectively.

ZINC BLENDE STRUCTURE

We have seen that the diamond structure is composed of two fcc
lattices displaced from each other by one-quarter of a body diagonal.
The cubic zinc sulfide structure results from the diamond structure
when Zn atoms are placed on one fcc lattice and S atoms on the other

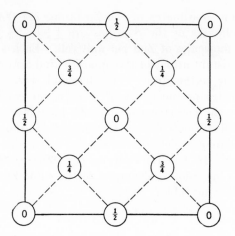

FIG. 1.10.   Atomic positions in the unit cell of the diamond structure projected on a cube face; fractions denote height above base in units of a cube edge.   The points at 0 and $\frac{1}{2}$ are on the fcc lattice; those at $\frac{1}{4}$ and $\frac{3}{4}$ are on a similar lattice displaced among the body diagonal by one-fourth of its length.

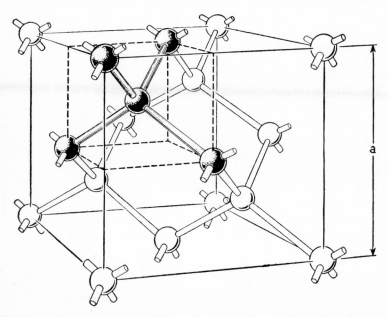

FIG. 1.11.   Crystal structure of diamond, showing the tetrahedral bond arrangement.   (After W. Shockley, *Electrons and holes in semiconductors*.   Copyright 1950.   Van Nostrand.)

fcc lattice.   The coordinates of the Zn atoms are 000; $0\frac{1}{2}\frac{1}{2}$; $\frac{1}{2}0\frac{1}{2}$; $\frac{1}{2}\frac{1}{2}0$; the coordinates of the S atoms are $\frac{1}{4}\frac{1}{4}\frac{1}{4}$; $\frac{1}{4}\frac{3}{4}\frac{3}{4}$; $\frac{3}{4}\frac{1}{4}\frac{3}{4}$; $\frac{3}{4}\frac{3}{4}\frac{1}{4}$. There are four molecules of ZnS per unit cell.   Each atom has about it four equally distant atoms of the opposite kind arranged at the corners of a regular tetrahedron.   The diamond structure possesses a center of symmetry at the midpoint of each line connecting nearest neighbor atoms; the ZnS structure does not have inversion symmetry. This is evident if we look at the arrangement of atoms along a body diagonal.   In diamond the order is CC···CC···CC, where the dots represent vacancies.   In ZnS the order is ZnS···ZnS···ZnS, which is not invariant under inversion.   Examples of the cubic ZnS structure are listed in the following table:

Crystal	a	Crystal	a
CuF	4.26 A	CdS	5.82 A
CuCl	5.41	InAs	6.04
AgI	6.47	InSb	6.46
ZnS	5.41	SiC	4.35
ZnSe	5.65	AlP	5.42

It is thought that the tetrahedral bond arrangement of the ZnS structure is a sign of covalent bonding; ionic bonds would tend to favor structures with a higher number of nearest neighbors (coordination number).

SODIUM CHLORIDE STRUCTURE

The sodium chloride, NaCl, structure is shown in Fig. 1.12a.   The space lattice is face-centered cubic, with a basis of one Na atom and

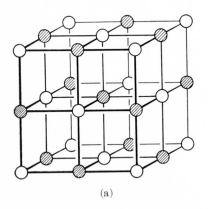
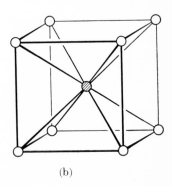

(a)   (b)

FIG. 1.12.   The (a) sodium chloride and (b) cesium chloride crystal structures.

one Cl atom separated by one-half the body diagonal of a unit cube. There are four molecules in a unit cube, with atoms in the positions:

$$\text{Na: } 000; \tfrac{1}{2}\tfrac{1}{2}0; \tfrac{1}{2}0\tfrac{1}{2}; 0\tfrac{1}{2}\tfrac{1}{2}.$$

$$\text{Cl: } \tfrac{1}{2}\tfrac{1}{2}\tfrac{1}{2}; 00\tfrac{1}{2}; 0\tfrac{1}{2}0; \tfrac{1}{2}00.$$

Each atom has as nearest neighbors six atoms of the opposite kind, so that the coordination number is six.

Representative crystals having the NaCl arrangement include those in the following table:

Crystal	a	Crystal	a
LiH	4.08 A	NH$_4$I	7.24 A
NaCl	5.63	AgBr	5.77
KBr	6.59	MgO	4.20
RbI	7.33	MnO	4.43
PbS	5.92	UO	4.92

CESIUM CHLORIDE STRUCTURE

The cesium chloride, CsCl, structure is shown in Fig. 1.12b. There is one molecule per unit cell, with atoms in the body-centered positions:

$$\text{Cs: } 000 \quad \text{and} \quad \text{Cl: } \tfrac{1}{2}\tfrac{1}{2}\tfrac{1}{2}.$$

The space lattice is simple cubic. Each atom is at the center of a cube of atoms of the opposite kind, so that the coordination number is eight. Representative crystals having the CsCl arrangement include those in the following table:

Crystal	a	Crystal	a
CsCl	4.11 A	CuZn (β-brass)	2.94 A
TlBr	3.97	AgMg	3.28
TlI	4.20	LiHg	3.29
NH$_4$Cl	3.87	AlNi	2.88
RbCl(190°C)	3.74	BeCu	2.70

CALCIUM FLUORIDE (FLUORITE) STRUCTURE

The cubic calcium fluoride, CaF$_2$, structure is shown in Fig. 1.13. The space lattice is fcc; the basis has a Ca atom at 000, one F atom at $\tfrac{1}{4}\tfrac{1}{4}\tfrac{1}{4}$, and the other F atom at $\tfrac{3}{4}\tfrac{3}{4}\tfrac{3}{4}$. Each Ca atom is at the center of eight F atoms at the corners of a surrounding cube, and each F atom

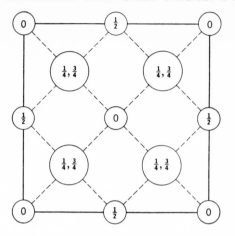

FIG. 1.13. Atom positions with the unit cell of fluorite projected on a cube face; small circles are Ca atoms, large circles F atoms.

is at the center of a tetrahedron of Ca atoms. Representative crystals having the CaF_2 arrangement include those in the following table:

Crystal	a	Crystal	a
CaF_2	5.45 A	Ir_2P	5.54 A
BaF_2	6.19	$AuAl_2$	6.00
UO_2	5.47	$PbMg_2$	6.84
K_2O	6.44	$SiMg_2$	6.39
Li_2Te	6.50	$PtGa_2$	5.91

COLLECTIONS OF CRYSTAL STRUCTURE DATA

The reader who wishes to look up the crystal structure of a substance may profitably consult the loose-leaf compilation by Wyckoff.[1] The *Strukturbericht* and *Structure Reports* are also valuable aids. The principal journals in the field are *Acta Crystallographica* and *Zeitschrift für Kristallographie*.

In Table 1.2 we list for convenience common crystal structures of a number of elements, and their lattice constants at room temperature. Hume-Rothery[2] has given a useful series of tables of crystal structures of elements arranged according to the groups in the periodic table.

[1] R. W. G. Wyckoff, *Crystal structures*, Interscience Publishers, New York, 1948.
[2] W. Hume-Rothery, *Structure of metals and alloys*, Institute of Metals, London, 1947, pp. 47–55.

TABLE 1.2
COMMON CRYSTAL STRUCTURES OF SELECTED ELEMENTS

Element	Structure	Density 20°C gram/cm³	Lattice Constants (at Room Temperature) (angstroms) a	c or Axial Angle	Atomic Volume (cm³/mole)	Nearest Neighbor Distance (A)
Aluminum	Fcc	2.70	4.04		9.99	2.86
Argon	Fcc		5.43(20°K)			3.83
Barium	Bcc	3.5	5.01		39	4.34
Beryllium	Hcp	1.82	2.27	3.59	4.96	2.22
Bismuth	Rhombohedral	9.80	4.74	$\alpha = 57°41'$	21.3	3.10
Boron	Complex	2.3			4.7	
Cadmium	Hcp	8.65	2.97	5.61	13.0	2.97
Calcium	Fcc	1.55	5.56		25.9	3.93
Carbon	Diamond	3.51	3.56			1.54
Cerium	Fcc	6.9	5.14		20	3.64
Cesium	Bcc	1.9	6.05(92°K)		70	5.24
Chromium	Bcc	7.19	2.88		7.23	2.49
Cobalt	Hcp	8.9	2.51	4.07	6.6	2.50
Copper	Fcc	8.96	3.61		7.09	2.55
Gadolinium	Hcp	7.95	3.62	5.75	19.7	3.55
Germanium	Diamond	5.36	5.65		13.5	2.44
Gold	Fcc	19.32	4.07		10.2	2.88
Helium	Hcp		3.57(2°K)	5.83		3.57
Iron (α)	Bcc	7.87	2.86		7.1	2.48
Lanthanum	Fcc	6.15	5.29			3.73
Lead	Fcc	11.34	4.94		18.27	3.49
Lithium	Bcc	0.53	3.50		13	3.03
Magnesium	Hcp	1.74	3.20	5.20	14.0	3.19
Manganese	Complex	7.43			7.39	2.24
Molybdenum	Bcc	10.2	3.14		9.41	2.72
Neon	Fcc		4.52(20°K)			3.20
Nickel	Fcc	8.90	3.52		6.59	2.49
Niobium	Bcc	8.57	3.29		10.8	2.85
Palladium	Fcc	12.0	3.88		8.89	2.74
Platinum	Fcc	21.45	3.92		9.10	2.77
Potassium	Bcc	0.86	5.33		45	4.62
Rubidium	Bcc	1.53	5.62(92°K)		55.9	4.87
Silicon	Diamond	2.33	5.43		12.0	2.35
Silver	Fcc	10.49	4.08		10.28	2.88
Sodium	Bcc	0.97	4.28		24	3.71

TABLE 1.2 (*Continued*)

Element	Structure	Density 20°C gram/cm³	Lattice Constants (at Room Temperature) (angstroms)		Atomic Volume (cm³/ mole)	Nearest Neighbor Distance (A)
			a	*c* or Axial Angle		
Strontium	Fcc	2.6	6.05		34	4.30
Tantalum	Bcc	16.6	3.30		10.9	2.85
Thalium	Hcp	11.85	3.45	5.51	17.24	3.40
Tin (gray)	Diamond	5.75	6.46			
Titanium	Hcp	4.54	2.95	4.73	10.6	2.91
Tungsten	Bcc	19.3	3.16		9.53	2.73
Uranium	Complex	18.7			12.7	2.76
Vanadium	Bcc	6.0	3.03		8.5	2.63
Xenon	Fcc		6.24(92°K)			4.41
Zinc	Hcp	7.13	2.66	4.94	9.17	2.66
Zirconium	Bcc	6.5	3.61(850°C)		14	3.16

EMPIRICAL CLASSIFICATION OF CRYSTAL BINDING

It is useful to make an approximate qualitative classification of crystals in terms of the dominant type of chemical binding displayed. It may not be possible or sensible to classify some solids, whereas with others it may be possible to make an approximate quantitative assessment of the contribution of the various types of binding to the total binding energy. The principal types of binding are given in Table 1.3.

The static forces binding atoms and molecules in solids are almost entirely electrostatic in nature, with only insignificant contributions from magnetic interactions. There are also important kinetic effects on the binding energy, arising from the motion of the atomic electrons. By and large, the important differences among the several types of crystal bonds may be attributed to qualitative differences in the distribution of electrons around the atoms and molecules.

There is an extraordinary and beautiful diversity in the structural composition of solid materials, ranging from the bare simplicity of the structure of diamond, the alkali halides, and monovalent metals through glasses, fibers, plastics, intermetallic compounds, organic crystals, and complex silicates of geological significance to the intricacies of biological substances. X-ray crystallography has made great progress in understanding structures over this broad spectrum. Solid state physics, however, is concerned at present largely with substances having simple structures and binding characteristics. The complexity of

TABLE 1.3
CLASSIFICATION OF CRYSTAL TYPES

The binding energy is the energy necessary to dissociate the solid into separated atoms, molecules, or ions, as appropriate. The binding energy is taken at room temperature, except for the molecular crystals where it is taken at the melting point. Note that 1 ev/molecule = 23.05 kcal/mole.

Crystal Type	Examples	Binding Energy (kcal/mole)	Characteristics of Type
Ionic	NaCl	180	Strong absorption in far infrared; low electrical conductivity at low temperatures; good conductivity by ions at high temperatures
	LiF	240	
Covalent	Diamond	∼170	Great hardness; low conductivity at low temperatures when specimens are pure
	SiC	283	
Metallic	Na	26	High electrical conductivity
	Fe	94	
Molecular	A	1.8	Low melting and boiling points; very compressible
	CH_4	2.4	
Hydrogen-bonded	H_2O (ice)	12	Tendency to polymerize (that is, to form groups of many molecules); increased binding energy of molecules in comparison with similar molecules without hydrogen bonds
	HF	7	

the observable phenomena in even the simple structures suggests that it would be most profitable to try to understand these first.

IONIC CRYSTALS

In ionic crystals electrons are transferred from atoms of one type to atoms of a second type, so that the crystal is made up of positive and negative ions. The ions arrange themselves so the Coulomb attraction between ions of opposite sign is stronger than the Coulomb repulsion between ions of the same sign. The *ionic bond* is thus essentially the bond resulting from the electrostatic interaction of oppositely charged ions. Two common crystal structures found for ionic crystals, the sodium chloride and the cesium chloride structures, are shown in Fig. 1.12.

The degree of ionization of the constituent atoms of an ionic crystal is often such that the electronic configurations of all ions correspond to closed electronic shells, as in the inert gas atoms.   In lithium fluoride the configuration[3] of the neutral atoms are, according to Table 1.4,

$$\text{Li:}\quad 1s^2 2s,$$
$$\text{F:}\quad 1s^2 2s^2 2p^5,$$

while the singly charged ions have the configurations

$$\text{Li}^+:\quad 1s^2,$$
$$\text{F}^-:\quad 1s^2 2s^2 2p^6,$$

as for helium and neon, respectively.   The inert gas atoms have closed shells, and the charge distributions are spherically symmetric.   We may expect accordingly that the charge distributions on each ion in an ionic crystal may have approximately spherical symmetry, with some distortion near the region of contact with neighboring atoms.

When we speak of ionic crystals we mean substances such as lithium fluoride and sodium chloride.   These are perhaps as simple as any chemical compound existing in nature, and for this reason they have been the subject of a great deal of theoretical calculation, and many of their physical properties have been investigated experimentally over a wide range of temperature.   The idealized model of an ionic crystal supposes that the constituents are positive and negative ions bearing charges which are multiples of the electronic charge, with the charge distributed with spherical symmetry on each ion as in the rare gas atoms.   The interactions between ions are assumed to be primarily the electrostatic interactions between spherical charge distributions.

A short estimate suggests that a large part of the binding energy of an ionic crystal is electrostatic.   The distance between a positive ion and the nearest negative ion in sodium chloride is known to be 2.81×10^{-8} cm, so that the attractive part of the potential energy of the two ions by themselves is

$$\frac{e^2}{r_0} = \frac{(4.8 \times 10^{-10})^2}{2.8 \times 10^{-8}} = 8 \times 10^{-12} \text{ erg},$$

[3] The notation used to describe the electronic configuration of atoms and ions is discussed in all textbooks of introductory atomic physics.   The letters s, p, d, $\cdots$ signify electrons having orbital angular momentum 0, 1, 2, $\cdots$ in units of $\hbar$; the number to the left of the letter denotes the principal quantum number of one orbit, and the superscript to the right denotes the number of electrons in the orbit.

TABLE 1.4

PERIODIC TABLE, WITH THE OUTER ELECTRON CONFIGURATIONS OF NEUTRAL ATOMS IN THEIR GROUND STATES

(Configuration assignments for the rare earth and actinide elements are somewhat uncertain.)

1 H $1s$
2 He $1s^2$

3 Li $2s$
4 Be $2s^2$
5 B $2s^22p$
6 C $2s^22p^2$
7 N $2s^22p^3$
8 O $2s^22p^4$
9 F $2s^22p^5$
10 Ne $2s^22p^6$

11 Na $2p^63s$
12 Mg $2p^63s^2$
13 Al $3s^23p$
14 Si $3s^23p^2$
15 P $3s^23p^3$
16 S $3s^23p^4$
17 Cl $3s^23p^5$
18 A $3s^23p^6$

19 K $3p^64s$
20 Ca $3p^64s^2$
21 Sc $3d4s^2$
22 Ti $3d^24s^2$
23 V $3d^34s^2$
24 Cr $3d^54s$
25 Mn $3d^54s^2$
26 Fe $3d^64s^2$
27 Co $3d^74s^2$
28 Ni $3d^84s^2$
29 Cu $3d^{10}4s$
30 Zn $3d^{10}4s^2$
31 Ga $4s^24p$
32 Ge $4s^24p^2$
33 As $4s^24p^3$
34 Se $4s^24p^4$
35 Br $4s^24p^5$
36 Kr $4s^24p^6$

37 Rb $4p^65s$
38 Sr $4p^65s^2$
39 Y $4d5s^2$
40 Zr $4d^25s^2$
41 Nb $4d^45s$
42 Mo $4d^55s$
43 Tc $4d^55s^2$
44 Ru $4d^75s$
45 Rh $4d^85s$
46 Pd $4d^{10}$
47 Ag $4d^{10}5s$
48 Cd $4d^{10}5s^2$
49 In $5s^25p$
50 Sn $5s^25p^2$
51 Sb $5s^25p^3$
52 Te $5s^25p^4$
53 I $5s^25p^5$
54 Xe $5s^25p^6$

55 Cs $5p^66s$
56 Ba $5p^66s^2$
57 La $5p^65d6s^2$
58 Ce $4f^26s^2$
59 Pr $4f^36s^2$
60 Nd $4f^46s^2$
61 Pm $4f^56s^2$
62 Sm $4f^66s^2$
63 Eu $4f^76s^2$
64 Gd $4f^75d6s^2$
65 Tb $4f^85d6s^2$
66 Dy $4f^{10}6s^2$
67 Ho $4f^{11}6s^2$
68 Er $4f^{12}6s^2$
69 Tm $4f^{13}6s^2$
70 Yb $4f^{14}6s^2$
71 Lu $4f^{14}5d6s^2$
72 Hf $5d^26s^2$
73 Ta $5d^36s^2$
74 W $5d^46s^2$
75 Re $5d^56s^2$
76 Os $5d^66s^2$
77 Ir $5d^9$
78 Pt $5d^96s$
79 Au $5d^{10}6s$
80 Hg $5d^{10}6s^2$
81 Tl $6s^26p$
82 Pb $6s^26p^2$
83 Bi $6s^26p^3$
84 Po $6s^26p^4$
85 At $6s^26p^5$
86 Rn $6s^26p^6$

87 Fr $6p^67s$
88 Ra $6p^67s^2$
89 Ac $6d7s^2$
90 Th $6d^27s^2$
91 Pa $5f^26d7s^2$
92 U $5f^36d7s^2$
93 Np $5f^57s^2$
94 Pu $5f^67s^2$
95 Am $5f^77s^2$
96 Cm $5f^76d7s^2$
97 Bk $5f^86d7s^2$
98 Cf $5f^96d7s^2$

which is about 5 ev.   This value may be compared with the known value 183 kcal/mole, or about 8 ev/molecule, of the heat of formation of the crystal starting with ions at infinite separation.   The order of magnitude agreement between the values of 5 and 8 ev/molecule is quite suggestive and is borne out by detailed calculation.

COVALENT CRYSTALS

When a covalent bond is formed, we imagine that an electron from each atom is transferred to the region between the two atoms joined by the bond.

In an ionic bond it is a good approximation to think of the valence electrons as attached to definite atoms.   The Pauli principle applied to ions with filled electronic shells ensures a low electron density in the region between the two ions where the charge shells make contact. Ions with filled shells do not generally form covalent bonds.   In a covalent or homopolar bond the charge density between the two atoms may be rather high, and the valence electrons are to an appreciable extent shared between two atoms.   The covalent bond is the normal electron-pair bond of chemistry, encountered particularly in organic chemistry.   It is characterized by a high density of electrons between the ions and also by marked directional properties.   The carbon bond is a good example of the directional properties of the covalent bond: carbon atoms often prefer to join onto each other or to other atoms by four bonds making tetrahedral angles with each other.   That is, each carbon atom will be at the center of the tetrahedron formed by the nearest neighbor atoms.   Diamond and methane, CH_4, are typical examples of the tetrahedral covalent bond.   The diamond structure is loosely packed in a geometrical sense: the tetrahedral bond allows only four nearest neighbors, whereas a closest-packed structure would require twelve nearest-neighbor atoms.   The covalent bond is usually formed from two electrons, one from each atom participating in the bond.   The spins of the two electrons in the bond are antiparallel. The carbon atom $(2s^2 2p^2)$ tends, in a sense, to fill up the $2p^6$ electron shell by sharing electrons with four neighbors.

There is apparently a continuous range of crystals between the ionic and the covalent limits.   It is often of importance to estimate the extent to which a given bond is ionic or covalent, but this may be difficult to do with any confidence.   We think of NaF as an ionic crystal, and perhaps of InSb as largely covalent, but it is at present difficult to know what to say about the nature of the bonding of ZnS or PbS, for example.   Pauling has formulated (Fig. 1.14) on a semi-empirical basis an electronegativity scale of some of the elements.

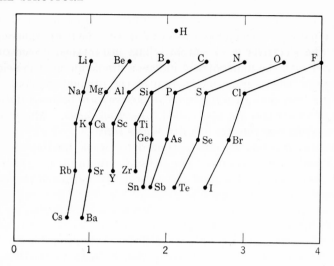

FIG. 1.14. The electronegativity scale of the elements, showing relation to the periodic table. The electronegativities are plotted against the horizontal scale, and different columns of the periodic table are separated vertically. (After L. Pauling, *Nature of the chemical bond*, Cornell University Press.)

Electronegativity is a chemical term meaning the power of an atom in a molecule to attract electrons to itself.

METAL CRYSTALS

Metals are characterized by high electrical conductivity, and so a portion of the electrons in a metal must be free to move about. The electrons available to participate in the conductivity are called conduction electrons. In some metals such as the alkali metals the interaction of the ion cores with the conduction electrons is largely responsible for the binding energy. We may think of an alkali metal crystal as an array of positive ions embedded in a more-or-less uniform sea of negative charge. In some metals such as the transition metals it has been suggested that there may also be binding effects from covalent-type bonds among the inner electron shells. Transition group elements have incomplete *d*-electron shells and are characterized by high binding energy.

MOLECULAR CRYSTALS

Inert gas atoms and saturated molecules are bound together in the solid phase by weak electrostatic forces known as *van der Waals forces*. These forces arise in the following way: even in an atom or molecule which has on the average an electric dipole moment of zero there will be a fluctuating dipole moment associated with the instantaneous position of the electrons in the atom. The instantaneous electric field associated with the moment will induce a dipole moment in neighboring atoms. The average interaction of the original moment and of the induced moment gives rise to an attractive force between the atoms. Forces of this origin are also called *dispersion forces*. Many organic solids are held together by van der Waals forces.

Molecular crystals are characterized by weak binding, with low melting and boiling points. The crystal structures are often those with dense packing. The inert gas crystals crystallize with cubic close packing.

HYDROGEN-BONDED CRYSTALS

As neutral hydrogen has only one electron, it should form a covalent bond with only one other atom. It is known, however, that under certain conditions an atom of hydrogen is attracted by rather strong forces to two atoms, thus forming what is called a *hydrogen bond* between them, with a bond energy of about 5 kcal/mole. It is believed that the hydrogen bond is largely ionic in character, being formed only between the most electronegative atoms. The hydrogen atom loses its electron to one of the other atoms in the molecule; the proton forms the hydrogen bond. The small size of the proton permits only two nearest-neighbor atoms because they are so close that more than two of them would get in each other's way; thus the hydrogen bond connects only two atoms.

The hydrogen bond is an important interaction between H_2O molecules and is responsible, together with the electrostatic attraction of the electric dipole moments, for the striking physical properties of water and ice. The hydrogen bond restrains protein molecules to their normal geometrical arrangements. It is also responsible for the polymerization of hydrogen fluoride and formic acid, for example. It is important in certain ferroelectric crystals, such as potassium dihydrogen phosphate.

IONIC RADII

It is found that the interatomic distances in the alkali halides are approximately additive, so that to a certain extent the ions may be regarded as rigid spheres. The distance at which the ions come into contact is the equilibrium interionic distance. The approximate validity of the ionic radius concept is a consequence of the very strong dependence of the repulsive forces on interionic distance.

The tailing-off of the radial wave functions according to quantum mechanics tells us that no absolute significance may be attached to a table of ionic radii, but for many purposes a set of radii, such as those in Tables 1.5 to 1.7, may be of value. It is necessary to assign one

TABLE 1.5
IONIC CRYSTAL RADII ACCORDING TO ZACHARIASEN
(Unpublished)

The interionic distance D is represented by $D_N = R_C + R_A + \Delta_N$, for ionic crystals, where N is the coordination number of the cation, R_C and R_A are the standard radii of the cation and anion, and Δ_N is a correction for coordination number. Room temperature.

(a)

Δ_N			Δ_N			Δ_N	
N	(A)		N	(A)		N	(A)
1	-0.50		5	-0.05		9	$+0.11$
2	-0.31		6	0		10	$+0.14$
3	-0.19		7	$+0.04$		11	$+0.17$
4	-0.11		8	$+0.08$		12	$+0.19$

(b)   *Standard Radii (in A) for Ions with Inert Gas Configurations*

-2		O 1.46	S 1.90	Se 2.02	Te 2.22	Po 2.30
-1		F 1.33	Cl 1.81	Br 1.96	I 2.19	At 2.27
$+1$	Li 0.68	Na 0.98	K 1.33	Rb 1.48	Cs 1.67	Fr 1.75
$+2$	Be 0.30	Mg 0.65	Ca 0.94	Sr 1.10	Ba 1.29	Ra 1.37
$+3$	B 0.16	Al 0.45	Sc 0.68	Y 0.88	La 1.04	Ac 1.11
$+4$		Si 0.38	Ti 0.60	Zr 0.77	Ce 0.92	Th 0.99
$+5$				Nb 0.67		Pa 0.90
$+6$						U 0.83

(c)   *Actinide Ions*

	Ac	Th	Pa	U	Np	Pu	Am
$+3$	1.11	1.08	1.05	1.03	1.01	1.00	0.99
$+4$		0.99	0.96	0.93	0.92	0.90	0.89
$+5$			0.90	0.89	0.88	0.87	0.86
$+6$				0.83	0.82	0.81	0.80

radius somewhat arbitrarily in constructing a table, as a constant distance may be added to the cations and subtracted from the anions without changing the observed lattice constants in diatomic structures. It is usual in empirical treatments to take the radius of F^- as 1.33 A, when the coordination number (number of nearest neighbors) is 6. The radii in Table 1.6 were calculated theoretically by Pauling with

TABLE 1.6

IONIC CRYSTAL RADII ACCORDING TO PAULING, IN ANGSTROMS

(L. Pauling, *Nature of the chemical bond*, Cornell University Press, Ithaca, 1945, p. 346.)

H^- Li^+ Be^{2+} B^{3+} C^{4+} N^{5+} O^{6+} F^{7+}

				H^-	Li^+	Be^{2+}	B^{3+}	C^{4+}	N^{5+}	O^{6+}	F^{7+}
				2.08	0.60	0.32	0.20	0.15	0.11	0.09	0.07
C^{4-}	N^{3-}	O^{2-}	F^-	Na^+	Mg^{2+}	Al^{3+}	Si^{4+}	P^{5+}	S^{6+}	Cl^{7+}	
2.60	1.71	1.40	1.36	0.95	0.65	0.50	0.41	0.34	0.29	0.26	
Si^{4-}	P^{3-}	S^{2-}	Cl^-	K^+	Ca^{2+}	Sc^{3+}	Ti^{4+}	V^{5+}	Cr^{6+}	Mn^{7+}	
2.71	2.12	1.84	1.81	1.33	0.99	0.81	0.68	0.59	0.52	0.46	
				Cu^+	Zn^{2+}	Ga^{3+}	Ge^{4+}	As^{5+}	Se^{6+}	Br^{7+}	
				0.96	0.74	0.62	0.53	0.47	0.42	0.39	
Ge^{4-}	As^{3-}	Se^{2-}	Br^-	Rb^+	Sr^{2+}	Y^{3+}	Zr^{4+}	Nb^{5+}	Mo^{6+}		
2.72	2.22	1.98	1.95	1.48	1.13	0.93	0.80	0.70	0.62		
				Ag^+	Cd^{2+}	In^{3+}	Sn^{4+}	Sb^{5+}	Te^{6+}	I^{7+}	
				1.26	0.97	0.81	0.71	0.62	0.56	0.50	
Sn^{4-}	Sb^{3-}	Te^{2-}	I^-	Cs^+	Ba^{2+}	La^{3+}	Ce^{4+}				
2.94	2.45	2.21	2.16	1.69	1.35	1.15	1.01				
				Au^+	Hg^{2+}	Tl^{3+}	Pb^{4+}	Bi^{5+}			
				1.37	1.10	0.95	0.84	0.74			

TABLE 1.7

EMPIRICAL IONIC RADII

(After Pauling)

NH_4^+	1.48 A	Mn^{2+}	0.80 A	Ti^{3+}	0.69 A
Tl^+	1.44 A	Fe^{2+}	0.75 A	V^{3+}	0.66 A
		Co^{2+}	0.72 A	Cr^{3+}	0.64 A
		Ni^{2+}	0.70 A	Mn^{3+}	0.62 A
				Fe^{3+}	0.60 A

Trivalent rare earth ions, 0.90 ± 0.05 A

the help of certain empirical data. Empirical radii values for other ions, based on $O^{2-} = 1.40$ A, are given in Table 1.7.

As an example of the use of the tables, we consider sodium chloride, which is probably principally ionic: we have $D_6 = 0.98 + 1.81 = 2.79$, or $a = 5.58$ A, while 5.63 A is observed at room temperature.

PROBLEMS

1.1. Show that the maximum proportion of the available volume which may be filled by hard spheres arranged in various structures is

Simple cubic	$\pi/6$ $(= 0.52)$
Body-centered cubic	$\pi 3^{1/2}/8$ $(= 0.68)$
Face-centered cubic	$\pi 2^{1/2}/6$ $(= 0.74)$
Hexagonal close-packed	$\pi 2^{1/2}/6$ $(= 0.74)$
Diamond	$\pi 3^{1/2}/16$ $(= 0.34)$

We may note that by experiment [O. K. Rice, *J. Chem. Phys.* **12**, 1 (1944)] it is found that the volume of an arrangement of spheres packed at random into a container exceeds that of the cubic and hexagonal close-packed arrangements by 15 to 20 percent. For further details on the packing of spheres, see A. H. Boerdijk, *Philips Research Repts.* **7**, 303 (1952), and references cited therein.

1.2. Show that the c/a ratio for an ideal hexagonal close-packed structure is $(\frac{8}{3})^{1/2} = 1.633$. Compare this with the experimental values of the ratios for twelve metals possessing hcp structures.

1.3. Hard spheres of radius b are arranged in contact in sc, bcc, and fcc structures. Find the radius s of the largest sphere which can fit into the largest interstice in the several structures.

1.4. Describe and discuss the crystal structures of ZnO, NiAs, TiO_2, and α-quartz.

1.5. Show that a bcc lattice may be decomposed into two sc lattices A, B with the property that none of the nearest neighbor lattice points to a lattice point on A lie on A, and similarly for the B lattice. Show that to obtain the same property a sc lattice is decomposed into two fcc lattices, and a fcc lattice into four sc lattices. These considerations are of interest for antiferromagnetism.

1.6. Show that among the nearest neighbor sites in a fcc lattice there are groups of three sites such that each site is a vertex of an equilateral triangle.

1.7. Prove that in a cubic crystal a direction [*uvw*] is perpendicular to a plane (*uvw*) having the same indices.

REFERENCES

W. L. Bragg, *The crystalline state*, Vol. I, G. Bell and Sons, Ltd., London, 1933.

M. J. Buerger, *Elementary crystallography*, John Wiley and Sons, New York, 1956.

C. W. Bunn, *Chemical crystallography*, Clarendon Press, Oxford, 1945.

P. H. Groth, *Chemische Krystallographie*, 5 volumes, W. Engelmann, Leipzig, 1906.

W. Hume-Rothery, *The structure of metals and alloys*, Institute of Metals, London, 1947.

International tables for x-ray crystallography, Kynoch Press, Birmingham, 1952.

Internationale Tabellen zur Bestimmung von Kristallstrukturen, Borntraeger, Berlin, 1935.

R. W. James, *The optical principles of the diffraction of x-rays*, G. Bell and Sons, Ltd., London, 1948.

K. Lonsdale, *Crystals and x-rays*, G. Bell and Sons, Ltd., London, 1948.

C. Palache, H. Berman, and C. Frondel, *Dana's system of mineralogy*, Vols. I and II, John Wiley and Sons, New York, 7th ed., 1944, 1951.

L. Pauling, *Nature of the chemical bond*, Cornell University Press, Ithaca, 1945.

F. C. Phillips, *An introduction to crystallography*, Longmans, London, 1946.

Strukturbericht, 7 vols.; Akademische Verlagsgesellschaft, Leipzig, 1913–1939; continued as *Structure Reports*, published by the International Union of Crystallography.

W. Voigt, *Lehrbuch der Kristallphysik*, Teubner, Leipzig and Berlin, 1910.

W. A. Wooster, *A textbook on crystal physics*, Cambridge University Press, Cambridge, 1938.

R. W. G. Wyckoff, *Crystal structures*, Interscience Publishers, New York, 1948.

W. H. Zachariasen, *Theory of x-ray diffraction in crystals*, John Wiley and Sons, New York, 1945.

2 Diffraction of waves by crystals

Many of the most interesting topics in solid state physics are concerned with the propagation of waves in crystal lattices. The types of waves include: electromagnetic waves (photons), elastic waves (phonons), spin waves (magnons), polarization waves (excitons), and neutron and electron waves. The most spectacular phenomena in the whole field of wave propagation on periodic lattices are the related phenomena of Bragg reflection and forbidden energy bands.

In this chapter we introduce the topic of diffraction in lattices using x-ray diffraction as an example. We find at certain angles and wavelengths that a crystal will reflect an x-ray beam strongly. The effect is a wave diffraction effect, and the simplest explanation was given by Bragg.

BRAGG'S LAW

W. L. Bragg found that one could account for the position of the diffracted beams produced by a crystal in an x-ray beam by a simple model which assumes that x-rays are reflected specularly from the various planes of atoms in the crystal. The diffracted beams are found only for special situations when the reflections from parallel planes of atoms interfere constructively. The original derivation of the Bragg law is indicated in Fig. 2.1.

We consider in the crystal a series of atomic planes which are considered to be partly reflecting for radiation of wavelength λ and which are spaced equal distances d apart. The radiation is incident in the plane of the paper. The path difference for rays reflected from adjacent planes is $2d \sin \theta$. Reinforcement of the radiation reflected from successive planes will occur when the path difference is an integral number n of wavelengths. The condition for constructive reflection is that

(2.1) $$2d \sin \theta = n\lambda.$$

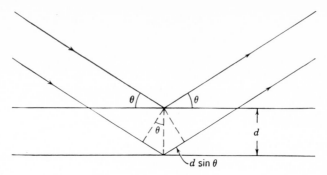

FIG. 2.1.   Derivation of the Bragg equation $2d \sin \theta = n\lambda$; here d is the spacing of parallel atomic planes and $2n\pi$ is the difference in phase between reflections from successive planes.

This is the Bragg law.   We shall derive this relation below in a more sophisticated manner, considering in detail the atomic nature of the crystal.   It should be emphasized that the Bragg equation results from the fundamental periodicity of the structure, and the equation does not refer to the actual composition or arrangement of the atoms associated with the reflecting planes.   The latter considerations will be seen below to affect the intensity of the diffracted radiation and to determine the relative intensity of the various orders n of diffraction. An important consequence of (2.1) is that wavelengths $\lambda \leq 2d$ are essential if Bragg reflection is to occur.

We may get an idea of the magnitude of the diffraction angle θ by considering $CuK\alpha_1$ radiation incident on a cubic crystal with a lattice constant of 4.00 A.   The wavelength of the $CuK\alpha_1$ line is 1.54 A.   In the first order ($n = 1$) reflection from (100) planes, $\theta = \sin^{-1} (1.54/8.00) = 11.1°$.   As the wavelength is decreased, the angle is decreased: for gamma-rays glancing angles must be used.

LAUE DIFFRACTION EQUATIONS

The Laue equations are derived from a simple static atomic model of a crystal structure.   They illustrate effectively the conditions for the formation of a diffracted beam.   The Bragg equation (2.1) will be derived as a direct consequence of the Laue equations.

We consider the nature of the x-ray diffraction pattern produced by identical scattering centers located at the lattice points of a space lattice.   We first look at the scattering from any two lattice points, P_1 and P_2 in Fig. 2.2, separated by the vector $\mathbf{r}$.   The unit incident wave normal is $\mathbf{s}_0$, and the unit scattered wave normal is $\mathbf{s}$.   We

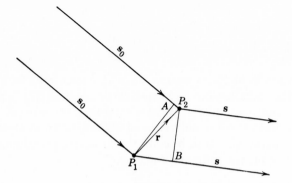

FIG. 2.2.   Calculation of the phase difference of the waves scattered from two
lattice points.

examine at a point a long distance away the difference in phase of the
radiation scattered by P_1 and P_2.

If P_2A and P_1B are the projections of $\mathbf{r}$ on the incident and scattered
wave directions, the path difference between the two scattered waves is

$$(2.2) \qquad P_2A - P_1B = \mathbf{r} \cdot \mathbf{s}_0 - \mathbf{r} \cdot \mathbf{s} = \mathbf{r} \cdot (\mathbf{s}_0 - \mathbf{s}).$$

The vector $\mathbf{s}_0 - \mathbf{s} = \mathbf{S}$ has a simple interpretation (Fig. 2.3) as
the direction of the normal to a plane that would reflect the incident
direction into the scattering direction.   This plane is a useful mathematical construction and may be spoken of as the *reflecting plane*.   If
2θ is the angle $\mathbf{s}$ makes with $\mathbf{s}_0$, then θ is the angle of incidence, and
from the figure we see that $|S| = 2 \sin \theta$, as $\mathbf{s}$ and $\mathbf{s}_0$ are unit vectors.

The phase difference ϕ is $2\pi/\lambda$ times the path difference between
the waves scattered between the two lattice points.   That is, if the
path difference is a whole wavelength λ, the phase difference is 2π.

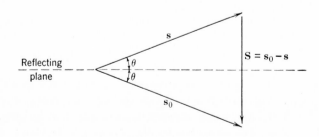

FIG. 2.3.   Construction of the normal to the reflecting plane.

We have

(2.3)
$$\phi = \frac{2\pi}{\lambda} (\mathbf{r} \cdot \mathbf{S}).$$

The amplitude of the scattered wave is a maximum in a direction such that the contributions from each lattice point differ in phase only by integral multiples of 2π. For this condition, the separate scattered amplitudes add up constructively and the intensity in the diffracted beam is a maximum. If $\mathbf{a}$, $\mathbf{b}$, $\mathbf{c}$ are the primitive translation vectors, we must have for the diffraction maxima

$$\phi_a = \frac{2\pi}{\lambda} (\mathbf{a} \cdot \mathbf{S}) = 2\pi h;$$

(2.4)
$$\phi_b = \frac{2\pi}{\lambda} (\mathbf{b} \cdot \mathbf{S}) = 2\pi k;$$

$$\phi_c = \frac{2\pi}{\lambda} (\mathbf{c} \cdot \mathbf{S}) = 2\pi l;$$

where h, k, l are integers. If α, β, γ are the direction cosines of $\mathbf{S}$ with respect to a, b, c, we have

$$\mathbf{a} \cdot \mathbf{S} = 2a\alpha \sin \theta = h\lambda;$$

(2.5)
$$\mathbf{b} \cdot \mathbf{S} = 2b\beta \sin \theta = k\lambda;$$

$$\mathbf{c} \cdot \mathbf{S} = 2c\gamma \sin \theta = l\lambda.$$

These are the Laue equations. They have solutions only for special values of θ and the wavelength λ.

The Laue equations (2.5) have a direct geometrical interpretation, which the reader may establish with a little contemplation. We recall that α, β, γ are the direction cosines of $\mathbf{S}$, the normal to the reflecting plane, referred to the basis vectors $\mathbf{a}$, $\mathbf{b}$, $\mathbf{c}$. The Laue equations state that in a diffraction direction the direction cosines are proportional to h/a, k/b, l/c, respectively. Now the adjacent lattice planes (hkl) intersect the axes at intervals a/h, b/k, c/l, by the definition of the Miller indices h, k, l in Chapter 1. By elementary plane geometry the direction cosines of the normal to (hkl) are proportional to h/a, k/b, l/c. Therefore the lattice planes (hkl) must be parallel to the reflecting plane, and the diffraction maxima occur when the scattering direction may be derived from the incident direction by reflection in a lattice plane.

If $d(hkl)$ is the spacing between two adjacent planes of a set (hkl), we have by projection

$$(2.6) \qquad d(hkl) = \frac{a\alpha}{h} = \frac{b\beta}{k} = \frac{c\gamma}{l}.$$

Then, from (2.5), we have

$$(2.7) \qquad 2d(hkl)\sin\theta = \lambda.$$

Now the integers, h, k, l of the Laue equations are not necessarily identical with the Miller indices of an actual crystal plane, as the h, k, l of the Laue equations may contain a common integral factor n, whereas in the Miller indices the common factor n has been eliminated. We may then write

$$(2.8) \qquad 2d\sin\theta = n\lambda,$$

where d is the spacing between adjacent planes with Miller indices $(h/n, k/n, l/n)$. This is the *Bragg equation* (2.1), and we have derived it here from the Laue equations. The integer n is called the order of reflection.

We may interpret (2.7) by giving an extended meaning to the spacing $d(hkl)$ when h, k, l have a common factor n: the diffracted wave actually arises from the nth order reflection from the true lattice planes, but, as a mathematical device, we may think of the diffracted wave as a first order reflection from a set of planes parallel to the true lattice planes but with a spacing $d(hkl)$ equal to $1/n$ of the true spacing.

It is useful to discuss the interference conditions in terms of a mathematical transformation known as the reciprocal lattice. This method is developed in the following section.

INTERFERENCE CONDITIONS AND THE RECIPROCAL LATTICE

The conditions for an x-ray beam to be diffracted by a crystal may be expressed in an elegant form with the help of the reciprocal lattice transformation. The reciprocal lattice is very widely used in x-ray crystallography and in the quantum theory of metals. We let **a**, **b**, **c** be the primitive translations of the crystal lattice. We define the primitive translations **a***, **b***, **c*** of the reciprocal lattice by the relations

$$(2.9) \qquad \mathbf{a}^* \cdot \mathbf{a} = \mathbf{b}^* \cdot \mathbf{b} = \mathbf{c}^* \cdot \mathbf{c} = 1;$$

$$\mathbf{a}^* \cdot \mathbf{b} = \mathbf{a}^* \cdot \mathbf{c} = \mathbf{b}^* \cdot \mathbf{c} = \mathbf{b}^* \cdot \mathbf{a} = \mathbf{c}^* \cdot \mathbf{a} = \mathbf{c}^* \cdot \mathbf{b} = 0.$$

Equations (2.9) define the magnitude and direction of **a***, **b***, **c***. The directions are such that, for example, **a*** is perpendicular to the plane

b and **c**, and in fact is given by

$$(2.10) \qquad\qquad \mathbf{a}^* = \frac{\mathbf{b} \times \mathbf{c}}{\mathbf{a} \cdot [\mathbf{b} \times \mathbf{c}]}.$$

Similar expressions obtain for the other vectors. The reciprocal lattice has a definite orientation relative to the crystal lattice.

The properties of the reciprocal lattice that make it of value in diffraction problems are: (1) The vector $\mathbf{r}^*(hkl)$ from the origin to the point (h, k, l) of the reciprocal lattice is normal to the (hkl) plane of the crystal lattice. (2) The length of the vector $\mathbf{r}^*(hkl)$ is equal to the reciprocal of the spacing of the planes (hkl) of the crystal lattice. As proof of (1) we note that $(\mathbf{a}/h) - (\mathbf{b}/k)$ is a vector in the (hkl) plane. Then

$$\mathbf{r}^*(hkl) \cdot \left(\frac{\mathbf{a}}{h} - \frac{\mathbf{b}}{k}\right) = (h\mathbf{a}^* + k\mathbf{b}^* + l\mathbf{c}^*) \cdot \left(\frac{\mathbf{a}}{h} - \frac{\mathbf{b}}{k}\right) = 0.$$

We can do the same thing for a second vector in the plane, say $(\mathbf{a}/h) - (\mathbf{c}/l)$, proving the first result. Furthermore, if **n** is the unit normal to the plane, $\mathbf{a} \cdot \mathbf{n}/h$ is the interplanar spacing, and, as $\mathbf{n} = \mathbf{r}^*/|r^*|$,

$$(2.11) \qquad\qquad d(hkl) = \frac{\mathbf{n} \cdot \mathbf{a}}{h} = \frac{\mathbf{r}^* \cdot \mathbf{a}}{h|r^*|} = \frac{1}{|r^*|},$$

using (2.9). This proves the second result.

It is effective to write the Bragg equation in the form $2d(hkl) \sin \theta = \lambda$. If h, k, l have a common factor n, the diffracted ray may be considered either as an nth order reflection from lattice planes with their true spacing, or else as a first order reflection from a set of planes parallel to the true lattice planes but with a spacing $d(hkl)$ equal to $1/n$ of the true spacing. The vector $\mathbf{r}^*$ (hkl) in the reciprocal lattice is in the same direction but n times as long as the vector corresponding to the true crystal plane. That is, the nth point from the origin in a given row in the reciprocal lattice corresponds to the nth order reflection from the associated crystal planes. Every point in the reciprocal lattice corresponds to a possible reflection from the crystal lattice.

The Bragg equation has a simple geometrical significance in the reciprocal lattice. In Fig. 2.4 we draw AO as a vector of length $1/\lambda$ in the direction of the incident radiation and terminating at the origin of the reciprocal lattice. Following Ewald, we draw a sphere of radius $1/\lambda$ about A as center; then the possible directions of the diffracted

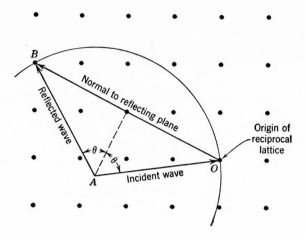

FIG. 2.4.   Ewald's construction in the reciprocal lattice.

rays for this incident ray are determined by the intersections of the sphere with the points of the reciprocal lattice.   That is, the direction AB is the direction of a diffraction maximum; here B is a point of the reciprocal lattice.

We prove the Ewald result by noting that OB is normal to one of the lattice planes (hkl) and of length $1/d(hkl)$; it is also equal in length to $(2/\lambda) \sin \theta$, where θ is the glancing angle between the planes (hkl) and the incident and reflected rays.   Therefore $2d(hkl) \sin \theta = \lambda$, which is just the Bragg condition.   This result may be written in vector form.   If $\mathbf{G}$ is 2π times the vector from the origin to a lattice point in the reciprocal lattice, and $\mathbf{k}$ is the propagation vector (of magnitude $2\pi/\lambda$) of the incident x-ray, then the condition for Bragg reflection is, from Fig. 2.4,

$$(\mathbf{k} + \mathbf{G})^2 = k^2,$$

or

(2.12) $2\mathbf{k} \cdot \mathbf{G} + G^2 = 0.$

We shall encounter the condition (2.12) again in later chapters in connection with the study of Brillouin zones.

ATOMIC SCATTERING FACTOR

The intensity of a given diffracted wave depends on a number of factors.   One of these is the atomic scattering factor, which describes the result of interference effects within the scattering atoms arising

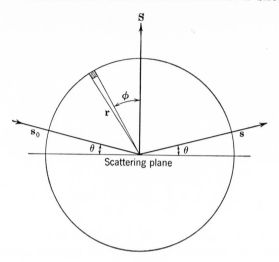

FIG. 2.5.   Calculation of the atomic scattering factor f.   The normal to the
scattering plane is **S**.

from the finite extent of the atoms in relation to the wavelength.   We
give below an approximate classical calculation of the coherent atomic
scattering factor.

    We arrange the coordinate system in Fig. 2.5 so that the incident
and reflected wave normals make equal angles with the vertical axis,
corresponding to Bragg reflection from the horizontal plane at angle θ.
The difference in phase between the radiation scattered by an element
of charge at (r, ϕ) and the radiation which would be scattered by the
same amount of charge located at the center of the atom is $\phi = (2\pi/\lambda)$
$(\mathbf{r} \cdot \mathbf{S})$, according to (2.3).   Then the amplitude scattered by one electron in the actual atom referred to the amplitude which would be scat-
tered by an electron at the center of the atom is, by superposition,

$$(2.13) \qquad\qquad f = \int \rho(\mathbf{r}) e^{i(2\pi/\lambda)\,(\mathbf{r}\cdot\mathbf{S})}\, d\tau,$$

where $\rho(\mathbf{r})\, d\tau$ is the probability of finding the electron in the element
of volume $d\tau$ at $\mathbf{r}$.

    If $\mathbf{r}$ makes an angle ϕ with $\mathbf{S}$, then

$$\frac{2\pi}{\lambda}\,(\mathbf{s}\cdot\mathbf{r}) = \frac{4\pi}{\lambda}\,\sin\theta r \cos\phi = \mu r \cos\phi,$$

where $\mu = 4\pi(\sin \theta)/\lambda$. If the charge density is spherically symmetric,

$$f = \int \rho(r)e^{i\mu r \cos \phi} \, 2\pi r^2 \sin \phi \, dr \, d\phi$$

$$= \int_0^\infty 4\pi r^2 \rho(r) \frac{\sin \mu r}{\mu r} \, dr.$$

Writing $U(r) \, dr = 4\pi r^2 \rho(r) \, dr$ as the probability that an electron lies between radii r and $r + dr$, we have

$$(2.14) \qquad f = \int_0^\infty U(r) \frac{\sin \mu r}{\mu r} \, dr$$

for the *atomic scattering factor*. It is the ratio of the radiation amplitude scattered by the charge distribution in an atom to that scattered by a point electron. At $\theta = 0$ our calculation gives $f = Z$, the number of atomic electrons.

GEOMETRICAL STRUCTURE FACTOR

The Laue and Bragg equations determine the reflections (hkl) which are possible for a given crystal lattice, but the relative intensities of the various reflections depend on the contents of the unit cell, that is, on the number, type, and distribution of atoms in the cell. We must now determine the amplitude of the wave scattered in a given direction by all the atoms in the unit cell. The *structure amplitude* $|F(hkl)|$ for a given hkl reflection is the reflection amplitude divided by the amplitude of the wave scattered by a single point electron for the same wavelength.

The value of $F(hkl)$ will be given by

$$(2.15) \qquad F(hkl) = \sum_i f_i e^{i\phi_i} = \sum_i f_i e^{i(2\pi/\lambda)(\mathbf{r}_i \cdot \mathbf{S})},$$

where the sum is extended over all atoms in a unit cell; ϕ_i is the phase of the wave scattered by the ith atom referred to that of the origin, $\mathbf{r}_i$ is the vector from the origin to the ith atom; f_i is the atomic structure factor of the ith atom.

$$(2.16) \qquad \mathbf{r}_i = u_i\mathbf{a} + v_i\mathbf{b} + w_i\mathbf{c}.$$

By the Laue equations

$$(2.17) \qquad (\mathbf{r}_i \cdot \mathbf{S}) = \lambda(hu_i + kv_i + lw_i),$$

so that

(2.18) $$F(hkl) = \sum_i f_i e^{i2\pi(hu_i+kv_i+lw_i)},$$

and

(2.19) $$|F|^2 = \left[\sum f_i \cos 2\pi(hu_i + kv_i + lw_i)\right]^2 + \left[\sum f_i \sin 2\pi(hu_i + kv_i + lw_i)\right]^2.$$

When all the atoms are identical we have, from (2.18), $F(hkl) = f\mathcal{S}$, where $\mathcal{S}$ is called the geometrical structure factor and is given by

(2.20) $$\mathcal{S} = \sum e^{i2\pi(hu_i+kv_i+lw_i)}.$$

The usual basis of a body-centered cubic structure of identical atoms has atoms at 000 and $\frac{1}{2}\frac{1}{2}\frac{1}{2}$. We find

(2.21) $$\mathcal{S} = 1 + e^{i\pi(h+k+l)}.$$

When $h + k + l$ is odd, $\mathcal{S} = 0$, and the intensities of all spectra for which (hkl) satisfy this condition are zero. For example, metallic sodium has a bcc structure; its diffraction spectrum does not contain lines such as (100), (300), (111), or (221), but lines such as (200), (110), and (222) will be present; here the planes are referred to a cubic unit cell. For each of the possible space groups there are characteristic absences of reflections, and from these the space group is determined.

There is a simple physical interpretation of the result that, in particular, the (100) reflection vanishes for the bcc lattice. The (100) reflection normally occurs when the reflections from the first and third planes in Fig. 2.6 are out of phase by 2π. However, in the bcc lattice

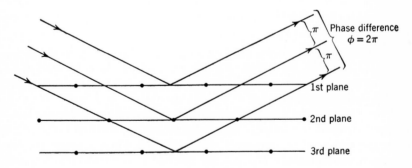

FIG. 2.6.   Explanation of the absence of a (100) reflection from a body-centered cubic lattice.

there is an intervening plane of atoms, labeled the second plane in the figure, which is equal in scattering power to the other planes and which, situated midway between them, gives a reflection out of phase by π, thereby canceling the contribution from another plane. The cancellation of the (100) reflection occurs only if the various planes are identical in composition; thus, in the CsCl structure (Fig. 1.12b) the cancellation does not occur, as the planes of Cs and Cl atoms alternate.

This discussion has assumed that the crystal is large and perfect. The effect of thermal motion on the structure factors may be quite important, as well as the effect of the mosaic or block structure of actual crystals.

EXPERIMENTAL X-RAY DIFFRACTION METHODS

The Bragg law,

$$2d \sin \theta = n\lambda,$$

for x-ray diffraction requires that θ and λ be matched; that is, x-rays of wavelength λ striking a crystal at an arbitrary angle of incidence in general will not be reflected. To satisfy the Bragg law it is necessary to provide experimentally for a continuous range of values of either λ or θ. The standard methods of diffraction used in crystal structure analysis accomplish this.

Laue Method. A single crystal is held stationary in a beam of continuous wavelength x-ray radiation. The crystal selects out and diffracts the discrete values of λ for which planes exist of spacing d and incidence angle θ satisfying the Bragg law.

Rotating-Crystal Method. A single crystal is rotated about a fixed axis in a beam of monochromatic x-rays. The variation in θ brings different atomic planes into position for reflection.

Powder Method (Debye-Scherrer-Hull method). A powdered sample of crystalline material is placed in a fixed position in a monochromatic beam. Among the distribution of crystallite orientations there will be some for which the angle of incidence satisfies the Bragg law.

All three of the foregoing methods are employed, sometimes with modifications, in current research. The Laue method is convenient for the rapid determination of crystal orientation and symmetry and also for studying the extent of crystalline imperfection under mechanical and thermal treatment. The rotating-crystal method is the principal method used for structure determination when a single crystal specimen is available. The powder method is convenient in applied and in metallurgical work because single crystals are not required. Accounts of the essential features of these methods are given below.

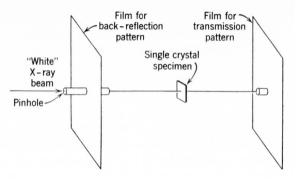

FIG. 2.7.   Arrangement of a camera for Laue patterns.

LAUE METHOD

A Laue camera is illustrated schematically in Fig. 2.7.   A source is used which produces a beam of x-rays over a wide range of wavelengths, perhaps from 0.2 to 2 A; a pinhole arrangement is employed to produce a well-collimated beam.   The dimensions of the single crystal specimen need not be greater than 1 mm.   Flat film is placed to receive either the transmitted diffracted lines or the reflected diffracted lines.   The diffraction pattern consists of a series of spots, as shown for a silicon crystal in Fig. 2.8.

Each reflecting plane in the crystal selects from the incident beam a wavelength satisfying the Bragg equation $2d \sin \theta = n\lambda$.   The pattern must show the symmetry of the crystal in the orientation used; thus, if a cubic crystal is oriented with a body-diagonal or [111] direction parallel to the beam, then the Laue pattern will show the threefold symmetry appropriate to the [111] axis.   This feature makes the Laue pattern particularly convenient for checking the orientation of crystals in solid state experiments.

The Laue method has certain disadvantages for crystal structure determination.   Because of the wide range of wavelengths, it is possible for several wavelengths to reflect in different orders from a single plane, and different orders of reflection may superpose on a single spot. This feature makes the determination of reflected intensity difficult.

ROTATING-CRYSTAL METHOD

A simple rotating-crystal camera is shown in Fig. 2.9.   The film is mounted with cylindrical geometry concentric with a rotating spindle on which the single crystal specimen is mounted.   The dimensions of the crystal are usually less than 1 mm.   The incident monochromatic beam is diffracted from a given crystal plane of interplanar spacing d whenever in the course of rotation the value of θ satisfies the Bragg equation. In particular, all planes parallel to the rotation axis will reflect in the horizontal plane. Planes with other orientations will reflect in layers above and below the horizontal plane.

Several variations of the rotating-crystal method are in common use. In *oscillating-crystal* photographs the crystal is oscillated through a limited angular range, instead of being rotated through 360°. The limited range reduces the possibility of overlapping reflections. The *Weissenberg goniometer* shifts the film in synchronism with the oscillation of the crystal. This procedure eliminates overlapping reflections

FIG. 2.8.   Laue pattern of a silicon crystal in approximately the [100] orientation.
(Courtesy of J. Washburn.)

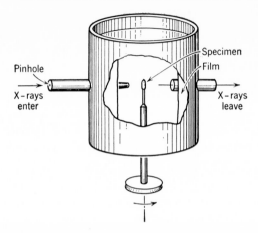

FIG. 2.9.   A rotating-crystal camera.   (By permission from *Structure of metals*, by C. S. Barrett.   Copyright 1943.   McGraw-Hill Book Co. 1943.)

and is also convenient for analytical reasons.   For details of the moving-film methods, which are now widely applied in structure-determination problems, the reader is referred to the book by Buerger listed at the end of the chapter.   In the *Bragg spectrometer* an ionization chamber is used to detect the diffracted radiation; it is well suited for absolute intensity measurements.

POWDER METHOD

In the powder method illustrated in Fig. 2.10 the incident mono-chromatic radiation strikes a finely powdered specimen or a fine-

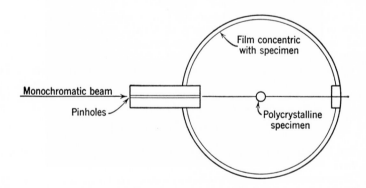

FIG. 2.10.   Schematic arrangement of a powder camera.

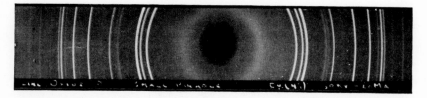

FIG. 2.11. Powder pattern for ZnO. (Courtesy of J. M. Jolliffe.)

grained polycrystalline specimen contained in a thin-walled capillary tube. Diffracted rays go out from individual crystallites which happen to be oriented with planes, making an incident angle θ with the beam satisfying the Bragg equation. An example of a powder-pattern photograph is given in Fig. 2.11. Diffracted rays leave the specimen along the generators of cones concentric with the original beam. The generators make an angle 2θ with the direction of the original beam, where θ is the Bragg angle. The cones intercept the film in a series of concentric rings.

An important use of the powder method is in the study of phase diagrams of alloy systems. Special cameras are constructed to permit the specimen to be at an elevated temperature, up to 1000°C or more.

PROBLEMS

2.1. Show that the perpendicular distance between adjacent planes of a set (hkl) in a simple cubic lattice of lattice constant a is

$$d(hkl) = \frac{a}{(h^2 + k^2 + l^2)^{1/2}}.$$

Hint: If one plane of the set passes through the origin, the equation of the nearest plane parallel to this plane is $xh + yk + zl = a$.

2.2. Design on paper a rotating-crystal experiment to determine the crystal structure of a single crystal specimen of NaBr. Consider voltage, target material, distances, spacing of different reflections, and other relevant experimental factors.

2.3. Show that a body-centered cubic lattice has as its reciprocal a face-centered cubic lattice.

2.4. Show that the geometrical structure factor for a face-centered cubic lattice referred to a cubic unit cell is

$$S = 1 + e^{i\pi(h+k)} + e^{i\pi(h+l)} + e^{i\pi(l+k)}.$$

Show that no reflections can occur for which the indices are partly even and partly odd.

2.5. Discuss several of the principal methods of growing inorganic and metal single crystals in the laboratory. (Reference: H. E. Buckley, *Crystal growth*, John Wiley and Sons, New York, 1951.)

2.6. The electron charge density $\rho(\mathbf{r})$ in a crystal may be expressed as a Fourier series

$$\rho(\mathbf{r}) = \sum_{\mathbf{k}} \rho_{\mathbf{k}} e^{i\mathbf{k}\cdot\mathbf{r}}.$$

If we write $\mathbf{k}$ in terms of the primitive translations of the reciprocal lattice, as follows:

$$\mathbf{k} = k_1 \mathbf{a}^* + k_2 \mathbf{b}^* + k_3 \mathbf{c}^*,$$

show that the requirement that $\rho(\mathbf{r})$ be invariant under all translations by lattice vectors of the form

$$\mathbf{T} = n_1 \mathbf{a} + n_2 \mathbf{b} + n_3 \mathbf{c}$$

may be satisfied by setting k_1, k_2, k_3 equal to integral multiples of 2π. Thus, if we write

$$\mathbf{r} = u\mathbf{a} + v\mathbf{b} + w\mathbf{c},$$

and, taking h, k, l as integers,

$$\mathbf{k} = 2\pi(h\mathbf{a}^* + k\mathbf{b}^* + l\mathbf{c}^*),$$

we have

$$\rho = \sum_{hkl} \rho(hkl) e^{2\pi i(hu+kv+lw)}.$$

We note that the values of $\mathbf{k}$ which occur in the Fourier series are equal to 2π times the vectors from the origin to the lattice points of the reciprocal lattice.

REFERENCES

Most of the references listed at the end of Chapter 1 are pertinent also to this chapter.

G. E. Bacon, *Neutron diffraction*, Clarendon Press, Oxford, 1955.

C. S. Barrett, *Structure of metals*, McGraw-Hill Book Co., New York, 2nd ed., 1952.

L. Brillouin, *Wave propagation in periodic structures*, McGraw-Hill Book Co., New York, 1946.

M. J. Buerger, *X-ray crystallography*, John Wiley and Sons, New York, 1942.

H. Lipson and W. Cochran, *The determination of crystal structures*, G. Bell and Sons, Ltd., London, 1953.

3 Thermal properties of solids

We discuss in this chapter the heat capacity of solids, and we give the theory for several idealized models. We shall make repeated use of a central result of statistical mechanics, the celebrated Boltzmann theorem.[1] The Boltzmann theorem or Boltzmann distribution law allows us to calculate the average properties of a system of particles in thermal equilibrium. According to the theorem, the ratio of the probability P_1 of finding the system in a state 1 to the probability P_2 of finding the system in a state 2 is given by

$$(3.1) \qquad \frac{P_1}{P_2} = \frac{e^{-E_1/KT}}{e^{-E_2/KT}},$$

where E_1, E_2 are the energies in the states 1, 2. Here k is the Boltzmann constant and T is the absolute temperature. The value of k is 1.38×10^{-16} erg/°K or 1.38×10^{-23} joule/°K. The precise definition of a *state* of the system is considered in books on statistical mechanics.

Example. Calculate the average kinetic energy and heat capacity of a free particle of mass M in thermal equilibrium at temperature T.

The Boltzmann probability factor is

$$e^{-E/kT} = e^{-Mv^2/2kT}$$

where **v** is the velocity of the particle. We denote thermal average by angular parentheses $\langle \ \rangle$. Thus the thermal average kinetic energy

$$(3.2) \qquad \langle E \rangle = \langle \tfrac{1}{2}Mv^2 \rangle = \frac{\iiint (\tfrac{1}{2}Mv^2)e^{-Mv^2/2kT} \, dv_x \, dv_y \, dv_z}{\iiint e^{-Mv^2/2kT} \, dv_x \, dv_y \, dv_z}$$

[1] For an introduction, see J. C. Slater, *Introduction to chemical physics*, McGraw-Hill, New York, 1939, pp. 32-64; also M. Born, *Atomic physics*, Hafner, New York, 5th ed., 1951, Chapter I; C. Kittel, *Elementary statistical physics*, John Wiley and Sons, New York, 1958.

where the denominator normalizes the total probability properly. The
integrals are taken from $-\infty$ to $+\infty$. In spherical coordinates the
volume element is $4\pi v^2\, dv$, so that

$$(3.3) \qquad \langle E \rangle = \frac{1}{2} M \int_0^\infty v^4 e^{-Mv^2/2kT}\, dv \bigg/ \int_0^\infty v^2 e^{-Mv^2/2kT}\, dv.$$

Setting $x = (M/2kT)^{\frac{1}{2}}v$, we have

$$(3.4) \qquad \langle E \rangle = kT \int_0^\infty x^4 e^{-x^2}\, dx \bigg/ \int_0^\infty x^2 e^{-x^2}\, dx.$$

We can look up the values of these definite integrals in standard tables,
but it is easy to get their ratio directly. The denominator may be
written as, letting $y^2 = \alpha x^2$,

$$(3.5) \qquad \int_0^\infty x^2 e^{-\alpha x^2}\, dx = \alpha^{-\frac{3}{2}} \int_0^\infty y^2 e^{-y^2}\, dy = C\alpha^{-\frac{3}{2}},$$

where C is some number. But

$$(3.6) \qquad -\frac{d}{d\alpha} \int_0^\infty x^2 e^{-\alpha x^2}\, dx = \int_0^\infty x^4 e^{-\alpha x^2}\, dx = \frac{3}{2} C\alpha^{-\frac{5}{2}},$$

so that the ratio of the definite integrals in (3.4) is, for $\alpha = 1$, just $\frac{3}{2}$.
Thus

$$(3.7) \qquad\qquad\qquad \langle E \rangle = \tfrac{3}{2}kT,$$

and the heat capacity is

$$(3.8) \qquad\qquad\qquad C_v = \frac{\partial \langle E \rangle}{\partial T} = \tfrac{3}{2}k.$$

These are familiar results.

It is interesting to follow the historical order of the growth of our
understanding of the heat capacity of dielectric or insulating solids.
The contribution of conduction electrons will be discussed in the chapter on the free electron theory of metals. The central experimental
facts are that the heat capacity of a representative monatomic solid
is about 6 cal per mole per deg K at room temperature and above. The
heat capacity falls off at low temperatures and approaches absolute
zero as T^3 in insulators and as T in metals. An experimental curve
for silver is shown in Fig. 3.1.

The first approach one might make to the thermal motion of the
atoms in a monatomic crystal is to picture each atom as bound by a

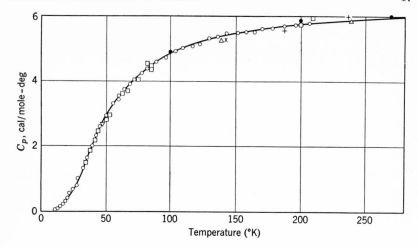

FIG. 3.1.   Heat capacity of metallic silver as a function of temperature.   The heat capacity at constant pressure C_p is the quantity measured, but for solids below room temperature the difference between C_p and C_v is small and usually may be neglected.

linear restoring force to a fixed position in the crystal.   On this picture each atom vibrates harmonically at a frequency ν common to all atoms of the crystal.   This model, when treated classically, gives a heat capacity independent of temperature and having a value in excellent agreement with experiment at room temperature and above, but which fails to account for the decrease in heat capacity observed at low temperatures.   The same model treated by quantum theory (by Einstein) does decrease at low temperatures but approaches zero too rapidly. Debye showed that a simple attempt to describe the elastic vibrations of the entire solid would account for the observed T^3 approach of the heat capacity to zero.   Born and von Kármán gave a more complete account of the spectrum of the lattice vibrations.

HARMONIC OSCILLATOR MODEL—CLASSICAL MECHANICS

We treat first the heat capacity of a simple harmonic oscillator in one dimension according to classical mechanics.   The energy of the oscillator is

$$(3.9) \qquad E = \tfrac{1}{2}Mv^2 + \tfrac{1}{2}M\omega^2 x^2,$$

where $\omega = 2\pi\nu$ is the angular frequency and x is the displacement from the position of static equilibrium.   The thermal average energy is, following the method used in the example just given,

$$(3.10) \quad \langle E \rangle = \frac{\frac{1}{2}M \iint (v^2 + \omega^2 x^2) e^{-M(v^2+\omega^2 x^2)/2kT} \, dx \, dv}{\iint e^{-M(v^2+\omega^2 x^2)/2kT} \, dx \, dv}$$

$$= \frac{\frac{M}{2} \int v^2 e^{-Mv^2/2kT} \, dv}{\int e^{-Mv^2/2kT} \, dv} + \frac{\frac{1}{2}M\omega^2 \int x^2 e^{-M\omega^2 x^2/2kT} \, dx}{\int e^{-M\omega^2 x^2/2kT} \, dx}$$

If in the first integral we put $y^2 = Mv^2/2kT$ and in the second integral $y^2 = M\omega^2 x^2/2kT$, we find that

$$(3.11) \qquad \langle E \rangle = 2kT \int_{-\infty}^{\infty} y^2 e^{-y^2} \, dy \, \Big/ \int_{-\infty}^{\infty} e^{-y^2} \, dy = kT,$$

for the simple harmonic oscillator in one dimension.

The internal energy of N harmonic oscillators in three dimensions is seen to be

$$(3.12) \qquad\qquad\qquad U = 3NkT,$$

or, for a mole of substance,

$$(3.13) \qquad\qquad\qquad U_M = 3RT.$$

The gas constant $R = Lk$, where L is Avogadro's number, 6.025×10^{23}. The theory predicts the lattice contribution to the molar heat capacity at constant volume

$$(3.14) \qquad\qquad\qquad C_v = \left(\frac{\partial U_M}{\partial T} \right)_v$$

of a solid should be, for a mole of atoms,

$$(3.15) \qquad\qquad\qquad C_v = 3R \cong 6 \text{ cal/deg mole.}$$

This value, which is known as the Dulong and Petit value, is in quite good agreement with the observed total heat capacity of many solids, including metals, at somewhat elevated temperatures, and often down to room temperature, but the agreement fails at low temperatures. As shown for silver in Fig. 3.1, the heat capacity falls drastically at low temperatures.

EINSTEIN MODEL OF THE LATTICE HEAT CAPACITY

Einstein[2] developed a simple model to account for the tendency of the lattice heat capacity to decrease at low temperatures below the

[2] A. Einstein, *Ann. d. Physik* **22**, 180 (1907); **34**, 170 (1911).

value $3R$ per mole found at elevated temperatures. He treated as above the thermal properties of the vibrations of a lattice of N atoms as a set of $3N$ independent harmonic oscillators in one dimension, each oscillator having the identical frequency ν. He then quantized the energies of the oscillators according to the prescription developed earlier by Planck in connection with the theory of blackbody radiation.

We recall that Planck[3] was faced with a critical failure of classical theory as applied to electromagnetic radiation in thermal equilibrium with matter. Classical theory predicted too much energy in the radiation spectrum at high frequencies. The departure of the observed radiation spectrum from the classical prediction occurred at lower and lower frequencies as the temperature was lowered, so that in some respects the failure at low temperature of the classical theory of heat capacity is reminiscent of the earlier difficulties with the blackbody radiation law.

The radiation problem is usually formulated by treating the light waves as equivalent to a set of harmonic oscillators. Planck was led to the correct law for the distribution of energy among the oscillators by postulating that the energy of an oscillator of frequency ν was quantized in discrete units $h\nu$. This was the first revolutionary step in the formulation of quantum mechanics, the set of physical laws, and principles governing the behavior of atoms, molecules, and solids. In classical theory an oscillator can have any amplitude of oscillation and hence any energy. According to Planck the energy E may have only the values

$$(3.16) \qquad E = nh\nu, \qquad n = 0, 1, 2, \cdots,$$

where n is any positive integer; ν is the frequency; and h is an experimental constant known as Planck's constant. The value of h has been determined to be 6.624×10^{-27} erg-sec. In modern work one often sees the relation (3.16) written as

$$(3.17) \qquad E = n \frac{h}{2\pi} 2\pi\nu = n\hbar\omega,$$

where ω is the angular frequency, and $\hbar$ (pronounced h-bar) has the value 1.054×10^{-27} erg-sec. An energy level is labeled by the value of the integer n, called the quantum number.

[3] For a detailed discussion of the Planck radiation law the reader may consult any textbook on modern atomic physics or on heat and thermodynamics. We mention a few examples of such textbooks: F. K. Richtmeyer and E. H. Kennard, *Introduction to modern physics*, McGraw-Hill, New York, 1947, 4th ed., pp. 178–183; M. Born, *Atomic physics*, Hafner, New York, 5th ed., 1951, Chapter VIII.

Quantization of the energy is approximately equivalent to quantization of the amplitude x_0 of the oscillator. If $\frac{1}{2}M\omega^2 x_0^2 = E$, then

$$(3.18) \qquad x_0 = \left(\frac{2n\hbar}{M\omega}\right)^{\frac{1}{2}}.$$

The uncertainty principle tells us that it is impossible to determine x_0 exactly.

The expression for the average energy of an oscillator on quantum theory is different from the average energy kT on classical theory. According to the Boltzmann distribution law the average energy is given by

$$(3.19) \qquad \langle E \rangle = \sum_{n=0}^{\infty} n\hbar\omega e^{-n\hbar\omega/kT} \Bigg/ \sum_{n=0}^{\infty} e^{-n\hbar\omega/kT}$$

$$= \frac{\hbar\omega(e^{-\hbar\omega/kT} + 2e^{-2\hbar\omega/kT} + \cdots)}{(1 + e^{-\hbar\omega/kT} + e^{-2\hbar\omega/kT} + \cdots)},$$

where as usual the denominator ensures that the normalization is correct. Writing $x = -\hbar\omega/kT$, we have after a little rearrangement

$$\langle E \rangle = \hbar\omega \frac{d}{dx} \log (1 + e^x + e^{2x} + \cdots)$$

$$= \hbar\omega \frac{d}{dx} \log \frac{1}{1 - e^x} = \frac{\hbar\omega}{e^{-x} - 1},$$

or, finally,

$$(3.20) \qquad \langle E \rangle = \frac{\hbar\omega}{e^{\hbar\omega/kT} - 1}.$$

This function is plotted in Fig. 3.2. We note that at high tempera-

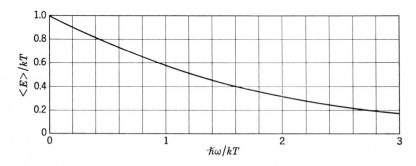

FIG. 3.2. Plot of average energy in units of kT for an Einstein oscillator of angular frequency ω.

tures ($kT \gg \hbar\omega$) the denominator can be expanded as

$$e^{\hbar\omega/kT} - 1 = 1 + \frac{\hbar\omega}{kT} + \cdots - 1 \cong \frac{\hbar\omega}{kT},$$

and so $\langle E \rangle \cong kT$. At high temperatures the average energy using the Planck-Einstein distribution law (3.20) for the harmonic oscillator approaches the classical average energy kT. The new feature is introduced at low temperatures ($kT \ll \hbar\omega$), as here $e^{\hbar\omega/kT} \gg 1$ and

$$(3.21) \qquad\qquad \langle E \rangle \cong \hbar\omega e^{-\hbar\omega/kT};$$

thus as $T \to$ zero the heat capacity approaches zero as

$$(3.22) \qquad\qquad C_v \cong Nk\left(\frac{\hbar\omega}{kT}\right)^2 e^{-\hbar\omega/kT},$$

for N atoms. The exponential factor is dominant in the limit, and so the low-temperature limiting variation of the heat capacity on the Einstein model is as $e^{-\hbar\omega/kT}$. Experimentally the variation for the lattice contribution at low temperatures is not exponential, but as T^3 in a dielectric. The Debye model, shortly to be discussed, gives a satisfactory account of the T^3 variation.

The Einstein model does, however, give a fairly good representation of the drop in heat capacity at low temperatures, provided we make an appropriate choice of the oscillator frequency ω. It is convenient to discuss results in terms of a characteristic temperature Θ_E (called the Einstein temperature) defined by

$$(3.23) \qquad\qquad \hbar\omega = k\Theta_E.$$

For many solids Θ_E is in the range 100 to 300°K, although instances are known which fall above or below this range. When we say Θ_E has a particular value, we mean that the heat capacity

$$(3.24) \qquad C = \frac{\partial U}{\partial T} = \frac{\partial(N\langle E \rangle)}{\partial T} = Nk\left(\frac{\hbar\omega}{kT}\right)^2 \frac{e^{\hbar\omega/kT}}{(e^{\hbar\omega/kT} - 1)^2}$$

$$= Nk\left(\frac{\Theta_E}{T}\right)^2 \frac{e^{\Theta_E/T}}{(e^{\Theta_E/T} - 1)^2}$$

gives a moderately good fit (for that value of Θ_E) to the experimental values over a wide range of temperature in which the heat capacity is varying appreciably with temperature.

If Θ_E is expressed in degrees and ω in radians per second, we have $\omega \approx 10^{11} \Theta_E$. For $\Theta_E = 300°K$, the characteristic frequency $\nu \doteq \omega/2\pi$ is of the order of 5×10^{12} cps. This is a reasonable magnitude for a characteristic atomic oscillation frequency: it is of the order of the frequency associated with an acoustical wavelength equal to an interatomic distance.

DEBYE MODEL OF THE LATTICE HEAT CAPACITY

The Einstein model is not an accurate representation of the thermal motion of the lattice at very low temperatures. On the Einstein model each atom is treated as an independent oscillator which executes harmonic motion about a fixed point in space regardless of what the neighboring atoms are doing. Actually the atoms oscillate relative to their neighbors in the lattice. For long wavelengths relative to the lattice spacing the motions of adjacent atoms are not independent, but large regions of the crystal move together coherently. It is an oversimplification to assign to all $3N$ oscillations the identical frequency—the long wavelength motions may have quite low frequencies, as in ordinary elastic waves at audio frequencies.

The long wavelength motions are particularly important at low temperatures, as there will always be modes of vibration in an infinite crystal for which $\hbar\omega \ll kT$. Thus even at low temperatures some degrees of freedom of the crystal will behave classically, and each such mode will make an approximate contribution kT to the energy, so that the total energy need not approach zero exponentially, as on the Einstein model.

Debye[4] assumes that the acoustical spectrum of a monatomic solid may be treated as if the solid were a homogeneous medium, except that the total number of independent elastic waves is cut off at $3N$, to agree with the number of degrees of freedom of N atoms. Debye assumes that the ordinary velocity of sound observed in a crystal at acoustical frequencies will hold approximately up to the cut-off frequency. It is usual to consider that the solid is elastically isotropic, so that the velocities v_l, v_t of longitudinal and transverse waves are independent of the propagation direction relative to the crystal axes. Elastic isotropy does *not* mean that the longitudinal wave velocity is equal to the transverse wave velocity.

In order to avoid confusion we first work out the contribution of the *longitudinal* elastic waves alone to the heat capacity of a Debye solid. If there are N atoms, there will be N longitudinal elastic modes of vibration labeled by the wave vector $\mathbf{k}$. The waves will have the

[4] P. Debye, *Ann. Physik* **39**, 789 (1912).

form $e^{i(\omega_k t - \mathbf{k}\cdot\mathbf{r})}$ if they are to be described as traveling waves. The internal energy is the sum of N Einstein functions, one for each mode:

$$(3.25) \qquad U_l = \sum_k \frac{\hbar\omega_k}{e^{\hbar\omega_k/kT} - 1}.$$

On the Debye model the dispersion relation connecting angular frequency and wave vector is

$$(3.26) \qquad \omega = v_l k,$$

where v_l is the longitudinal sound velocity. Thus

$$(3.27) \qquad U_l = \sum_k \frac{\hbar v_l k}{e^{\hbar v_l k/\tau} - 1},$$

where we have written τ for the Boltzmann constant times T to avoid confusing the different uses of k:

$$(3.28) \qquad \tau = k_B T.$$

The real problem now is to carry out the sum in (3.27) over all the longitudinal modes. If we want to replace the sum over $\mathbf{k}$ by an integral over the three-dimensional $\mathbf{k}$ space, we need to know $\rho(\mathbf{k})$, the number of modes per unit volume in $\mathbf{k}$ space. Then

$$(3.29) \qquad U_l = \iiint \frac{\hbar v_l k}{e^{\hbar v_l k/\tau} - 1} \rho(\mathbf{k}) \, dk_x \, dk_y \, dk_z.$$

Now $\rho(\mathbf{k})$ is determined by the boundary conditions on the vibrations of the solid. The boundary conditions determine $\rho(\mathbf{k})$, but the value of the function may be proved to be remarkably insensitive to the particular boundary conditions imposed, such as free ends or fixed ends.

The simplest boundary condition to calculate is the periodic boundary condition, which requires that the motion be the same at a point x, y, z as at a point $x + L$, $y + L$, $z + L$, where L is a macroscopic dimension. If the solid is in the form of a cube, then L can be taken as the edge of the cube. The application of this periodic boundary condition requires that

$$e^{i\mathbf{k}\cdot\mathbf{r}} = e^{i(\mathbf{k}\cdot\mathbf{r} + k_x L + k_y L + k_z L)}.$$

Thus

$$(3.30) \qquad e^{i(k_x L + k_y L + k_z L)} = 1,$$

which has the general solution

$$(3.31) \qquad k_x = \frac{2\pi l}{L}; \qquad k_y = \frac{2\pi m}{L}; \qquad k_z = \frac{2\pi n}{L};$$

where l, m, n are positive or negative integers. That is, the boundary conditions are that $k_i L/2\pi$ have integral values.

There is thus one allowed value of the vector $\mathbf{k}$ for each element of volume $(2\pi/L)^3$ in $\mathbf{k}$ space, so that the number of points $\rho(\mathbf{k})$ per unit volume in $\mathbf{k}$ space is

$$(3.32) \qquad \rho(\mathbf{k}) = \frac{L^3}{(2\pi)^3} = \frac{V}{(2\pi)^3},$$

where $V = L^3$ is the volume of the specimen. The situation in two dimensions is illustrated in Fig. 3.3.

By using this result for the density of states, the internal energy is

$$(3.33) \qquad U_l = \frac{V}{8\pi^3} \iiint \frac{\hbar v_l k}{e^{\hbar v_l k/\tau} - 1} \, dk_x \, dk_y \, dk_z$$

In spherical polar coordinates

$$(3.34) \qquad U_l = \frac{V}{2\pi^2} \int_0^{k_m} \frac{\hbar v_l k^3}{e^{\hbar v_l k/\tau} - 1} \, dk,$$

where the upper limit k_m of the integral is to be determined by the

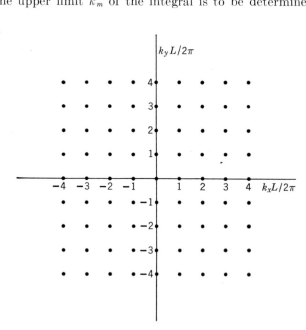

FIG. 3.3. Values of k_x, k_y satisfying periodic boundary conditions in a square of side L. In this two-dimensional problem the density of states is in $\mathbf{k}$ space $\rho(\mathbf{k}) = L^2/(2\pi)^2$.

condition that the total number of longitudinal modes shall be equal to N, the number of atoms. That is, in the Debye approximation we allow all $\mathbf{k}$ for which $k_i L/2\pi$ is integral, within a sphere in $\mathbf{k}$ space of radius

$$\frac{4\pi}{3} k_m{}^3 \rho(\mathbf{k}) = N,$$

or, using (3.32),

$$(3.35) \qquad k_m{}^3 = (2\pi)^3 \frac{N}{V} \frac{3}{4\pi} = \frac{6\pi^2 N}{V}.$$

We proceed with the evaluation of U_l and set

$$(3.36) \qquad x = \hbar v_l{}^{k/\tau}.$$

Then

$$(3.37) \qquad U_l = \frac{V}{2\pi^2} \frac{\tau^4}{\hbar^3 v_l{}^3} \int_0^{x_{ml}} \frac{x^3}{e^x - 1} \, dx,$$

where $x_{ml} = \hbar v_l k_m/\tau$, relating the upper limit on the integral to the cut-off wave vector k_m. The internal energy of the transverse vibrational modes is

$$(3.38) \qquad U_t = 2 \left(\frac{V}{2\pi^2} \right) \frac{\tau^4}{\hbar^3 v_t{}^3} \int_0^{x_{ml}} \frac{x^3}{e^x - 1} \, dx;$$

the factor of 2 arises because there are two transverse modes for each longitudinal mode.

If we define a suitable average elastic wave velocity as v, then the total lattice internal energy is given by

$$(3.39) \qquad U = 3 \left(\frac{V}{2\pi^2} \right) \frac{k_B{}^4 T^4}{\hbar^3 v^3} \int_0^{x_m} \frac{x^3}{e^x - 1} \, dx,$$

where k_B is the Boltzmann constant. It is usual to introduce the Debye temperature Θ by the relation

$$(3.40) \qquad x_m = \frac{\Theta}{T},$$

so that

$$(3.41) \qquad \Theta = \frac{\hbar v}{k_B} \left(\frac{6\pi^2 N}{V} \right)^{1/3}.$$

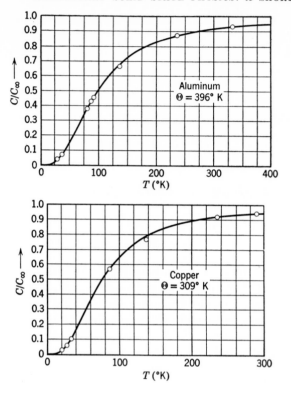

FIG. 3.4. Observed values, and curves calculated on the Debye model of the heat capacity of aluminum and copper, taking Θ = 396°K and 309°K, respectively. [After P. Debye, *Ann. Physik* **39**, 789 (1912).]

The heat capacity is given by dU/dT and is plotted in Fig. 3.4, together with observed values for aluminum and copper.

At high temperatures $x \ll 1$ the integrand in (3.39) may be approximated by

$$\frac{x^3}{e^x - 1} \cong \frac{x^3}{1 + x + \cdots - 1} \cong x^2,$$

and the integral in (3.39) has the value $x_m^3/3$ in this limit, so that

(3.42) $$U \cong 3Nk_BT,$$

in agreement with the classical result (3.12).

At very low temperatures we may approximate (3.39) by letting the upper limit go to infinity. We have[5]

$$(3.43) \qquad \int_0^\infty \frac{x^3 \, dx}{e^x - 1} = 6\zeta(4) = 6\sum_1^\infty \frac{1}{n^4} = \frac{\pi^4}{15},$$

where $\zeta(4)$ is the Riemann zeta function. Thus, for $T \ll \Theta$,

$$(3.44) \qquad U = \frac{3\pi^4 N k_B T^4}{5\Theta},$$

and from $C_v = dU/dT$,

$$(3.45) \qquad C_v = \frac{12\pi^4 N k_B}{5} \left(\frac{T}{\Theta}\right)^3 = 234 N k_B \left(\frac{T}{\Theta}\right)^3,$$

exhibiting the Debye T^3 approximation. For sufficiently low temperatures the Debye approximation should be quite good, as here only long wavelength acoustic waves are excited, and these are just the waves which may be treated as in an elastic continuum having macroscopic elastic constants.

We can understand the T^3 region qualitatively by a simple argument. It is reasonable to suppose that only those lattice modes having $\hbar\omega \lesssim k_B T$ will be excited to any appreciable extent at a low temperature T and, further, the excitation of these modes will be approximately classical, that is, each mode defined as "excited" will have an energy close to $k_B T$. Now we can see that the volume in $\mathbf{k}$ space occupied by the excited modes is of the order of $(k/k_m)^3$ or $(T/\Theta)^3$ of the total volume in $\mathbf{k}$ space; thus there are of the order of $N(T/\Theta)^3$ excited modes, each having energy $k_B T$. This gives rise to an internal energy of the order of $N k_B T (T/\Theta)^3$ and a heat capacity of the order of $N k_B (T/\Theta)^3$. However, attention is called to the large numerical factor, 234, in (3.45). The large factor is caused essentially by our inclusion (in accordance with convention) of the factor $(6\pi^2)^{1/3}$ in the definition of Θ in Eq. (3.41).

Representative values of the Debye characteristic temperature for a number of substances are given in Table 3.1. These data are quite useful in solid state problems, as Θ enters into a number of different phenomena, including electrical resistivity, thermal conductivity, and x-ray diffraction intensity.

[5] E. T. Whittaker and G. N. Watson, *Modern analysis*, Cambridge University Press, Cambridge, 4th ed., 1935, pp. 265–266.

TABLE 3.1

REPRESENTATIVE VALUES OF THE DEBYE Θ
(Compiled by P. H. Keesom and N. Pearlman)

Substance	(°K)	Substance	(°K)	Substance	(°K)
Be	1160	Fe	467	Al	418
Mg	406	Co	445	In	109
Ca	(219)	Ni	456	Tl	89
La	132	Pd	275	C (diamond)	(2000)
Ti	278	Pt	229	Si	658
Zr	270	Cu	339	Ge	366
V	273	Ag	225	Sn (gray)	212
Nb	252	Au	165	Sn (white)	189
Ta	231	Zn	308	Pb	94.5
Cr	402	Cd	300	Bi	117
Mo	425	Hg	(60–90)		
W	(379)				

The values of Θ obtained from thermal data at low temperatures are in quite good agreement with values of Θ calculated by Alers and Neighbours from elastic data when a suitable averaging over possible propagation directions is carried out:

	Θ (calorimetric) (°K)	Θ (elastic) (°K)
NaCl	320	322
KBr	174	173
Ag	226.5	226.4
Zn	305	327
Cu	345	344

We must emphasize that the Debye theory is not an exact theory because it is based on dispersion relations $\omega_i = v_i k$ which are valid only in the limit of long wavelengths ($ka \ll 1$, where a is an interatomic distance). The Debye theory usually fits experimental data fairly well because the heat capacity is not very sensitive to the details of the frequency distribution of normal modes.

HEAT CAPACITY OF CONDUCTION ELECTRONS IN METALS

When atoms are assembled to make a metal, the valence electrons of the atoms become the conduction electrons of the metal. In a certain sense the conduction electrons are free to move through the metal, and they may be accelerated by an applied electric field, leading to a flow of electric current. If the conduction electrons behaved as free classical particles, they would make a contribution $C(el) = \frac{3}{2}Nk$ to the heat capacity, where N is the number of conduction electrons per unit volume. That is, one would be led to expect (for $T \gg \Theta$) a total heat capacity of $3R$ per mole for insulators and $(3 + \frac{3}{2})R = 9R/2$ per mole for metals. In fact, the heat capacity of metals at high temperatures usually is not particularly different from that of insulators. There is no evidence that the electrons contribute to the heat capacity to anything like the extent envisaged by classical statistics.

The actual thermal behavior of the conduction electron gas in metals is affected profoundly by the Pauli exclusion principle, which expresses the prohibition against two electrons occupying the same quantum state. We shall develop these matters at considerable length in a later chapter on the free electron theory of metals. It is useful to anticipate the result for the heat capacity here in order that we may employ it in the discussion of thermal conductivity which follows directly.

For free electrons of mass m, the quantum theory result is that the electronic heat capacity at low temperatures is given by

$$(3.46) \qquad C_v(el) = \gamma T; \qquad \gamma = \frac{\pi^2 N^{1/3} km}{(3\pi^2)^{2/3}\hbar^2}.$$

For normal metals the definition of a low temperature for the present purpose is by comparison with a temperature of the order of perhaps 30,000°K. We note especially that $C_v(el)$ is linear in the temperature; the numerical value of γ is often of the order of 10^{-4} cal/mole-deg^2, so that at room temperature the electronic contribution is only of the order of 3×10^{-2} cal/mole-deg, quite small in comparison with the Dulong and Petit value for the lattice heat capacity, 6 cal/mole-deg.

At sufficiently low temperatures, usually below 4°K, the electronic contribution to the heat capacity becomes larger than the lattice contribution: the electronic term decreases as T, whereas at low temperatures the lattice term decreases as T^3, so that if we go low enough in temperature the electronic term will always be dominant in metals. Therefore it is possible to determine the coefficient γ in (3.46) by measurements at low temperatures. We observe that, for $T \ll \Theta$,

$$(3.47) \qquad C_v = C_v(\text{lattice}) + C_v(\text{electronic}) = \alpha T^3 + \gamma T,$$

where α is a constant defined by reference to Eq. (3.45). If we plot (C_v/T) versus T^2:

$$(3.48) \qquad \frac{C_v}{T} = \gamma + \alpha T^2,$$

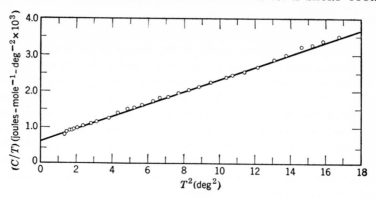

FIG. 3.5.   Heat capacity of metallic silver. (According to Corak, Garfunkel, Satterthwaite, and Wexler.)

we should have a straight line with the property that the extrapolated intercept on the vertical axis at $T = 0$ gives the value of γ, whereas the slope of the line gives α and therefore the value of the Debye Θ. A plot of this kind for silver is shown in Fig. 3.5.

A table of experimental values of γ is given in Table 3.2. It is found experimentally that the temperature dependence of the conduction electron heat capacity is actually linear in T for most metals; however, the coefficient γ sometimes has values quite different from those calculated from (3.46).

TABLE 3.2

SELECTED VALUES OF THE ELECTRONIC HEAT CAPACITY COEFFICIENT

Metal	$\gamma \times 10^4$ (cal/mole-deg^2)
Cu	1.65
Ag	1.46
Au	1.78
α-Mn	33
α-Fe	12
Co	12
Ni	17
Cd	1.7
Zn	1.3

PHONONS

In the derivation of the Debye theory we were led to the quantization of elastic waves in a crystal. The energy of an elastic wave of circular frequency ω must be equal to an integral multiple of $\hbar\omega$. The unit of elastic vibrational energy $\hbar\omega$ is called a *phonon*. We are already familiar with the fact that the unit of energy in an electromagnetic wave is also $\hbar\omega$; here the unit is called a photon. The names emphasize the particle aspects of the waves—energy exchange processes usually involve the creation or destruction of integral numbers of phonons, photons, etc.

It is natural to try to associate a momentum p with the phonon by the de Broglie relation $\lambda = h/p$, or

$$(3.49) \qquad \mathbf{p} = \hbar\mathbf{k},$$

which was first used to associate a wavelength with the momentum of an electron. In many respects a phonon behaves *as if* it had just this momentum. What happens is that in processes where the numbers or wave vectors of phonons change one finds that the momentum of the center of mass of the body often changes just as if $\mathbf{p}$ in (3.49) were a real momentum. However, in a finite body the normal modes of vibration are standing waves in coordinates relative to the center of mass, and such normal modes cannot in themselves carry momentum. But in exciting these waves by an external agency one transfers momentum to the center of mass. This is a delicate point. The quantity $\hbar\mathbf{k}$ is often called the *crystal momentum*, a name intended to distinguish it from the true momentum of the center of mass of the crystal.

In Bragg reflection of incident x-rays by a crystal, the photon momentum is changed by 2π times a reciprocal lattice vector of the crystal, and this is precisely the momentum given to the center of mass of the crystal. No phonons are excited (in a pure Bragg reflection), and thus the sum of $\hbar\mathbf{k}$ for the phonons is unchanged.

THERMAL CONDUCTIVITY OF SOLIDS

The thermal conductivity coefficient K of a solid is most easily defined with respect to the steady state flow of heat down a long rod within which there exists a temperature gradient $\partial T/\partial x$:

$$(3.50) \qquad Q = K\frac{\partial T}{\partial x},$$

where Q is the flux of thermal energy (energy transmitted across unit area per unit time); K is often expressed in units cal/cm-sec-deg or watts/cm-deg. To convert to watts/cm-deg, multiply K in cal/cm-sec-deg by 4.186. Some experimental curves of K versus temperature are given in Figs. 3.6 and 3.7.

The form of the equation (3.50) defining the conductivity implies that the process of thermal energy transfer is a random process. The energy does not simply enter one end of the specimen and proceed directly in a straight path to the other end, but the energy diffuses through the specimen, suffering frequent collisions. If the energy were propagated directly through the specimen without deflection,

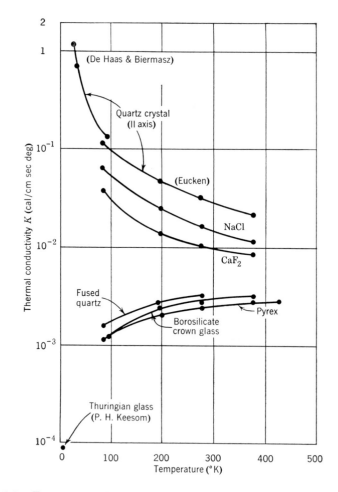

FIG. 3.6. Temperature dependence of the thermal conductivity of various crystals and glasses.

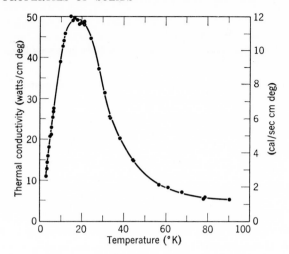

FIG. 3.7.   The thermal conductivity of copper.   (After Berman and MacDonald.)

then the expression for the thermal flux would not depend on the temperature gradient, but only on the difference in temperature ΔT between the ends of the specimen, regardless of the length of the specimen.   It is the random nature of the conductivity process that brings the temperature gradient into the expression for the thermal flux.

In gas-kinetic theory we find in a certain approximation the following expression for the thermal conductivity:

$$(3.51) \qquad\qquad K = \tfrac{1}{3}Cu\Lambda,$$

where C is the heat capacity per unit volume, u is the average particle velocity, and Λ is the mean free path of a particle between collisions. The result was applied first by Debye to describe thermal conductivity in dielectric solids, C being the heat capacity of the lattice waves or phonons, u the velocity of sound, and Λ the mean free path of the phonons.   Several representative values of the mean free path are given in Table 3.3.

It is instructive to bring out the random nature of the conductivity process.   The usual heat conduction equation for the flux of thermal energy in a linear specimen is

$$(3.52) \qquad\qquad Q = \frac{K(T_1 - T_2)}{L}.$$

TABLE 3.3

PHONON MEAN FREE PATH VALUES

(Calculated from (3.51), taking $u = 5 \times 10^5$ cm/sec as the average
sound velocity)

Crystal	$T(°C)$	$C(\text{cal/cm}^3\text{-deg})$	$K(\text{cal/cm-deg-sec})$	$\Lambda(\text{cm})$
Quartz†	0	0.48	0.03	40×10^{-8}
	−190	0.13	0.12	540×10^{-8}
NaC	0	0.45	0.17	23×10^{-8}
	−190	0.24	0.064	100×10^{-8}

† Parallel to optic axis.

Here Q = heat transfer across unit area per unit time; $T_1 - T_2$ = temperature drop between ends; L = length of specimen. On substituting for K the expression given by (3.51), we have

$$(3.53) \qquad Q = \tfrac{1}{3}C(T_1 - T_2)\frac{\Lambda u}{L}.$$

In this form the equation may be interpreted very simply: $C(T_1 - T_2)$ is the excess energy density at one end of the specimen with respect to the other end; this excess is propagated down the specimen with an effective transport velocity which is just the carrier velocity reduced by the ratio of the mean free path to the length of the specimen.

The phonon mean free path Λ is determined principally by two processes, geometrical scattering and scattering by other phonons. If the forces between atoms were purely harmonic, there would be no mechanism for collisions between different phonons, and the mean free path would be limited solely by collisions of a phonon with the crystal boundary, and by lattice imperfections. There are situations to be discussed below where these effects are dominant. With anharmonic lattice interactions there is a coupling between different phonons which limits the value of the mean free path.

The theory of the effect of anharmonic coupling on thermal conductivity is one of the more complicated problems in solid state physics. An approximate calculation given by Debye,[6] and Peierls,[7] has considered the problem in great detail. They both show that Λ is proportional to $1/T$ at high temperatures, in agreement with many

---

[6] P. Debye, in *Vorträge über die kinetische Theorie der Materie und Elektrizität*, by M. Planck et al., Teubner, Leipzig, 1914.

[7] R. Peierls, *Ann. Physik* **3**, 1055 (1929); see also C. Herring, *Phys. Rev.* **95**, 954 (1954).

experiments. We can understand this dependence in terms of the number of phonons with which a given phonon can interact: at high temperature the excitation of phonons is proportional to T.

THERMAL EXPANSION

We may understand the origin of thermal expansion by considering the effect of anharmonic terms in the potential energy on the separation of a pair of atoms at a temperature T. We take the potential energy of the atoms at a displacement x from their equilibrium separation at $0°K$ as

$$(3.54) \qquad V(x) = cx^2 - gx^3 - fx^4,$$

where the term in x^3 represents the asymmetry of the mutual repulsion of the atoms and the term in x^4 represents the general "softening" of the vibration at large amplitudes.

We calculate the average displacement by using the Boltzmann distribution function, which weights the possible values of x according to their thermodynamic probability:

$$(3.55) \qquad \bar{x} = \frac{\int_{-\infty}^{\infty} x e^{-V(x)/kT}\, dx}{\int_{-\infty}^{\infty} e^{-V(x)/kT}\, dx}.$$

For small displacement (low anharmonic energy) we expand the integrands:

$$\int x e^{-V/kT}\, dx \cong \int e^{-cx^2/kT}\left(x + \frac{gx^4}{kT} + \frac{fx^5}{kT}\right) dx = \frac{g}{kT}\left(\frac{kT}{c}\right)^{5/2}\frac{3\pi^{1/2}}{4},$$

$$\int e^{-V/kT}\, dx \cong \int e^{-cx^2/kT}\, dx = \left(\frac{\pi kT}{c}\right)^{1/2};$$

and so

$$(3.56) \qquad \bar{x} = \frac{3kTg}{4c^2},$$

giving a constant value of the temperature coefficient of thermal expansion. Several values of the linear expansion coefficient are given in Table 3.4.

TABLE 3.4

LINEAR COEFFICIENTS OF THERMAL EXPANSION NEAR ROOM TEMPERATURE

$$l_t = l_0(1 + \beta t)$$

Substance	$10^6 \times \beta$ (per deg C)	Substance	$10^6 \times \beta$ (per deg C)
Au	14	CsCl	50
Li	56	Jena glass (2954—III)	6
Na	71	$AlBr_3$	400
K	83	Zn (parallel to axis)	64
Ni	13	(perpendicular to axis)	14
Pt	9	Te (parallel to axis)	−1.6
		(perpendicular to axis)	27

PROBLEMS

3.1. Show that the heat capacity of a monatomic lattice in one dimension in the Debye approximation is proportional to T/Θ for low temperatures such that $T \ll \Theta$, where Θ is the effective Debye temperature in one dimension and is defined as $\Theta = \hbar\omega_m/k = \hbar\pi v_0/ka$, k being the Boltzmann constant and a the interatomic separation.

3.2. Show that the expression for the average energy of a classical system may be written as

$$\langle E \rangle = \frac{kT^2 d(\log Z)}{dT},$$

where the partition function Z is defined by

$$Z = \iint e^{-E(p,q)/kT} \, dp \, dq;$$

here p is the momentum.

3.3. Using the anharmonic potential $V(x) = cx^2 - gx^3 - fx^4$, show that the approximate heat capacity of the classical anharmonic oscillator is

$$C \cong k \left[1 + \left(\frac{3f}{2c^2} + \frac{15g^2}{8c^3} \right) kT \right].$$

Note: $\log (1 + x) \cong x - \frac{1}{2}x^2$ for $x \ll 1$; the calculation is shorter if the partition function (Problem 3.2) is employed.

3.4. Show by thermodynamics that

$$C_p - C_v = \frac{9\beta^2 T}{K},$$

where C_p is the heat capacity per unit volume at constant pressure, C_v at constant volume, β is the temperature coefficient of linear expansion, and K is the compressibility. Estimate $C_p - C_v$ for copper at 300°K and at 1000°K. The derivation is given in standard textbooks on thermodynamics.

3.5. By equating the elastic energy per unit cell $\frac{1}{2}ce^2a^3$ with kT, show that the local thermal strain in a crystal at room temperature may be of the order of 0.1; here e is the strain; c is an average elastic constant; and a is the lattice constant.

3.6. Does the classical result (3.15) depend on the assumption that all atomic oscillators have the identical frequency? Why?

3.7. Let us suppose that we have a system of N molecules each of which can be oriented independently relative to some fixed direction in two ways, parallel or antiparallel. We suppose further that the energy of a molecule when it is directed in one of the orientations is higher by an amount ΔE than when directed in the opposite orientation. We have then the simple energy level system indicated in Fig. 3.8. In thermal equilibrium the ratio of the

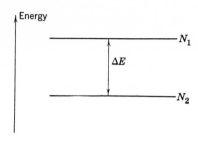

FIG. 3.8. Two-level systems with populations N_1, N_2.

number of atoms N_1 in the upper energy state to the number in the lower energy state is given simply by the Boltzmann factor

$$\frac{N_1}{N_2} = e^{-\Delta E/kT}.$$

Show that the internal energy of the system is

$$U = N_1 \Delta E = \frac{N \Delta E}{1 + e^{\Delta E/kT}},$$

where $N = N_1 + N_2$. Show further that the heat capacity is

$$C = Nk \frac{(\Delta E/kT)^2 e^{\Delta E/kT}}{(1 + e^{\Delta E/kT})^2}.$$

Plot N_1 and C as functions of the parameter $x = kT/\Delta E$. Peaks of this type in the heat capacity are often known as Schottky anomalies.

REFERENCES

R. Berman, "Thermal conductivity in dielectric solids at low temperatures," *Advances in Physics* **2**, 103–140 (1953).

A. Eucken, *Handbuch der Experimentalphysik, Akademische Verlagsgesellschaft,* Leipzig, Vol. 8/1, 1929.

R. H. Fowler and E. A. Guggenheim, *Statistical thermodynamics,* Cambridge University Press, Cambridge, 1939.

J. L. Olsen and H. M. Rosenberg, "Thermal conductivity of metals at low temperatures," *Advances in Physics* **2**, 28–66 (1953).

J. C. Slater, *Introduction to chemical physics,* McGraw-Hill Book Co., New York, 1939, Chapters XIII–XV.

4 Dielectric properties

In this chapter we discuss first the relationship between the applied electric field and the local electric field acting on an atom. The interaction of the local field with the atom determines the polarization, yet the local field may itself be a function of the polarization. We then discuss the electric polarization of atoms, molecules, and crystals in static fields and at high frequencies. The polarization is defined as the dipole moment per unit volume, the dipole moment $\wp$ of the specimen as a whole being defined as $\wp = \Sigma\ e_i \mathbf{r}_i$. The sum is extended over all charges in the system; on the supposition that the system is neutral the sum is independent of the origin chosen for the position vector $\mathbf{r}_i$.

LOCAL ELECTRIC FIELD

The calculation of the local field at an atom or ion as affected by the polarization of the specimen as a whole is a problem of central importance in dielectric and magnetic theory. We consider first a solid dielectric with a cubic crystal structure; we suppose that the specimen is in the form of an ellipsoid with one of the axes parallel to the applied electric field (Fig. 4.1).

The field $\mathbf{E}_{loc}$ at any atom may be written as a sum

$$(4.1) \qquad \mathbf{E}_{loc} = \mathbf{E}_0 + \mathbf{E}_1 + \mathbf{E}_2 + \mathbf{E}_3,$$

where $\mathbf{E}_0$ is the electric field applied from external sources; $\mathbf{E}_1$ is the "depolarization field" resulting from polarization charges on the outer surface of the specimen. We imagine as a mathematical fiction a small sphere cut out of the specimen around the reference point; then $\mathbf{E}_2$ is the field of the polarization charges on the inside of the cavity left by the sphere, and $\mathbf{E}_3$ is the field of the atoms within the cavity.

The addition $\mathbf{E}_1 + \mathbf{E}_2 + \mathbf{E}_3$ to the local field is just the total effect at one atom of the dipole moments of all the other atoms in the specimen:

(4.2)

$$(\text{esu}) \qquad \mathbf{E}_1 + \mathbf{E}_2 + \mathbf{E}_3 = \sum_i \frac{3(\mathbf{p}_i \cdot \mathbf{r}_i)\mathbf{r}_i - r_i^2 \mathbf{p}_i}{r_i^5};$$

$$(\text{MKS}) \qquad \mathbf{E}_1 + \mathbf{E}_2 + \mathbf{E}_3 = \frac{1}{4\pi\epsilon_0} \sum_i \frac{3(\mathbf{p}_i \cdot \mathbf{r}_i)\mathbf{r}_i - r_i^2 \mathbf{p}_i}{r_i^5};$$

where $\mathbf{p}_i$ is the dipole moment of atom i, and $\epsilon_0 = 8.85 \times 10^{-12}$ farad/ meter is the permittivity constant. If we are far enough away from the individual dipoles of a uniformly polarized specimen, we may, according to an elementary transformation occurring in electrostatic theory, calculate the field of the specimen as equal to the field of a surface charge distribution of density P_n on the surfaces of the specimen, P_n being the normal component of the polarization $\mathbf{P}$ at the surfaces. The idea in creating the cavity is that we may treat the field $\mathbf{E}_3$ of the dipoles within the cavity on a microscopic basis by such a sum as (4.2), whereas the rest of the specimen is treated macroscopically by means of integrals over the effective surface charges. One integral is taken over the outer surface, and it gives $\mathbf{E}_1$; the other integral is taken over the

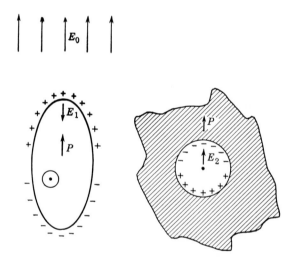

FIG. 4.1.   Contributions to the local electric field at the ion at the center of the spherical cavity, showing the applied field E_0, the depolarization field E_1, and the Lorentz field E_2.   The local field is the sum of these plus the field of the dipoles within the cavity.

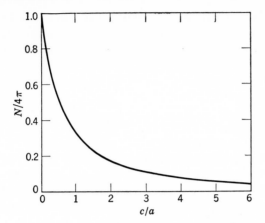

FIG. 4.2. Demagnetization factor N parallel to the figure axis of ellipsoids of revolution as a function of the axial ratio c/a.

surface of the spherical cavity, and it gives $\mathbf{E}_2$.   The field $\mathbf{E}_1$ is readily seen from Fig. 4.1 to be opposite in direction to the polarization and hence is called the *depolarization field*.

DEPOLARIZATION FIELD

The calculation of the depolarization field is a well-known problem in classical electricity, and we summarize the results here.   It is found that specimens of homogeneous composition will be uniformly polarized when placed in a uniform external field as long as the external shape of the specimen is that of a general ellipsoid or a limiting case of a general ellipsoid.   If the ellipsoid is oriented with one of the principal axes parallel to the applied field, the polarization will be parallel to the applied field, as will the depolarization field E_1, which it is found may be calculated from the polarization P by a relation of the form

$$\text{(esu)} \qquad E_1 = -NP;$$

(4.3)
$$\text{(MKS)} \qquad E_1 = \frac{-NP}{4\pi\epsilon_0}.$$

The constant N is known as the *depolarization factor;* it is precisely the same as the *demagnetization factor*, and its value depends on the axial ratio.   It is exceptionally important in the field of magnetism.   Values of N are plotted in Fig. 4.2 for ellipsoids of revolution, and additional cases have been calculated by Osborn[1] and Stoner.[2]   As defined here N has the same value in both esu and MKS units.   In the several limiting cases we have the following values:

Shape	Axis	N
Sphere	any	$4\pi/3$
Thin slab	normal	4π
Thin slab	in plane	0
Long circular cylinder	longitudinal	0
Long circular cylinder	transverse	2π

The demagnetization factor has a rigorous meaning only for homogeneous general ellipsoids in uniform applied fields.   An important property of the demagnetization factor is that $N_a + N_b + N_b = 4\pi$, where N_a, N_b, N_c are the demagnetization factors along the three principal axes of a general ellipsoid.   Sometimes the demagnetization factors are defined such that their sum is unity, but we have not done this.

LORENTZ FIELD

The field $\mathbf{E}_2$ due to the polarization charges on the surface of the fictitious cavity was calculated first by Lorentz.   If θ is the polar angle (Fig. 4.3) referred to the polarization direction as axis, the surface charge density on the surface of the cavity is $-P \cos \theta$.   The electric field at the center of the spherical cavity of radius a is

$$(4.4) \quad (\text{esu}) \quad \mathbf{E}_2 = \int_0^\pi (a^{-2})(2\pi a \sin \theta)(a \, d\theta)(\mathbf{P} \cos \theta)(\cos \theta) = \frac{4\pi \mathbf{P}}{3};$$

in MKS units the result is $\mathbf{E}_2 = \mathbf{P}/3\epsilon_0$.   The cavity field is actually uniform, but for our purpose we need only the field at the center, which is what we have just calculated.

FIELD OF DIPOLES INSIDE CAVITY

The field $\mathbf{E}_3$ caused by the dipoles within the cavity is the only term in the sum which depends on the crystal structure.   We shall first consider a cubic structure, for which it is readily shown that $\mathbf{E}_3 = 0$ if all the atoms may be replaced by point dipoles parallel to each other.

[1] J. A. Osborn, *Phys. Rev.* **67**, 351 (1945).

[2] E. C. Stoner, *Phil. Mag.* **36**, 803 (1945); for approximate values for non-ellipsoidal shapes, see J. Würschmidt, *Theorie des Entmagnetisierungsfaktor,* Vieweg, Braunschweig, 1925; J. L. Snoek, *Physica* **1**, 649 (1933); R. M. Bozorth and D. M. Chapin, *J. Appl. Phys.* **13**, 320 (1942).

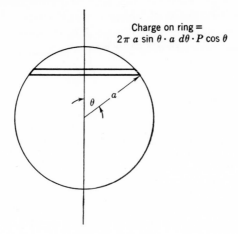

FIG. 4.3. Calculation of the field in a spherical cavity in a uniformly polarized
medium (esu).

The axis of the dipoles is taken as the z axis; at the reference point
the field caused by the other dipoles p_i is

(4.5)

$$\text{(esu)} \qquad E_3{}^z = \sum_i \frac{3p_i z_i{}^2 - p_i r_i{}^2}{r_i{}^5};$$

$$\text{(MKS)} \qquad E_3{}^z = \sum_i \frac{3p_i z_i{}^2 - p_i r_i{}^2}{4\pi\epsilon_0 r_i{}^5}.$$

By the symmetry of the lattice and the cavity, $\Sigma\ (z_i{}^2/r_i{}^5) = \Sigma\ (y_i{}^2/r_i{}^5)$
$= \Sigma\ (x_i{}^2/r_i{}^5)$, so that $\Sigma\ (r_i{}^2/r_i{}^5) = 3\ \Sigma\ (z_i{}^2/r_i{}^5)$, whence $\mathbf{E}_3 = 0$.

The proof we have given for the vanishing of $\mathbf{E}_3$ actually obtains
for all cases in which the environment of the reference point is cubic
as long as the dipoles are parallel. Thus $\mathbf{E}_3 = 0$ for induced polarization on simple cubic, body-centered cubic, and face-centered cubic lattices, as well as for an isotropic distribution. Later, in considering
the ferroelectric properties of barium titanate, we shall see that here
$\mathbf{E}_3 \neq 0$; although the crystallographic symmetry is cubic, the environment of the oxygen ions is not cubic.

FIELD IN DIELECTRIC BETWEEN CONDENSER PLATES

The classical definition of the macroscopic (average) electric field
intensity $\mathbf{E}$ inside a dielectric is that $\mathbf{E}$ is the average field inside a long

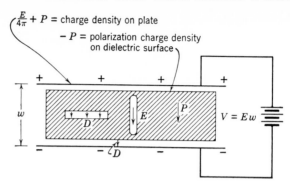

FIG. 4.4. Definitions of D and E; the voltage V across the condenser plates is E times the separation w, if we neglect the air gaps between the plates and the dielectric. Figure is for esu.

needle-shaped cavity, parallel to the polarization (Fig. 4.4), whereas the displacement $\mathbf{D}$ is defined as the average field inside a disk-shaped cavity normal to the polarization. The difference

$$(4.6) \qquad \text{(esu)} \qquad \mathbf{D} - \mathbf{E} = 4\pi\mathbf{P}$$

is caused by the field $4\pi\mathbf{P}$ of the polarization charge density $\mathbf{P}$ on the flat surfaces of the disk cavity; the polarization charges on the needle cavity may be neglected. Inside a spherical cavity the local field is $\mathbf{E} + (4\pi/3)P$. In MKS, (4.6) becomes $\mathbf{D} - \epsilon_0\mathbf{E} = \mathbf{P}$, and the field inside a spherical cavity is $\mathbf{E} + \mathbf{P}/3\epsilon_0$.

Measurements of the polarization $\mathbf{P}$ or of the dielectric constant $\epsilon = D/E$ (in esu) or $\epsilon = D/\epsilon_0 E$ (in MKS) are usually made by measuring the capacity $C = Q/V$ of a condenser filled with the dielectric. In the absence of the dielectric we suppose that the field between the condenser plates is E', so that the surface charge density on each plate is $\pm E'/4\pi$ in esu or $\pm\epsilon_0 E'$ in MKS. When the dielectric is inserted, polarization charge densities $\pm P$ are induced on the surfaces of the dielectric, and these charges are then effectively neutralized by a flow of charge around the condenser circuit. The field E in esu inside the needle-shaped cavity is the sum of a field $-4\pi P$ from the polarization charges and $E' + 4\pi P$ from the original and the neutralization charges on the condenser plates. Thus for the condenser arrangement $E = E'$, and from (4.1), (4.3), and (4.4), $E_{\text{loc}} = E_0 + E_1 + E_2 + E_3 =$

$(E + 4\pi P) + (-4\pi P) + (4\pi P/3) + (0)$ for structures such that $E_3 = 0$. Then

$$\text{(esu)} \qquad E_{\text{loc}} = E + \frac{4\pi}{3} P;$$

(4.7)

$$\text{(MKS)} \qquad E_{\text{loc}} = E + \frac{1}{3\epsilon_0} P.$$

That is, the value of the macroscopic average field E is the same as the field existing between the condenser plates before the dielectric is inserted; the field acting at the center of an atom is E plus a contribution $4\pi P/3$ or, in MKS, $P/3\epsilon_0$ from the field produced by the polarization of the other atoms in the specimen. It is seen further that the condenser plates, if put in close contact with the dielectric, have the effect of shorting-out the depolarization charge. Evidence for the approximate validity of (4.7) in ionic crystals is given by Tessman, Kahn, and Shockley.[3]

DIELECTRIC CONSTANT AND POLARIZABILITY

The dielectric constant ϵ has the identical value in esu and MKS, and it is defined for an isotropic medium as

$$\text{(esu)} \qquad \epsilon = \frac{D}{E} = 1 + 4\pi \frac{P}{E} = 1 + 4\pi\chi;$$

(4.8)

$$\text{(MKS)} \qquad \epsilon = \frac{D}{\epsilon_0 E} = 1 + \frac{P}{\epsilon_0 E} = 1 + 4\pi\chi,$$

where χ is the electric susceptibility. The use of the factor 4π before χ in (4.8) (MKS) is not entirely orthodox, but is introduced to make the numerical value of χ independent of the system of units employed. The polarizability α is defined as

$$\text{(4.9)} \qquad \text{(esu)} \qquad \alpha_i = \frac{p_i}{E_{\text{loc}}{}^i},$$

where the index i refers to a particular type of atom, p_i is the dipole moment. The polarization is then

$$\text{(esu)} \qquad P = \sum_i E_{\text{loc}}{}^i N_i \alpha_i,$$

where N_i is the number per unit volume of atoms of type i.

[3] J. Tessman, A. Kahn, and W. Shockley, *Phys. Rev.* **92**, 890 (1953).

If the local field is connected with the applied field by the Lorentz relation (4.7), we have

$$(4.10) \qquad \text{(esu)} \qquad \frac{P}{E} = \frac{\Sigma\, N_i \alpha_i}{1 - (4\pi/3)\,\Sigma\, N_i \alpha_i} = \frac{\epsilon - 1}{4\pi};$$

which may be solved for $\Sigma\, N_i \alpha_i$ to give

$$(4.11) \qquad \text{(esu)} \qquad \frac{\epsilon - 1}{\epsilon + 2} = \frac{4\pi}{3}\, \Sigma\, N_i \alpha_i;$$

This is a common form of the relation between the dielectric constant and the atomic polarizabilities; (4.11) may be rewritten as the Clausius-Mossotti equation (or, with $\epsilon = n^2$, the Lorenz-Lorentz equation),

$$(4.12) \qquad \text{(esu)} \qquad \frac{M}{\rho} \frac{\epsilon - 1}{\epsilon + 2} = \frac{4\pi}{3}\, L\alpha,$$

where M is the molecular weight, ρ the density, L Avogadro's number, n the refractive index, and α the total polarizability per molecule. The left-hand side of this equation is called the *molar polarizability*.

MEASUREMENT OF DIELECTRIC CONSTANTS

The usual methods of measuring dielectric constants are based on a comparison of the capacity C'' of a capacitor filled with the substance and the capacity C' of the empty capacitor. The ratio $C''/C' = \epsilon$, the dielectric constant. The determination of the value of the capacity may in principle be accomplished by an LC resonant circuit as shown in Fig. 4.5, where C_s is a calibrated variable capacitor and C is the condenser in which the specimen may be placed. By varying the

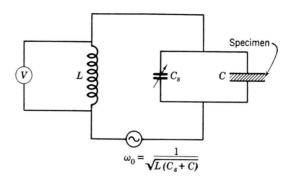

FIG. 4.5. Schematic diagram of apparatus for the measurement of dielectric constants.

calibrated capacitor so as to keep the resonance frequency $\omega_0 = [L(C_s + C)]^{-\frac{1}{2}}$ constant when C is inserted and then filled, we may determine C' and C'', and thus ϵ. The dielectric loss may be obtained from the sharpness of the tuning near resonance.

Descriptions of the actual circuits employed are abundant in the literature. At microwave frequencies the technique of measurement is altered somewhat, and here one often measures essentially the wavelength λ of the microwave radiation in the specimen, obtaining the dielectric constant from the relation $\lambda(\text{vacuum})/\lambda(\text{specimen}) = (\epsilon\mu)^{\frac{1}{2}}$, where μ is the permeability.

ELECTRONIC POLARIZABILITIES

The total polarizability of an atom or ion may usually be separated into three parts:[4] electronic, ionic, and orientational. The electronic contribution arises from the displacement of electrons in an atom relative to the nucleus; that is, from the deformation of the electron shell about a nucleus. The ionic or atomic contribution comes from the displacement and deformation of a charged ion with respect to other ions. The orientational or dipolar polarizability arises when the substance is built up of molecules possessing a permanent electric dipole moment which may be more or less free to change orientation in an applied electric field. It is possible to separate experimentally the different contributions, and one way of doing this is indicated in Fig. 4.6. The usual situation is that both the ionic and the dipolar contributions are seldom large together in the same substance: in ordinary ionic crystals there is no dipolar contribution.

In the optical range of frequency the dielectric constant arises almost entirely from the electronic polarizability, so that in the optical range (4.11) reduces to

$$(4.13) \qquad (\text{esu}) \qquad \frac{n^2 - 1}{n^2 + 2} = \frac{4\pi}{3} \Sigma N_i \alpha_i \text{ (electronic)};$$

here we have used the relation $n^2 = \epsilon$, where n is the refractive index. By applying this relation to large numbers of crystals we may determine empirical values of the electronic polarizabilities which are reasonably consistent with the observed values of the refractive index. Values obtained in this way are given in Table 4.1. The scheme is not entirely self-consistent, as the electronic polarizability of an ion may depend slightly on the environment in which it is placed.

[4] In heterogeneous materials there is usually also an *interfacial polarization* arising from the accumulation of charge at structural interfaces. This is of little fundamental interest, but of considerable practical interest as commercial insulating materials are usually heterogeneous.

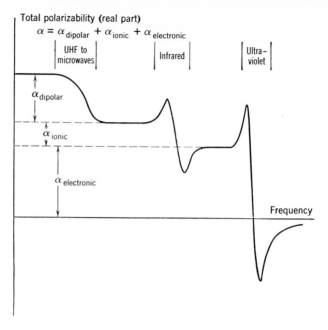

FIG. 4.6.   Frequency dependence of the several contributions to the polarizability (schematic).

CLASSICAL THEORY OF ELECTRONIC POLARIZABILITY

According to classical mechanics an electron bound harmonically to an atom will show resonance absorption at a frequency $\omega_0 = (\beta/m)^{\frac{1}{2}}$, where β is the force constant.   The average displacement of the electron occasioned by the application of a field E_{loc} will be given by

$$eE_{\text{loc}} = \beta\bar{x} = m\omega_0{}^2\bar{x},$$

so that the static electronic polarizability is

(4.14)   (esu) $\alpha(\text{electronic}) = \dfrac{p}{E_{\text{loc}}} = \dfrac{e\bar{x}}{E_{\text{loc}}} = \dfrac{e^2}{m\omega_0{}^2}.$

The electronic polarizability will depend on frequency, and it is shown in the following example that the result is, for frequency ω,

(4.15) $\alpha(\text{electronic}) = \dfrac{e^2/m}{\omega_0{}^2 - \omega^2},$

TABLE 4.1
ELECTRONIC POLARIZABILITIES OF IONS

Values from L. Pauling, *Proc. Roy. Soc.* (*London*) **A114,** 181 (1927) and from Tessman, Kahn, and Shockley, *Phys. Rev.* **92,** 890 (1953). The TKS polarizabilities are for the D lines of sodium.

Units cm^3 $\times$ 10^{-24}

	He	Li$^+$	Be^{2+}	Br^{3+}	C^{4+}
Pauling	0.201	0.029	0.008	0.003	0.0013
TKS		0.03			

	O^{2-}	F$^-$	Ne	Na$^+$	Mg^{2+}	Al^{3+}	Si^{4+}
Pauling	3.88	1.04	0.390	0.179	0.094	0.052	0.0165
TKS	(2.4)	0.652		0.41			

	S^{2-}	Cl$^-$	A	K$^+$	Ca^{2+}	Sc^{3+}	Ti^{4+}
Pauling	10.2	3.66	1.62	0.83	0.47	0.286	0.185
TKS	(5.5)	2.97		1.33	1.1		(0.19)

	Se^{2-}	Br$^-$	Kr	Rb$^+$	Sr^{2+}	Y^{3+}	Zr^{4+}
Pauling	10.5	4.77	2.46	1.40	0.86	0.55	0.37
TKS	(7.)	4.17		1.98	1.6		

	Te^{2-}	I$^-$	Xe	Cs$^+$	Ba^{2+}	La^{3+}	Ce^{4+}
Pauling	14.0	7.10	3.99	2.42	1.55	1.04	0.73
TKS	(9.)	6.44		3.34	2.5		

but in the visible region the dispersion is not usually very important in most dielectric materials.

Example. Find the frequency dependence of the electronic polarizability of an electron having the resonance frequency ω_0, treating the system as a simple harmonic oscillator.

The equation of motion in the electric field $E_0 e^{i\omega t}$ is

$$m\ddot{x} + m\omega_0{}^2 x = eE_0 e^{i\omega t},$$

so that, for $x = x_0 e^{i\omega t}$,

$$m(-\omega^2 + \omega_0{}^2)x_0 = eE_0.$$

The dipole moment is $p_0 e^{i\omega t}$, where

$$p_0 = ex_0 = \frac{e^2 E_0}{m(\omega_0{}^2 - \omega^2)},$$

from which (4.15) follows.

The electronic polarizability is of the order of magnitude, for hydrogen,

$$\alpha \approx \frac{e^2}{m\omega_0^2} \approx \frac{e^2}{m}\left(\frac{\hbar^3}{me^4}\right)^2 = \frac{\hbar^6}{m^3e^6} = a_H^3 \approx 10^{-25} \text{ cm}^3.$$

IONIC POLARIZABILITIES

In sodium chloride the square of the refractive index is $(1.50)^2 = 2.25$, and the static dielectric constant is 5.62. The difference $\Delta\epsilon$ between the static and optical dielectric constants may be ascribed in ionic crystals to the ionic polarizability; in sodium chloride we see that $\Delta\epsilon = 3.37$. The ionic polarization arises from the displacement of ions of opposite sign when an electric field is applied, and also from the deformation of the electronic shells of the ions as a result of the relative motion of the ions.

In a sodium chloride crystal when a uniform external field E_0 is applied each Na^+ ion is displaced in one direction, and each Cl^- ion in the opposite direction. The dipole moment is given by e times the displacement. A comparison of static dielectric constants $\epsilon(0)$ and the square of the optical refractive indices is given in Table 4.2.

TABLE 4.2

DIELECTRIC DATA FOR ALKALI HALIDES HAVING THE SODIUM
CHLORIDE STRUCTURE

	e_0	n^2
LiF	9.27	1.92
NaF	6.0	1.74
NaCl	5.62	2.25
NaI	6.60	2.91
KCl	4.68	2.13
KBr	4.78	2.33
KI	4.94	2.69
RbCl	5	2.19
RbBr	5	2.33
RbI	5	2.63

ORIENTATIONAL POLARIZABILITIES

The polarizability arising from the orientation in an applied electric field of molecules possessing a permanent electric dipole moment is usually discussed only with reference to gases and liquids, but it is of importance in some solids. This type of polarization was first discussed by Debye (1912), who showed that by assuming that molecules could have permanent dipole moments one could explain the high dielectric constant of water, alcohol, and similar liquids, and the temperature dependence of their dielectric constants. The problem of the dielectric constant of water is that the static dielectric constant is 81 (at room temperature), whereas the dielectric constant at optical frequencies is $(1.33)^2 = 1.77$. It is now known that the difference is caused chiefly by the orientational polarization which is effective at low frequencies, but is damped out for wavelengths shorter than about 1 cm. The characteristic temperature dependence of the orientational polarizability is shown in Fig. 4.7: CH_3Cl has a permanent electric dipole moment; CH_4 and CCl_4 do not.

In the absence of thermal agitation and of interactions among themselves, molecules with permanent dipole moments would all line up completely on application of an arbitrarily small electric field, so that the dielectric constant would be infinite. Actually, the orienting tendency of the electric field is partly compensated by the thermal agitation, and in solids and some liquids the orientation is hindered by close-range mutual interactions of the molecules.

We consider the effect of the thermal motion on molecules which are free to move. The potential energy of a molecule of permanent

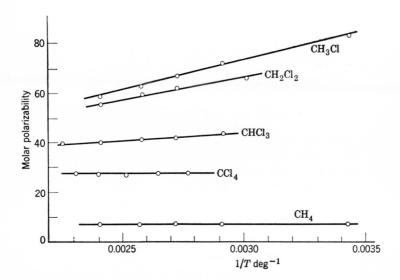

FIG. 4.7. Plot of the quantity $\dfrac{M}{\rho} \dfrac{\epsilon - 1}{\epsilon + 1} = \dfrac{4\pi}{3} L\alpha$ (known as the molar polarizability) for polar and nonpolar substituted methane compounds in gaseous form. [After R. Sänger, *Physik Z.* **27**, 556 (1926).]

moment **p** in a field **E** is

(4.23)   (esu) $V = -\mathbf{p} \cdot \mathbf{E} = -pE \cos \theta,$

where θ is the angle between the moment and the field direction. The polarization will be

$$P = Np \,\overline{\cos \theta},$$

where N is the number of molecules per unit volume and $\overline{\cos \theta}$ is the average over a distribution in thermal equilibrium.

According to the Boltzmann distribution law the relative probability of finding a molecule in an element of solid angle $d\Omega$ is proportional to $e^{-V/kT}$, and

(4.24) $\overline{\cos \theta} = \int e^{-V/kT} \cos \theta \, d\Omega \Big/ \int e^{-V/kT} \, d\Omega.$

The integration is to be carried out over all solid angles, so that

$$\overline{\cos \theta} = \int_0^\pi 2\pi \sin \theta \cos \theta \, e^{pE\cos\theta/kT} \, d\theta \Big/ \int_0^\pi 2\pi \sin \theta \, e^{pE\cos\theta/kT} \, d\theta.$$

We let $x = \cos \theta$ and $a = pE/kT$, so that

(4.25) $\overline{\cos \theta} = \int_{-1}^1 e^{ax} x \, dx \Big/ \int_{-1}^1 e^{ax} \, dx = \dfrac{d}{da} \ln \int_{-1}^1 e^{ax} \, dx$

$$= \text{ctnh } a - \frac{1}{a} \equiv L(a).$$

This may be viewed as the definition of the Langevin function $L(a)$, which was first introduced in connection with the magnetic susceptibility of paramagnetic substances. The function is plotted in Fig. 4.8, and the saturation property for $pE \gg kT$ is clearly seen.

The most important situation experimentally is when $pE \ll kT$. Dipole moments are of the order of 10^{-18} esu, so that for $E = 3000$ volts/cm $= 10$ statvolts/cm, $pE \approx 10^{-17}$ erg, and at room temperature $kT \approx 4 \times 10^{-14}$ erg. Thus $pE/kT \approx 1/4000$, and our condition is satisfied. In this limit of $a \ll 1$,

(4.26)   (esu) $L(a) \cong \dfrac{a}{3} = \dfrac{pE}{3kT},$

and so the polarization is

(4.27)   (esu) $P = Np \,\overline{\cos \theta} = \dfrac{Np^2E}{3kT},$

and the polarizability (per molecule) is

$$(4.28) \qquad \text{(esu)} \qquad \alpha(\text{dipolar}) = \frac{p^2}{3kT}.$$

At room temperature this is of the order of $(10^{-18})^2/10^{-13} \approx 10^{-23}$ cm^3, of the same order of magnitude as the electronic polarizability. The total polarizability may then be written, if we let α_0 denote the deformation polarizability (that is, the sum of the electronic and ionic contributions),

$$(4.29) \qquad \text{(esu)} \qquad \alpha = \alpha_0 + \frac{p^2}{3kT},$$

an expression which is known as the Langevin-Debye equation, and which has been of great importance in interpreting molecular structures. The dipole moment p is determined in practice by plotting either α or the molar polarizability (4.12) as a function of $1/T$ as in Fig. 4.7; the slope is simply related to p. In this way one obtains, for example, the following dipole moments: $p(\text{HCl}) = 1.03 \times 10^{-18}$ esu; $p(\text{HBr}) = 0.79 \times 10^{-18}$ esu; $p(\text{HI}) = 0.38 \times 10^{-18}$ esu; $p(\text{H}_2\text{O}) =$

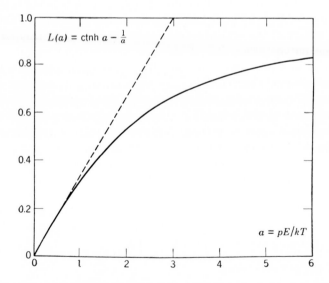

FIG. 4.8. Plot of Langevin function $L(a)$ as function of $a = pE/kT$; the initial slope is shown by the dashed line.

1.87×10^{-18} esu. The moments are often expressed in Debye units, where a Debye unit is 10^{-18} esu, of the order of the electronic charge times an interatomic distance.

DIPOLE ORIENTATION IN SOLIDS

We expect molecules in gases and liquids to be fairly free to rotate, and the permanent dipole moments may be expected to make their full orientational contribution to the polarizability, as just calculated. In molecular solids the ability of a molecule to rotate depends very much on its shape and on the strength of its interactions with the environment. The closer the approach to sphericity and the lower the dipole moment, the more easily the molecule will rotate. Thus solid methane (CH_4), which is a symmetrical nonpolar molecule, rotates quite freely in the solid state, and the molecules in solid hydrogen rotate so freely that the Raman lines of gaseous H_2 are found at nearly the same frequencies in the solid phase. In less symmetrical molecules such as HCl and H_2O, at high temperatures there appear to be several stable orientations for each molecule in the solid, and a molecule will change direction from one stable orientation to another in a time which is called the relaxation time.

DIPOLE RELAXATION AND DIELECTRIC LOSSES

The principal part of the difference between the low frequency dielectric constant and the high frequency dielectric constant as measured by the square of the optical refractive index may be attributed to the damping out or relaxation of the orientational contribution to the dielectric constant. We introduce the concept of *relaxation time* as the time interval characterizing the restoration of a disturbed system to its equilibrium configuration; the relaxation frequency is defined as the reciprocal of the relaxation time. In inhomogeneous dielectrics the Maxwell-Wagner interfacial polarization mechanism discussed in Problem 4.5 leads to another type of relaxation which is quite often important in engineering dielectrics. The orientational relaxation frequencies vary over a wide range and may be strongly dependent on the temperature. In water at room temperature, relaxation occurs at about 3×10^{10} cps, corresponding to a wavelength for electromagnetic radiation of 1 cm. In ice at $-20°C$ we see from Fig. 4.9 that the relaxation frequency is of the order of 1 kc.

DEBYE RELAXATION TIME

Debye has given an elegant discussion of dielectric relaxation in polar liquids and in solutions of polar molecules in nonpolar solvents;

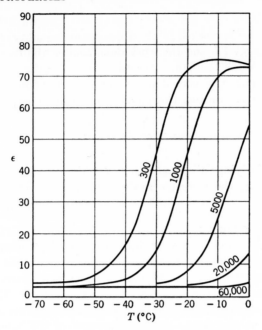

FIG. 4.9. Variation of the dielectric constant of ice with temperature and frequency, in cycles per second. [After Smyth and Hitchcock, *J. Am. Chem. Soc.* **54**, 4631 (1932).]

his central result is that the orientational part of the polarizability depends on frequency as

$$\alpha = \frac{\alpha_0}{1 + i\omega\tau},$$

(4.30)

where τ is the relaxation time and α_0 is the static orientational polarizability. Debye has suggested further that in liquids the relaxation time is related to the viscosity η by the approximate relation

$$\tau = \frac{4\pi\eta a^3}{kT},$$

(4.31)

where a is the radius of the molecule, which is supposed to be spherical. For water at room temperature we obtain $\tau \approx 10^{-11}$ sec, using $a \approx 10^{-8}$ cm and $\eta = 0.01$ poise, giving a relaxation frequency in approximate agreement with the experimental measurements on water. The form of the expression (4.31) for the relaxation time may be under-

stood by making the plausible supposition that the relaxation frequency $\omega_0 = 1/\tau$ is marked by the approximate equality of the thermal
rotational energy kT and the work done against the frictional torque
in rotation through 1 radian. According to Stokes the frictional torque
is $8\pi\eta a^3\omega$, whence the work done by the frictional torque acting for 1
radian is $8\pi\eta a^3\omega$. Setting this equal to kT for $\omega = \omega_0$, we have

$$\tau \equiv \frac{1}{\omega_0} \cong \frac{8\pi\eta a^3}{kT}.$$

The idea underlying this discussion is that the thermal energy is insuf-
ficient to rotate the molecule against the viscous resistance when ω
exceeds ω_0.

RELAXATION IN SOLIDS

Following Debye,[5] we may make a crude model of dielectric relaxation in dipolar solids by supposing that each molecule of the solid
carries a permanent electric moment p which can be oriented in two
directions, parallel (1) or antiparallel (2) to the field E. These orientations do not arise through quantization, but through the arrangement
of molecules in the solid. One consequence of the calculation is to
demonstrate that α will have a $1/T$ temperature dependence for a two-
orientation model just as for the continuous-orientation model considered earlier. We suppose that there are n_1, n_2 molecules in the two
groups at a given time and that the probability that a particle in
group 1 makes a transition to group 2 in time δt is $w_{12}\,\delta t$, while the
probability of the reverse process is $w_{21}\,\delta t$. Then

(4.32)

$$\frac{dn_1}{dt} = -w_{12}n_1 + w_{21}n_2;$$

$$\frac{dn_2}{dt} = w_{12}n_1 - w_{21}n_2.$$

For equilibrium $dn_1/dt = dn_2/dt = 0$; therefore we must have

(4.33) $$\frac{n_1}{n_2} = \frac{w_{21}}{w_{12}}.$$

However, in equilibrium n_1 and n_2 must satisfy the Boltzmann distribution, and so

(4.34) $$n_1 = Ae^{pE/kT}; \qquad n_2 = Ae^{-pE/kT},$$

[5] P. Debye, *Polar molecules*, Chemical Catalog Co., New York, 1929, Chapter V.

where A is a constant. According to (4.33) it is reasonable to take

$$(4.35) \qquad w_{12} = \frac{1}{2\tau} e^{-pE/kT}; \qquad w_{21} = \frac{1}{2\tau} e^{pE/kT}.$$

Taking $pE \ll kT$, we have from (4.32) and (4.35)

$$(4.36) \qquad 2\tau \frac{dn_1}{dt} = -(n_1 - n_2) + \frac{pE}{kT}(n_1 + n_2);$$

$$2\tau \frac{dn_2}{dt} = (n_1 - n_2) - \frac{pE}{kT}(n_1 + n_2).$$

If E varies with time as $e^{i\omega t}$, the equations (4.36) are seen to have the solution

$$(4.37) \qquad n_1 - n_2 = \frac{(n_1 + n_2)}{1 + i\omega\tau} \frac{pE}{kT},$$

and so τ as introduced in (4.35) plays the part of a relaxation time. If there are N molecules per unit volume, the polarizability is given by

$$(4.38) \qquad N\alpha = \frac{P}{E} = \frac{p(n_1 - n_2)}{E} = \frac{Np^2}{kT} \cdot \frac{1}{1 + i\omega\tau},$$

of essentially the same form as (4.30).

The relaxation times in solids are usually much longer than in liquids. This behavior is somewhat parallel to the behavior of diffusion rates in liquids and solids. Breckenridge[6] has related the observed dielectric losses in alkali halide crystals to the presence of lattice defects in the crystals, with considerable success.

COMPLEX DIELECTRIC CONSTANTS AND THE LOSS ANGLE

In the presence of relaxation effects the dielectric constant may conveniently be written as complex. For a polarizability

$$\alpha = \frac{\alpha_0}{1 + i\omega\tau}$$

[6] R. G. Breckenridge, in *Imperfections in nearly perfect crystals*, edited by Shockley, Hollomon, Maurer, and Seitz, John Wiley and Sons, New York, 1952.

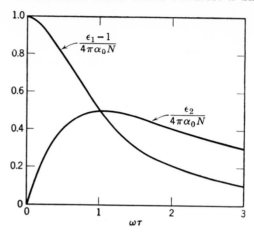

FIG. 4.10.   Frequency dependence of real and imaginary parts of the dielectric constant $\epsilon = \epsilon_1 - i\epsilon_2$, for a relaxation mechanism.

the dielectric constant is, taking the local field as equal to the applied field,

$$\epsilon = \epsilon_1 - i\epsilon_2 = 1 + \frac{4\pi\alpha_0 N}{1 + i\omega\tau}$$

$$= 1 + \frac{4\pi\alpha_0 N}{1 + \omega^2\tau^2} - i\,\frac{4\pi\alpha_0\omega\tau N}{1 + \omega^2\tau^2},$$

so

$$(4.39) \quad \epsilon_1 = \Re(\epsilon) = 1 + \frac{4\pi\alpha_0 N}{1 + \omega^2\tau^2}; \qquad \epsilon_2 = -\mathcal{I}(\epsilon) = \frac{4\pi\alpha_0\omega\tau N}{1 + \omega^2\tau^2};$$

where $\Re$ and $\mathcal{I}$ denote real and imaginary parts, respectively.   The variation of ϵ_1 and ϵ_2 with frequency is shown in Fig. 4.10.

The power dissipation per unit volume $\mathcal{P}$ is given by

$$(4.40) \qquad\qquad\qquad \mathcal{P} = j_p E,$$

where j_p is the component of the current density which is in phase with E.   We have

$$(\text{esu}) \qquad j = \sigma E + \frac{1}{4\pi}\frac{\partial D}{\partial t} = \left(\sigma + \frac{i\omega\epsilon}{4\pi}\right)E;$$

(4.41)

$$(\text{MKS}) \qquad j = \sigma E + \frac{\partial D}{\partial t} = (\sigma + i\omega\epsilon\epsilon_0)E,$$

which, for $\sigma = 0$ and $\epsilon = \epsilon_1 - i\epsilon_2$, becomes

$$\text{(esu)} \qquad j = \left(\frac{\epsilon_2\omega}{4\pi} + \frac{i\epsilon_1\omega}{4\pi}\right) E;$$

$$\text{(MKS)} \qquad j = (\epsilon_2\omega + i\epsilon_1\omega)\epsilon_0 E,$$

so that the power dissipation is

$$\text{(4.42)} \qquad \text{(esu)} \qquad \mathcal{P} = \frac{E^2}{4\pi}\omega\epsilon_2 = \frac{\epsilon_1 E^2}{4\pi}\omega \tan \delta;$$

$$\text{(MKS)} \qquad \mathcal{P} = \epsilon_1\epsilon_0 E^2\omega \tan \delta,$$

where the *loss angle* or *power factor* is defined as

$$\text{(4.43)} \qquad \tan \delta = \frac{\epsilon_2}{\epsilon_1}.$$

The Q *factor* of a system is defined as

$$\text{(4.44)} \qquad Q = \frac{\text{maximum stored energy}}{\text{average energy loss per radian}},$$

which in the dielectric case reduces to

$$\text{(4.45)} \qquad Q = \frac{\epsilon_1 E_0{}^2/8\pi}{(\epsilon_1\overline{E^2}/4\pi) \tan \delta} = \frac{1}{\tan \delta},$$

where we have used the fact that the average value of E^2 over a cycle is $E_0{}^2/2$, the amplitude being E_0. The result $Q = 1/\tan \delta$ is independent of the system of units.

Values of ϵ_1 and tan δ for several insulating materials at a frequency of 25,000 mc are given in Table 4.3. An excellent compilation of

TABLE 4.3

DIELECTRIC CONSTANT AND POWER FACTOR VALUES AT 25,000 MC

Material	ϵ_1	tan δ
Polystyrene	2.55	0.0012
Lucite	2.57	0.0032
Paraffin wax	2.26	0.0001
Lead glass	6.8	0.009
Ebonite	2.73	0.0038
Teflon		0.0006
Polyethylene		0.0006
Fused quartz		0.00025

dielectric data between 100 cps and 2.5×10^{10} cps has been made by von Hippel.[7]

FERROELECTRIC CRYSTALS

A ferroelectric crystal is defined as a crystal which exhibits a spontaneous electric dipole moment; in other words, a crystal for which even in the absence of an applied electric field the center of positive charge does not coincide with the center of negative charge. It can be shown that it is a necessary, but not sufficient, condition for ferroelectricity that the crystal lack a center of symmetry. All ferroelectrics will be piezoelectric, but not all piezoelectrics will be ferroelectric (e.g., quartz). The occurrence of ferroelectricity is generally interpreted to be the result of a polarization catastrophe.

After a ferroelectric crystal is polarized in a given direction, the action of the polarization outside the crystal is gradually neutralized by the collection on the crystal surface of free charges from the atmosphere and by conduction within the crystal. In a number of substances the polarization appears to have a very high coercive force— the direction of the spontaneous polarization may not be changed by an electric field of the maximum intensity which it is possible to apply without causing electrical breakdown of the crystal. We are often able to observe the spontaneous moment in these substances only when they are heated, as raising the temperature changes the value of the polarization. Thus crystals, such as tourmaline, which develop an observable spontaneous electric moment only on heating are called *pyroelectric*, while crystals with a lower coercive force, such that the direction of the spontaneous moment can be altered by an electric field, are called *ferroelectric* and often have very high dielectric constants.

ELECTRETS

There is another class of substances known as *electrets*, discovered by Eguchi in 1925, which may display "permanent" electric moments. Electrets are produced by the solidification of mixtures of certain organic waxes in a strong electric field. Some of the wax molecules carry permanent dipole moments; they are oriented by the electric field, and frozen in their orientation by the solidification. The moments produced in this way may persist for several years, yet it is generally believed that the polarized state of an electret is only metastable, and that the stable state would be unpolarized. We shall not

[7] A. R. von Hippel, editor, *Dielectric materials and applications*, John Wiley and Sons, New York, 1954.

consider electrets here; for a review of their properties the reader is referred to a paper by Gutmann.[8]

CLASSIFICATION OF FERROELECTRIC CRYSTALS

We list in Table 4.4 some of the crystals which are commonly con-

TABLE 4.4
DATA ON SOME FERROELECTRIC CRYSTALS
(The values of P_s are for room temperature unless otherwise marked)
(Compiled in part from a tabulation by Walter J. Merz)

Crystal	Structure	T_c (°K)	P_s (esu)	P_s(MKS)
$NaK(C_4H_4O_6) \cdot 4H_2O$ (Rochelle salt)	Complex	297 (upper) 255 (lower)	800	3×10^{-3}
$NaK(C_4H_2D_2O_6) \cdot 4D_2O$		308 (upper) 251 (lower)	1,100	4×10^{-3}
$LiNH_4(C_4H_4O_6) \cdot H_2O$		106	630	2×10^{-3}
KH_2PO_4	Complex	123	16,000	5×10^{-2}
KD_2PO_4		213	27,000	9×10^{-2}
RbH_2PO_4		147		
RbH_2AsO_4		111		
KH_2AsO_4		96.5		
KD_2AsO_4		162		
CsH_2PO_4		160		
CsH_2AsO_4		143		
CsD_2AsO_4		212		
$BaTiO_3$	Perovskite	393	78,000	0.26
$KTaO_3$	Perovskite			
$NaTaO_3$	Perovskite			
$KNbO_3$	Perovskite	708	80,000	0.27
$PbTiO_3$	Perovskite	763		
$LiTaO_3$	Ilmenite		70,000(425°C)	0.23
$LiNbO_3$	Ilmenite			
$Cd_2Nb_2O_7$	Pyrochlorite	185	5,400(100°K)	1.8×10^{-2}

sidered ferroelectric, along with the transition (Curie) temperature T_c at which the crystal changes from the low temperature polarized state to the high temperature unpolarized state. Rochelle salt has both an upper and a lower Curie point, between which the crystal is ferroelectric. The maximum value of the spontaneous polarization P_s is listed where known. It is useful in converting units to recall that P(esu) is obtained by multiplying $P(\mu\text{coul/cm}^2)$ by 3×10^3 and by multiplying the MKS value $P(\text{coul/meter}^2)$ by 3×10^5.

The crystals considered in the table may be classified into several

[8] F. Gutmann, *Revs. Modern Phys.* **20**, 457 (1948).

quite natural groups.   First there is Rochelle salt[9] and the associated isomorphous salts.   Rochelle salt is a quite complicated crystal, and little progress has been made toward understanding its behavior on a microscopic basis, although Mueller[10] and others have formulated a phenomenological theory which correlates a number of experimental facts.   It seems possible that the ferroelectric behavior of Rochelle salt is connected intimately with the action of the molecules of water of hydration in the crystal.   This is suggested by the observation that the substitution of D_2O for H_2O changes the range in which the crystal is ferroelectric from 41.7°C for the ordinary Rochelle salt to 57°C for the deuterated salt, which is quite a large effect.   It may be noted, however, that the observed spontaneous polarization 800 esu is considerably less than the polarization which would result from the parallel orientation of all the water molecules; there are 1.52×10^{22} of these per cubic centimeter, and the moment per molecule is 1.85×10^{-18} esu (in the vapor), corresponding to a polarization of 28,000 esu, whereas the observed spontaneous polarization is only 800 esu.

The second group of ferroelectric crystals consists of crystals with hydrogen bonds in which the motion of the protons is specifically connected with the ferroelectric properties; the group comprises potassium dihydrogen phosphate (KH_2PO_4) and the isomorphous salts.   The behavior of the deuterated crystal strongly suggests the hydrogen atoms are of central importance:

	KH_2PO_4	KD_2PO_4	KH_2AsO_4	KD_2AsO_4
Curie temperature	123°K	213°K	96°K	162°K
Saturation polarization	16,000 esu	27,000 esu		

The substitution of deuterons for protons nearly doubles both T_c and P_s, although the fractional change in the molecular weight of the compound is less than 2 percent.   This is an extraordinarily large isotope effect.

The third group of ferroelectrics consists of ionic crystals with crystal structures closely related to the perovskite and ilmenite structures. The perovskite structure is the simplest crystal structure (Figs. 4.11 and 4.12) to exhibit ferroelectricity, and we shall devote the rest of this chapter primarily to barium titanate, which has this structure and is the crystal in the third group about which most experimental and theoretical information is available.   The name perovskite applies to the

[9] Discovered by J. Valasek, *Phys. Rev.* **17**, 475 (1921); for summary of properties see H. Mueller, *Ann. N.Y. Acad. Sci.* **40**, 321 (1940).

[10] H. Mueller, *Phys. Rev.* **57**, 829 (1940); **58**, 565 (1940).

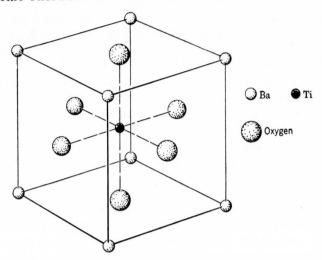

FIG. 4.11. The perovskite crystal structure of barium titanate. The structure is cubic, with Ba^{2+} ions at the cube corners, O^{2-} ions at the face centers, and a Ti^{4+} ion at the body center. Below the Curie temperature the structure is slightly deformed with respect to that described here. The prototype crystal is calcium titanate (perovskite).

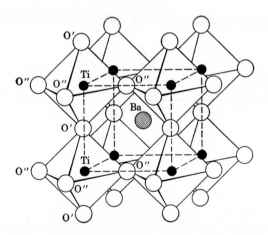

FIG. 4.12. Another view of the $BaTiO_3$ structure, showing the octahedra of oxygen atoms about the titanium atoms. For later application the oxygen atoms on the lines joining nearest neighbor titanium atoms are labeled O'.

mineral $CaTiO_3$. The ilmenite structure, named from the mineral $FeTiO_3$, is more complicated and we shall not discuss it here.

THEORY OF BARIUM TITANATE

We consider first the general order of magnitude of the ferroelectric effects in barium titanate. It is observed that barium titanate has at room temperature a saturation polarization of 78,000 esu (or 0.26 coul/meter^2). As the volume of a unit cube is $(4 \times 10^{-8})^3$ cm^3, the dipole moment per unit cube is 5×10^{-18} esu. If, for example, all the polarization were caused by a displacement of the central Ti^{4+} ion, we should require a displacement of $5 \times 10^{-18}/4(4.8 \times 10^{-10}) \approx 0.26 \times 10^{-8}$ cm, which seems fairly large.

We suppose that the Curie point is determined approximately by the interaction energy of a dipole with the local internal electric field caused by the polarization itself. The interaction energy is $-\frac{1}{2}(\mathbf{p} \cdot \mathbf{E})$; the factor $\frac{1}{2}$ is common to self-energy problems. Now E will be of the order of $-P_s$, so that the interaction energy is of the order of $\frac{1}{2}(5 \times 10^{-18})(8 \times 10^4) = 2 \times 10^{-13}$ erg. We obtain a rough estimate of the transition temperature by setting the interaction energy equal to kT_c, giving $T_c \approx (2 \times 10^{-13})/(1.4 \times 10^{-16}) \approx 1400°K$, appreciably higher than the observed $380°K$.

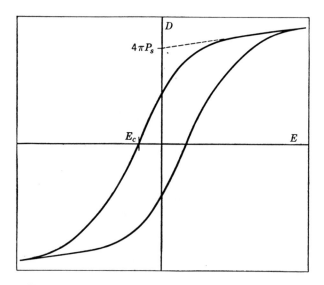

FIG. 4.13. Hysteresis loop in ferroelectric specimen, showing spontaneous polarization P_s and coercive field E_c. In barium titanate the value of $4\pi P_s$ may be of the order 3×10^8 volts/cm, and E_c of the order of 10^3 volts/cm.

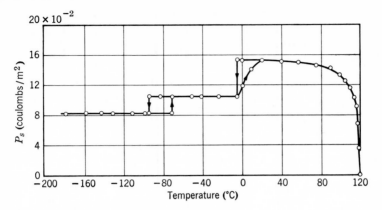

FIG. 4.14. Spontaneous polarization of barium titanate as a function of temperature. The discontinuities near 0°C and −80°C are caused by small changes in the
crystal structure.

The most striking indication of ferroelectricity in barium titanate
is provided by the hysteresis loops of the form shown in Fig. 4.13 as
observed at temperatures below the transition temperature, 120°C; at
temperatures above the transition the loop reduces to a straight line.
The spontaneous polarization as a function of temperature is shown in
Fig. 4.14, and the dielectric constant versus temperature is shown in
Fig. 4.15.   The dielectric constant is usually very much larger when
measured perpendicular to the c axis than when measured parallel to it.

THE POLARIZATION CATASTROPHE IN FERROELECTRICS

The occurrence of ferroelectricity in barium titanate is believed to
be the result of a polarization catastrophe in which the local electric
fields arising from the polarization itself increase faster than the elastic
restoring forces on the ions in the crystal, thereby leading ultimately
to an asymmetrical shift in ionic positions; the shift is limited to a
finite displacement by the onset of anharmonic restoring forces.   The
occurrence of ferroelectricity in an appreciable number of crystals with
the perovskite structure suggests that this structure is in some way
favorably disposed to the production of a polarizability catastrophe;
this suggestion is supported by the fact that the hexagonal modification of barium titanate is not ferroelectric, whereas the cubic (perovskite) form is ferroelectric.   Calculations by Slater[11] and others have
made clear the physical reason for the favored position of the perov-

[11] J. C. Slater, *Phys. Rev.* **78**, 748 (1950).

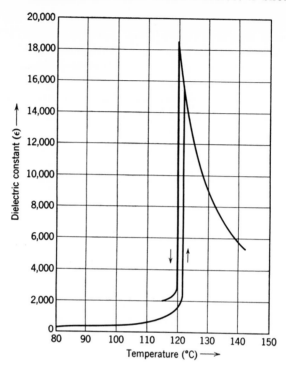

FIG. 4.15.   Dielectric constant of barium titanate versus temperature.   [After
M. E. Drougard and D. R. Young, *Phys. Rev.* **95**, 1152 (1954).]

skite structure.   We give first the simple form of the catastrophe
theory, supposing that the Lorentz factors are all $4\pi/3$.   The theory
given now assumes implicitly that the transition is a second order
transition, but the physical ideas involved can be carried over in part
to a first order transition.   In a first order transition there is a latent
heat and a discontinuity in the saturation polarization at the transition temperature; in a second order transition there is only a discontinuity in the heat capacity and in dP_s/dT.   The transition in pure
barium titanate is a first order transition.

We may rewrite (4.10) in the form

$$(4.46) \qquad \text{(esu)} \qquad \epsilon = \frac{1 + (8\pi/3)\, \Sigma\, N_i \alpha_i}{1 - (4\pi/3)\, \Sigma\, N_i \alpha_i},$$

where α_i is the polarizability of an ion of type i, and N_i the number of
ions i per unit volume, noting that the numerical factors multiplying

$\Sigma\ N_i\alpha_i$ are the consequence of the use of the Lorentz local field $E + (4\pi/3)P$. It is seen that the dielectric constant becomes infinite, corresponding to a finite polarization for zero applied field, when $\Sigma\ N_i\alpha_i = (4\pi/3)^{-1}$, and for this reason the polarization catastrophe is commonly known as the "$4\pi/3$ catastrophe."

We note that the value of ϵ is sensitive to small departures of $\Sigma\ N_i\alpha_i$ from the critical value $3/4\pi$; if we write

(4.47)
$$\frac{4\pi}{3}\ \Sigma\ N_i\alpha_i = 1 - s,$$

where $s \ll 1$, we have

(4.48)
$$\epsilon \cong \frac{3}{s}.$$

If we suppose that above the critical temperature the value of s varies with temperature in a linear fashion,

(4.49)
$$s \cong \beta(T - T_0),$$

where T_0 and β are constants, we have above the transition temperature a Curie-Weiss law for the dielectric constant

(4.50)
$$\epsilon \cong \frac{3/\beta}{T - T_c},$$

which is the form of the observed temperature variation.

The refractive index of barium titanate is 2.4; we estimate the electronic contribution to the polarizability from the relation

(4.51)
$$\frac{n^2 - 1}{n^2 + 2} = \frac{4\pi}{3}\ \Sigma\ N_i\alpha_i(\text{electronic}),$$

according to (4.11). Using Slater's values $\alpha(\text{Ba}) = 1.95 \times 10^{-24}\ \text{cm}^3$; $\alpha(\text{O}) = 2.4 \times 10^{-24}\ \text{cm}^3$; $\alpha(\text{Ti}) = 0.19 \times 10^{-24}\ \text{cm}^3$, we find that $(4\pi/3)\ \Sigma\ N_i\alpha_i(\text{electronic}) = 0.61$, so that a contribution of $1 - 0.61 = 0.39$ would be required from the ionic polarizabilities in order to explain the occurrence of a ferroelectric state. The value of $\alpha(\text{O})$ is selected to fit the observed refractive index. We saw earlier that, even if all the spontaneous polarization arose from the ionic displacement of the titanium ion in the center of each cube, a displacement of 0.26×10^{-8} cm would be required. There is nothing inherently unreasonable about an assumption that 39 percent of the total polarizability is ionic except that this is something of an *ad hoc* explanation; it does not give us any indication of why the perovskite structure is prone to ferroelectricity, nor does it suggest why crystals such as rutile (TiO_2) with an even higher refractive index [$n = 2.8$; $(4\pi/3) \Sigma N_i\alpha_i$(electronic) $= 0.70$] are not ferroelectric. We shall see in the following section that the actual local fields in the perovskite structure act to enhance the effect of the polarizability of the titanium ion by a factor of the order of 5 with respect to the situation where $E + 4\pi P/3$ is the local field.

LOCAL FIELD IN THE PEROVSKITE STRUCTURE

The Lorentz local field $E + 4\pi P/3$ holds for a crystal when all atoms have environments with cubic symmetry. In barium titanate the Ba and Ti ions see a cubic environment, but the O ions do not; there are, for example, only two nearest neighbor Ti ions adjacent to each O ion, so that the environment of the O ions cannot be cubic. It is necessary in this circumstance to derive a generalized form of the Lorentz formula; this has been done by several authors,[11,12] and Slater has actually carried out the calculations for barium titanate.

How we should go about obtaining an expression for the local field in barium titanate is quite obvious. We set up an expression for the local field at each lattice point as the sum of the applied field and the polarization of the several types of ions. We take the applied field parallel to a particular cube side, which we call the z direction; there are then four types of ions to be considered: Ba, Ti, O', O'', where the O' ions are on lines parallel to the z direction and passing through the Ti ions; the remaining oxygen ions are the O'' ions. We have four simultaneous equations for the polarizations:

$$E(\text{Ba}) = \frac{P(\text{Ba})}{N(\text{Ba})\alpha(\text{Ba})}$$
$$= E_0 + q_{11}P(\text{Ba}) + q_{12}P(\text{Ti}) + q_{13}P(\text{O}') + q_{14}P(\text{O}'');$$

$$E(\text{Ti}) = \frac{P(\text{Ti})}{N(\text{Ti})\alpha(\text{Ti})}$$
$$= E_0 + q_{21}P(\text{Ba}) + q_{22}(\text{Ti}) + q_{23}P(\text{O}') + q_{24}P(\text{O}'');$$

(4.52)

$$E(\text{O}') = \frac{P(\text{O}')}{N(\text{O}')\alpha(\text{O}')}$$
$$= E_0 + q_{31}P(\text{Ba}) + q_{32}P(\text{Ti}) + q_{33}P(\text{O}') + q_{34}P(\text{O}'');$$

$$E(\text{O}'') = \frac{P(\text{O}'')}{N(\text{O}'')\alpha(\text{O}'')}$$
$$= E_0 + q_{41}P(\text{Ba}) + q_{42}P(\text{Ti}) + q_{43}P(\text{O}') + q_{44}P(\text{O}'').$$

[12] G. J. Skanavi, *Doklady Akad. Nauk S.S.S.R.* **59**, 231 (1948); J. H. van Santen and W. Opechowski, *Physica* **14**, 545 (1948).

The coefficient of the P's are lattice sums for dipole arrays and may be calculated by the methods given by Kornfeld and others.[13]   The q's have the following values:

$$q_{11} = q_{22} = q_{21} = q_{12} = q_{33} = \frac{4\pi}{3};$$

$$q_{13} = q_{31} = \frac{4\pi}{3} - 8.668;$$

$$q_{34} = q_{43} = q_{14} = q_{41} = \frac{4\pi}{3} + 4.334$$

$$q_{23} = q_{32} = \frac{4\pi}{3} + 30.080$$

$$q_{24} = q_{42} = \frac{4\pi}{3} - 15.040$$

$$q_{44} = \frac{4\pi}{3} - 4.334$$

It should particularly be noted that the interaction between the Ti and O′ ions is especially strong, being $(4\pi/3) + 30.080$, which is approximately 8.2 times the ordinary value, $4\pi/3$.   It is this factor which is responsible for the great enhancement of the field at the central ion of the perovskite structure.

The ferroelectric catastrophe occurs when the determinant of the coefficients of the P's in (4.52) vanishes, as this is the condition that the P's have nontrivial solutions for $E = 0$.   We substitute the appropriate polarizabilities as used by Slater:

$$\alpha(\text{Ba}) = 1.95 \times 10^{-24} \text{ cm}^3,$$

$$\alpha(\text{O}') = \alpha(\text{O}'') = 2.4 \times 10^{-24} \text{ cm}^3,$$

$$\alpha(\text{Ti}) = 0.19 \times 10^{-24} \alpha_i(\text{Ti});$$

here we suppose that the polarizabilities are all electronic except for an ionic contribution $\alpha_i(\text{Ti})$ from the titanium ions.   We then determine the value of $\alpha_i(\text{Ti})$ which makes the determinant vanish, and find

$$\alpha_i(\text{Ti}) = 0.95 \times 10^{-24} \text{ cm}^3,$$

and $\qquad\qquad \dfrac{4\pi}{3} N(\text{Ti})\alpha_i(\text{Ti}) = 0.062,$

[13] H. Kornfeld, Z. Physik **22**, 27 (1924); L. W. McKeehan, Phys. Rev. **43**, 913 (1933); **72**, 78 (1947); J. M. Luttinger and L. Tisza, Phys. Rev. **70**, 954 (1946); **72**, 257 (1947).

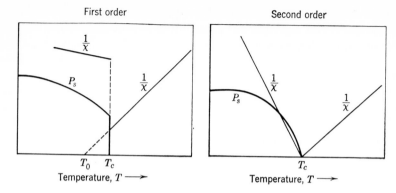

FIG. 4.16. Schematic variation of spontaneous polarization and reciprocal susceptibility for first order and second order transitions. The transition in barium titanate is first order, but is close to being second order.

as compared with 0.39 on the elementary theory, the magnification of about 6 being caused by the nature of the perovskite lattice. In particular the existence of lines of oxygen and titanium ions in the lattice is favorable for the high magnification.

The temperature dependences of P_s and $1/\chi$ for first and second order transitions are shown in Fig. 4.16. We note here that it can be shown by standard thermodynamic methods that a second order transition does not have a latent heat of transition, but is rather accompanied by a discontinuity in the heat capacity; such a transition is

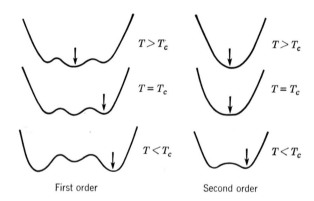

FIG. 4.17. Schematic potential energy wells for the two types of ferroelectric transitions, showing the variation of well shape with temperature. The horizontal coordinate is the polarization, taken from the center of each drawing.

known in thermodynamics as a second order transition; a first order transition is accompanied by a latent heat. Schematic diagrams of free energy versus lattice distortion from equilibrium, or polarization, for first and second order transitions are shown in Fig. 4.17. It is likely that ferroelectric transitions in perovskites are first order, but barium titanate probably comes very close to being second order in that T_0 is very close to T_c. The transitions in Rochelle salt and in KH_2PO_4 are probably second order. A good review of the detailed thermodynamic theory of ferroelectrics is given by Devonshire.[14]

FERROELECTRIC DOMAINS

We have seen that a crystal of barium titanate has cubic symmetry above the Curie point and tetragonal symmetry below the Curie point. On cooling a crystal through the Curie point, it is usually found that the entire crystal does not have the same tetragonal axis, but that in one part of the crystal one of the formerly cubic axes has become the tetragonal axis, whereas in some other region in the crystal another of the cubic axes has become the tetragonal axis. This means that different regions will have different directions of spontaneous polarization. A region within which the spontaneous polarization is in the same direction is called a *domain*. Crystals have been grown which consist entirely of a single domain, and this indeed is expected theoretically to be the stable configuration for a platelike crystal between condenser plates which are connected. But crystals appear more commonly to grow with inhomogeneous concentrations of impurities leading to mechanical strains in the lattice that may often be reduced by the establishment of a domain structure.

Ferroelectric domains in barium titanate may be observed by optical means, as the crystals are transparent and exhibit different indices of refraction parallel and perpendicular to the tetragonal axis of a domain. In barium titanate the difference of the refractive indices at room temperature is $n_c - n_a = -0.055$. A detailed optical examination of various types of domain structures has been carried out by Forsbergh,[15] and we reproduce Fig. 4.18 from his paper. Schematic domain arrangements are shown in Fig. 4.19.

Merz[16] has studied the kinetics of domain formation and domain

[14] A. F. Devonshire, *Advances in Physics* **3**, 85–130 (1954).

[15] P. W. Forsbergh, Jr., *Phys. Rev.* **76**, 1187 (1949); see also W. J. Merz, *Phys. Rev.* **88**, 421 (1952); E. A. Little, *Phys. Rev.* **98**, 978 (1955).

[16] W. J. Merz, *Phys. Rev.* **95**, 690 (1954); this paper contains a discussion of the theory of ferroelectric domains; for application to memory devices, see J. R. Anderson, *Am. Inst. Elect. Eng.* **71**, 916 (1952).

FIG. 4.18. Wedge-shaped laminar domains in barium titanate single crystal.
(After Forsbergh.)

wall motions in barium titanate grown as thin flat plates, the normal
to the plane of the plate being the c or polar direction of the crystal.
When the electric field along the c direction is reversed, new domains
are formed having opposite polarization. The growth of these domains
is rather surprising in view of experience with ferromagnetic materials
where domain boundary motion makes a large contribution to the magnetization change. In barium titanate the polarization is changed by
the formation of very many new antiparallel domains which are
extremely thin (10^{-4} cm) and appear to grow only in the forward
direction. It is likely that the thickness of the wall or transition region
is small, of the order of a few lattice constants; the wall energy is of
the order of 10 ergs/cm². As there is practically no sidewise motion
of the 180° domain walls in an applied electric field, there is no interference or crosstalk between one set of electrodes to another on the
same crystal plate even when they are spaced only 10^{-2} cm apart.
This feature is of great importance in the application of crystals of
barium titanate in memory devices.

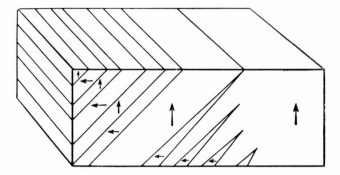

FIG. 4.10.   Directions of spontaneous polarization in polydomain barium titanate.

In Fig. 4.20 is shown the frequency dependence of the dielectric constant in polycrystalline barium titanate.   The decrease in the dielectric constant at microwave frequencies is not yet understood.

PROBLEMS

4.1. Consider a semiclassical model of the ground state of the hydrogen atom in an electric field normal to the plane of the orbit, and show that for this model $\alpha = a_H{}^3$, where a_H is the radius of the unperturbed orbit.   *Note:*

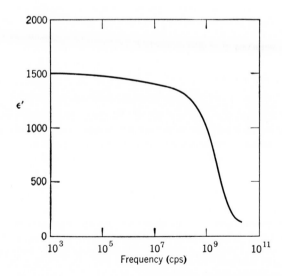

FIG. 4.20.   Frequency dependence of the real part of the dielectric constant in barium titanate, from smoothed data of von Hippel and Powles and Jackson.

If the applied field is in the x direction, then the x component of the field of the nucleus at the displaced position of the electron orbit must be equal to the applied field. The correct quantum-mechanical result is larger than this by the factor $\frac{9}{2}$.

4.2. In the local field problem the cavity need not be chosen as spherical, but may be a cube with a face normal parallel to the polarization. In this case the polarization charge density on the upper and lower faces of the cube is uniform and equal to $\pm P$, whereas the other faces do not carry any charge. Show that, for this cavity, $E_2 = 4\pi P/3$, just as for the spherical cavity, in esu.

4.3. Show that the polarizability of a conducting metallic sphere of radius a is $\alpha = a^3$; this result is most easily obtained by noting the $E = 0$ inside the sphere and then using the depolarization factor. This result gives values of α of the order of magnitude of the observed polarizabilities of atoms. A lattice of N conducting spheres per unit volume has dielectric constant $\epsilon = 1 + 4\pi N a^3$, for $Na^3 \ll 1$; this result has been used in the construction of artificial dielectrics for use in microwave lenses [W. E. Kock, *Bell System Tech. J.* **27**, 58 (1948)].

4.4. Show that the dielectric constant at frequency ω of a medium containing N free electrons per unit volume is, in esu,

$$\epsilon = 1 - \frac{4\pi Ne^2}{m\omega^2}.$$

The presence of the mass in the denominator suggests that we may neglect the contribution of the positive ions present. We suppose, following C. G. Darwin [*Proc. Roy. Soc. (London)* **A146**, 17 (1934); **A151**, 512 (1935)], that the local field in this case is equal to the applied field E_0.

4.5. Show that a parallel-plate condenser made up of two parallel layers of material, one layer with dielectric constant ϵ, zero conductivity, and thickness d, and the other layer with $\epsilon = 0$ for convenience, finite conductivity σ, and thickness qd, behaves as if the space between the condenser plates were filled with a homogeneous dielectric with dielectric constant, in esu,

$$\epsilon^* = \frac{\epsilon(1 + q)}{1 + (i\epsilon\omega q/4\pi\sigma)},$$

where ω is the angular frequency [K. W. Wagner, *Arch. Elecktrotech.* **2**, 371 (1914)]. Values of ϵ as high as 10^4 or 10^5, caused largely by the Maxwell-Wagner mechanism, are sometimes found, but the high values are always accompanied by large losses. An analysis of the dielectric properties of a nickel zinc ferrite is given by C. G. Koops, *Phys. Rev.* **83**, 121 (1951).

4.6. Consider a system consisting of two atoms separated by a fixed distance a, each dipole having a polarizability α. Find the relation between a and α for such a system to be ferroelectric.

4.7. Consider a system consisting of two dipoles separated by a fixed distance a along the x axis. Assume that the dipoles are so restrained that they may polarize only along the y axis, and let the polarizability along the y axis be α. Can such a system be ferroelectric? Find the relation between a and α for the system to be antiferroelectric.

4.8. Discuss the effect of an air gap between condenser plates and dielectric on the measurement of high dielectric constants. What is the highest apparent dielectric constant possible if the air gap thickness is 10^{-3} of the total thickness?

4.9. Discuss the operation of the dielectric amplifier [see W. P. Mason and R. F. Wick, *Proc. I.R.E.* **42**, 1606 (1954)].

REFERENCES

Baumgartner, Jona, and Känzig, "Seignetteelektrizität," *Ergebnisse der exacten Naturwissenschaften* **23**, 235 (1950).

C. J. F. Böttcher, *Theory of electric polarisation*, Elsevier, Amsterdam, 1952.

W. G. Cady, *Piezoelectricity*, McGraw-Hill Book Co., New York, 1946.

P. Debye, *Polar molecules*, Chemical Catalog Co., New York, 1929.

A. F. Devonshire, "Theory of barium titanate," *Phil. Mag.* **40**, 1040 (1949); **42**, 1065 (1951); "Theory of ferroelectrics," *Advances in Physics* **3**, 85–130 (1954).

H. Fröhlich, *Theory of dielectrics: dielectric constant and dielectric loss*, Clarendon Press, Oxford, 1949.

E. T. Jaynes, *Ferroelectricity*, Princeton University Press, 1953.

R. J. LeFèvre, *Dipole moments*, Methuen and Co., London, 3rd ed., 1953.

W. P. Mason, *Piezoelectric crystals*, Van Nostrand, Princeton, New Jersey, 1950.

L. Rosenfeld, *Theory of electrons*, Interscience Publishers, New York, 1951.

G. Shirane, F. Jona, and R. Pepinsky, "Some aspects of ferroelectricity," *Proc. I.R.E.* **43**, 1738–1793 (1955).

C. P. Smyth, *Dielectric behavior and structure*, McGraw-Hill Book Co., New York, 1955.

J. H. Van Vleck, *Theory of electric and magnetic susceptibilities*, Clarendon Oxford, 1932.

A. R. von Hippel, *Dielectrics and waves*, John Wiley and Sons, New York, 1954.

A. R. von Hippel, editor, *Dielectric materials and applications*, John Wiley and Sons, New York, 1954.

5 Free electron model of metals

It is possible to understand a number of important physical properties of some metals, in particular the simple monovalent metals, in
terms of the free electron model. According to this model the valence
electrons of the constituent atoms of the metal are able to move about
freely through the volume of the specimen. The valence electrons
are responsible for the conduction of electricity by the metal, and for
this reason these electrons are termed conduction electrons, as distinguished from the electrons of the filled shells of the ion cores. The
interaction of the conduction electrons with the ion cores of the original atoms is neglected in the free electron approximation, and all calculations proceed as if the conduction electrons were entirely free in
the space bounded by the surfaces of the specimen.

Even in the metals for which the free electron model is most useful,
such as sodium, copper, and silver, it is wrong to imagine that the
charge distribution of the electrons does not reflect the strong attractive electrostatic potential of the ion cores. The usefulness of the free
electron model for the discussion of certain properties of metals depends
on two circumstances: (1) the energy of a conduction electron may
depend on the square of the velocity, just as for an electron in free
space, without the implication that the charge distribution should be
that of a free electron; and (2) the electron-electron collision scattering cross section is relatively small, the coulomb interaction being
largely suppressed by electrostatic screening, and the number of
allowed collision events being drastically reduced by the Pauli
principle.

The concept that metallic properties may be described in terms of
free electrons was developed long before the invention of wave mechanics. The early theory had several conspicuous successes and several
remarkable failures. Among the successes were the derivation of the
functional form of Ohm's law connecting the electric current with the
electric field and, in particular, the validity of the Wiedemann-Franz

relation between the electrical conductivity and the thermal conductivity. The outstanding failures relate to major discrepancies between observed and calculated values of the electronic heat capacity and also of the paramagnetic susceptibility of the conduction electrons. There is a further difficulty: it is not possible to understand on the classical model the occurrence of long electronic mean free paths, which at low temperatures may be as much as 10^3 or more longer than the values expected on a classical hard sphere model of the scattering of electrons by the ion cores. In actual fact, according to quantum theory the ion cores do not scatter the conduction electrons at all, as long as the ion cores are arranged in a perfectly regular array; this is truly a remarkable result. We discuss these points in detail in the following sections.

ELECTRICAL CONDUCTIVITY AND OHM'S LAW

We shall first consider the effect of an electric field $\mathbf{E}$ on a classical gas of free electrons. We suppose that there are N electrons per unit volume. We imagine that the electrons are moving around in a random way, with a velocity distribution appropriate to a condition of thermal equilibrium at temperature T. In the absence of an applied electric field the average or drift velocity,

$$(5.1) \qquad \mathbf{v}_D = \frac{1}{N} \sum_{i=1}^{N} \mathbf{v}_i,$$

will be zero, as in equilibrium there are just as many electrons moving in one direction as in the opposite direction.

We introduce now the concept of the *relaxation time,* denoted by τ. The relaxation time is closely related to the mean time of flight between collisions and also to the mean free path of the conduction electrons, which is the average distance of undisturbed motion between collisions. All the details of the collision processes occurring in the electron gas are summarized for the present purpose when the relaxation time is given. The collisions are caused by thermal or structural imperfections in the lattice. The relaxation time is introduced as the characteristic time governing the establishment of equilibrium (through collisions) from an initial disturbed situation in which $\mathbf{v}_D \neq 0$. If we write as the equation of motion for the drift velocity

$$(5.2) \qquad m\left(\frac{d\mathbf{v}_D}{dt} + \frac{1}{\tau}\mathbf{v}_D\right) = \mathbf{F},$$

where $\mathbf{F}$ is the average external force acting on an electron, we see that in the absence of external forces the free motion satisfies

(5.3)
$$\frac{d\mathbf{v}_D}{dt} + \frac{1}{\tau} \mathbf{v}_D = 0,$$

or, if $\mathbf{v}_D(0)$ is the initial drift velocity in the nonequilibrium distribution, the approach to equilibrium is described by the appropriate solution of (5.3)

(5.4)
$$\mathbf{v}_D(t) = \mathbf{v}_D(0)e^{-t/\tau}.$$

We have thus arranged things so that a disturbance from equilibrium dies out exponentially, with the characteristic time τ. We note further that the term $m\mathbf{v}_D/\tau$ introduced in (5.2) has the familiar form of a frictional or damping force, with m/τ playing the part of a coefficient of friction.

   If there were no friction in the electron system, that is, if the relaxation time were infinitely long, the conduction electrons would accelerate without limit in a constant applied electric field. The equation of motion

(5.5)
$$m\dot{\mathbf{v}}_D = e\mathbf{E}$$

has the solution

(5.6)
$$\mathbf{v}_D(t) = \mathbf{v}_D(0) + \frac{e\mathbf{E}t}{m},$$

which does not give a steady state of the type described by Ohm's law.

   With a finite relaxation time the equation of motion in a constant electric field is

(5.7)
$$m\left(\frac{d\mathbf{v}_D}{dt} + \frac{1}{\tau} \mathbf{v}_D\right) = e\mathbf{E},$$

which has the particular solution

(5.8)
$$\mathbf{v}_D = \frac{e\tau\mathbf{E}}{m}.$$

This solution represents a situation in which the drift velocity does not change with time and is obtained from (5.7) by setting the term $d\mathbf{v}_D/dt = 0$. The latter term describes inertial effects and should be included in problems where $\mathbf{E}$ is not constant, but is time-dependent. If $\mathbf{E} = \mathbf{E}_0 e^{i\omega t}$,

(5.9)
$$\mathbf{v}_D = \frac{e\tau\mathbf{E}/m}{1 + i\omega\tau}.$$

The electric current density $\mathbf{j}$ is defined as the electric charge transported through unit area in unit time. The net number of electrons passing through a unit area in unit time is $N\mathbf{v}_D$, where N is the number of electrons per unit volume. The electric current density is therefore given by

$$(5.10) \qquad\qquad \mathbf{j} = Ne\mathbf{v}_D.$$

Using (5.8), we have in the steady state

$$(5.11) \qquad\qquad \mathbf{j} = \frac{Ne^2\tau}{m}\,\mathbf{E},$$

showing that the current is directly proportional to the electric field. We have thus established Ohm's law.

The electrical conductivity σ is defined by the relation

$$(5.12) \qquad\qquad \mathbf{j} = \sigma\mathbf{E},$$

and so, using (5.11), we have the important result

$$(5.13) \qquad\qquad \sigma = \frac{Ne^2\tau}{m}.$$

As the resistivity ρ is defined as the reciprocal of the conductivity, we have

$$(5.14) \qquad\qquad \rho = \frac{1}{\sigma} = \frac{m}{Ne^2\tau}.$$

It is easy to understand the result (5.13) for the conductivity. We expect the charge transported to be proportional to the charge density Ne; the factor e/m enters because the acceleration in a given electric field is proportional to e and inversely proportional to the mass m; the time τ describes the free time during which the field acts on the carrier, the next collision removing all memory of the drift velocity. Quantum theory does not alter the result (5.13) in any essential way; rather, it tells us how to make a theoretical calculation of the relaxation time starting from first principles.

It is instructive to estimate from the observed conductivity the order of magnitude of the relaxation time τ, using (5.13). We consider copper at room temperature. The handbook value of the resistivity is 1.7 microhm-cm, and so $\sigma = 6 \times 10^5$ (ohm-cm)$^{-1}$ or mho/cm. In MKS the unit of resistivity is the ohm-meter, and the numerical value of a resistivity in MKS units is 10^{-2} times the value in practical units; similarly the conductivity measured in mho/meter is 10^2 larger than the conductivity measured in mho/cm. To convert a conductivity given in mho/cm to esu we must multiply by $(10)^{-1}(3 \times 10^{10})(300) = 9 \times 10^{11}$. The factor $(10)^{-1}$ converts the current to absolute amperes and the factor 3×10^{10} converts to statamperes; the factor 300 is involved reciprocally in the conversion of volts/cm to statvolts/cm. That is, we are given

$$\mathbf{j} \text{ (practical)} = \sigma \text{ (practical) } \mathbf{E} \text{ (practical)}$$

and wish to find σ (esu) defined by

$$\mathbf{j} \text{ (esu)} = \sigma \text{ (esu) } \mathbf{E} \text{ (esu)}.$$

Thus on division

(5.15)
$$\frac{\sigma \text{ (esu)}}{\sigma \text{ (practical)}} = \frac{\mathbf{j} \text{ (esu)}}{\mathbf{j} \text{ (practical)}} \frac{\mathbf{E} \text{ (practical)}}{\mathbf{E} \text{ (esu)}}$$

$$= (3 \times 10^9)(300) = 9 \times 10^{11}.$$

In these conversions we have taken the value of the velocity of light to be 3×10^{10} cm/sec. For our problem we have then that σ (esu) $\cong 5 \times 10^{17}$ sec^{-1}, recalling that in esu the conductivity has the dimensions of a frequency.

It is reasonable to suppose that each atom of copper in the metal contributes one valence electron to the conduction band.[1] The concentration N of conduction electrons will be equal to the number of copper atoms per unit volume, which may be found from the Avogadro number divided by the molar volume. The molar volume is the molecular weight divided by the density, or

$$\text{Molar volume} = \frac{63.5}{8.94} = 7.1 \text{ cm}^3.$$

Hence

$$N = \frac{6.025 \times 10^{23}}{7.1} = 8.5 \times 10^{22} \text{ cm}^{-3}.$$

We have

$$\tau = \frac{\sigma m}{Ne^2} \cong \frac{(5 \times 10^{17})(9 \times 10^{-28})}{(9 \times 10^{22})(5 \times 10^{-10})^2}$$

$$\cong 2 \times 10^{-14} \text{ sec}.$$

We have not yet built up enough background material or carried the theory far enough along to enable the reader at this point to judge

---

[1] The configuration of the ground state of the free copper atom is $1s^2 2s^2 2p^6 3s^2$-$3p^6 3d^{10} 4s$; the valence electron of copper is the $4s$ electron, the other electrons in closed shells forming the ion core.

for himself if this estimated value of the relaxation time is reasonable on the basis of other evidence. One piece of evidence may be cited to suggest that the relevant relaxation time should be shorter than 10^{-11} sec, in agreement with the above estimate: the microwave attenuation of copper wave guide at a frequency of 2.4×10^{10} cps and at room temperature is known to be in quite good agreement with that calculated according to the ordinary theory of the r-f skin effect, provided the surfaces of the guide are well polished. The result of the theory is expressed in terms of the static electrical conductivity. If the inertial term $md\mathbf{v}_D/dt$ in the equation of motion

$$(5.16) \qquad m\left(i\omega + \frac{1}{\tau}\right)\mathbf{v}_D = e\mathbf{E}$$

were more important than the relaxation term $m\mathbf{v}_D/\tau$, we would not expect to find agreement with the waveguide losses as calculated using the d-c conductivity.

The relaxation term is dominant as long as $1/\tau \gg \omega$, or

$$(5.17) \qquad \tau \ll \frac{1}{\omega} = \frac{1}{2\pi f} \cong 7 \times 10^{-12} \text{ sec.}$$

It is satisfying that our time of 2×10^{-14} sec as estimated from the conductivity does indeed satisfy this inequality.

We may introduce the mean free path Λ by the relation

$$(5.18) \qquad \Lambda = \tau u,$$

where u is an appropriate average electron velocity. We shall see later in this chapter that the appropriate value of u for copper is about 1.6×10^8 cm/sec; with $\tau \cong 2 \times 10^{-14}$ sec at room temperature we have $\Lambda \cong 3 \times 10^6$ cm, or about 100 times the lattice constant of copper. There is some experimental evidence that this value is reasonable: for example, Reynolds and Stilwell[2] have measured the resistivity of good films of copper and silver as a function of the thickness of the film. The resistivity will have two contributions, one from collisions in the bulk of the material of the type that we are discussing and another contribution from diffuse scattering of the electrons at the surface of the film. In thick specimens the bulk scattering is dominant; in thin films the surface scattering is dominant. The theory of the combined scattering has been worked out by K. Fuchs[3] and is in good agreement

[2] F. W. Reynolds and G. R. Stilwell, *Phys. Rev.* **88**, 418 (1952); a review of theoretical and experimental work on the mean free path of electrons in metals is given by E. H. Sondheimer, *Advances in Physics* **1**, 1 (1952).

[3] K. Fuchs, *Proc. Cambridge Phil. Soc.* **34**, 100 (1938).

with the observations, provided the bulk mean free path is taken to be 4.5×10^{-6} cm in copper, in satisfactory agreement with our rough estimate. The results of more careful calculations are given in Table 5.1.

TABLE 5.1
CONDUCTIVITY DATA FOR METALS AT $0°c$

One free electron per atom is assumed: Λ is calculated by using Eq. (5.18); values after Mott and Jones, with an error of a factor of 2 in their Λ's corrected; u_F is calculated by setting $\frac{1}{2}mu_F^2 = E_F$, where the Fermi energy E_F is given by (5.44)

Metal	Free Electrons per cm³, N	Observed Conductivity at 0°C, σ (esu)	Calculated u_F (cm/sec)	Calculated Mean Free Path Λ (cm)
Li	4.6×10^{22}	1.06×10^{17}	1.31×10^8	110×10^{-8}
Na	2.5	2.09	1.07	350
K	1.3	1.47	0.85	370
Rb	1.1	0.78	0.80	220
Cs	0.85	0.49	0.75	160
Cu	8.5	5.76	1.58	420
Ag	5.8	6.12	1.40	570
Au	5.9	4.37	1.40	410

The ionic radius R of the Cu^+ ion core is about 0.96×10^{-8} cm. Now, according to simple dimensional reasoning or elementary kinetic theory, the mean free path should be given by $\Lambda \approx 1/(N\pi R^2) \approx 4 \times 10^{-8}$ cm if the interaction of a conduction electron with a copper ion core may be treated classically. However, we have seen that the actual mean free path is of the order of 5×10^{-6} cm at room temperature, and it may be as long as 10^{-3} cm or more at low temperatures. We conclude the problem cannot be treated classically.

The mobility μ is defined as the drift velocity per unit electric field

$$(5.19) \qquad \mu = \frac{\mathbf{v}_D}{\mathbf{E}} = \frac{e\tau}{m},$$

according to (5.8). To get an idea of the order of magnitude of the mobility, we consider copper at room temperature:

$$\mu \cong \frac{(5 \times 10^{-10})(2 \times 10^{-14})}{9 \times 10^{-28}} \cong 10^4 \text{ cm}^2/\text{statvolt-sec}$$

$$\cong 30 \text{ cm}^2/\text{volt-sec} \cong 3 \times 10^{-3} \text{ meter}^2/\text{volt-sec}.$$

The mobility is a particularly useful quantity in dealing with semi-conductors, because it is defined without reference to the concentration of charge carriers.

We have quoted (but not yet derived) the value 1.6×10^8 cm/sec for the intrinsic velocity of the conduction electrons in copper. The drift velocity acquired in an external electric field will be small in comparison with this as long as the electric field intensity does not exceed 10^6 volts/cm. For fields of this magnitude or higher we expect non-linear effects to modify the form of Ohm's law. Because of the high fields required, such effects are of only little importance in normal metals;[4] they are important however in semiconductors,[5] where high electric field intensities may exist at *p-n* junctions. The theory of *p-n* junctions is discussed in Chapter 6.

We must emphasize that the expression $\sigma = Ne^2\tau/m$ has been discussed here on a purely classical model, with no use of quantum mechanics or quantum statistics. It is shown later in this chapter that the result is preserved with quantum statistics.

WIEDEMANN-FRANZ RATIO

In Chapter 3 we discussed expressions for the thermal conductivity of conduction electrons. Using the free electron model and Fermi-Dirac statistics, we have for the thermal conductivity

(5.20)
$$K = \frac{\pi^2}{3} \frac{k^2 TN\tau}{m}.$$

The electrical conductivity is given by $\sigma = Ne^2\tau/m$, according to (5.13). Thus

(5.21)
$$\frac{K}{\sigma} = \frac{\pi^2}{3} \left(\frac{k}{e}\right)^2 T.$$

A relationship of this type was first observed by Wiedemann and Franz, and the ratio is named after them. The Lorenz number L is defined by

(5.22)
$$L = \frac{K}{\sigma T},$$

and according to (5.21) should be given on the free electron model by

(5.23) $$L = \frac{\pi^2}{3} \left(\frac{k}{e}\right)^2 = 2.72 \times 10^{-13} \text{ esu/deg}^2$$

$$= 2.45 \times 10^{-8} \text{ watt-ohm/deg}^2,$$

[4] See, for example, E. Guth and J. Mayerhöfer, *Phys. Rev.* **57**, 908 (1940).
[5] W. Shockley, *Bell System Tech. J.* **30**, 990 (1951).

TABLE 5.2
EXPERIMENTAL LORENZ NUMBERS

$L \times 10^8$ watt-ohms/deg^2			$L \times 10^8$ watt-ohms/deg^2		
Metal	0°C	100°C	Metal	0°C	100°C
Ag	2.31	2.37	Pb	2.47	2.56
Au	2.35	2.40	Pt	2.51	2.60
Cd	2.42	2.43	Sn	2.52	2.49
Cu	2.23	2.33	W	3.04	3.20
Ir	2.49	2.49	Zn	2.31	2.33
Mo	2.61	2.79			

for electronic conduction only. This is a remarkable result, as it involves neither N, m, nor τ. A more detailed study of the quantum theory of transport processes in metals shows that the Lorenz number is expected to be independent of temperature only above the Debye temperature,[6] as the differences among the types of collision averages involved in electrical and thermal conductivity become important when at low temperatures small angle electron-phonon collisions are dominant. At room temperature the values observed are in quite good agreement with the theoretical value given in (5.23), as shown in Table 5.2.

HEAT CAPACITY OF CONDUCTION ELECTRONS

According to the classical theory discussed in Chapter 3, the conduction electrons of a metal should make a contribution

$$C \text{ (electronic)} = \tfrac{3}{2}Rz$$

to the molar heat capacity of the metal; here R is the gas constant and z is the number of valence electrons per atom. As discussed earlier, there is no experimental evidence for an electronic contribution of anything like this magnitude. The value of the total heat capacity of metals at room temperature and above is usually quite close to the value 6 cal/mole-deg, just as for dielectric solids, and this value may be attributed to lattice vibrations, to a fair approximation. The discrepancy represents an outstanding failure of the classical free electron gas model. It was a particularly puzzling failure in the light of the partial successes of the model in explaining electrical and thermal conductivity in metals: it is difficult to see classically how the electrons

---

[6] Experimental studies of the temperature dependence of L at low temperatures in sodium and copper have been carried out by R. Berman and D. K. C. MacDonald, *Proc. Roy. Soc.* (*London*) **A209**, 368 (1951;) **A211**, 122 (1952).

can participate in transport processes as if they were free and yet give only a very small contribution to the heat capacity.

PARAMAGNETIC SUSCEPTIBILITY OF CONDUCTION ELECTRONS

The classical free electron theory also gives an unsatisfactory account of the paramagnetic susceptibility of the conduction electrons. We know from elementary atomic physics that an electron has associated with it a magnetic moment of value equal to a Bohr magneton:

$$(5.24) \qquad \mu_B = \frac{e\hbar}{2mc} = -0.927 \times 10^{-20} \text{ erg/oersted}$$

$$= -9.27 \times 10^{-18} \text{ joule/meter}^2\text{/weber}$$

One would expect that the conduction electrons, according to the results of a later chapter, would make a paramagnetic contribution [Eq. (8.13)],

$$\chi = \frac{N\mu_B{}^2}{3kT}$$

to the susceptibility of the metal. This result is the magnetic analog of (4.28) for electric dipole moments. Instead it is observed that the susceptibility of normal nonferromagnetic metals is independent of temperature and of magnitude at room temperature perhaps only $\frac{1}{100}$ of that expected.

QUANTUM THEORY OF FREE PARTICLES IN A BOX

The difficulties encountered by the classical free electron theory in attempting to explain the observations of the heat capacity and magnetic susceptibility of simple metals are corrected in a simple and satisfying way on taking account of the requirements of the Pauli exclusion principle. We are familiar with the central and crucial part played by the Pauli principle in accounting for the composition and even the existence of the periodic table of elements.[7] The most elementary statement of the Pauli principle as applied to isolated atoms is that no two electrons of the same atom may have all their individual quantum numbers equal. The individual quantum numbers in an atom may be taken as n, the principal quantum number; l, the orbital quantum number; m_l, the azimuthal quantum number representing the projection of l on a given direction; m_s, the spin quantum number, which may be either $\pm\frac{1}{2}$.

---

[7] For introductory discussions of the Pauli principle the reader may refer to the following references, among others: J. C. Slater, *Introduction to chemical physics*, McGraw-Hill, New York, 1939, Chapter XXI; M. Born, *Atomic physics*, Hafner, New York, 5th ed., 1951, Chapter VI.

We remind the reader of an elementary application of the exclusion principle. If we take the quantum numbers for the ground state of hydrogen to be $n = 1$, $l = 0$, $m_l = 0$, $m_s = \frac{1}{2}$, then the next electron added in forming the ground state of helium, which has two electrons, must occupy the set of quantum numbers $n = 1$, $l = 0$, $m_l = 0$, $m_s = -\frac{1}{2}$. In helium all the sets of quantum numbers associated with $n = 1$ are occupied, so that when we go on to the lithium atom the third electron in the ground state must start with $n = 2$, and we can complete the set by taking $l = 0$, $m_l = 0$, $m_s = +\frac{1}{2}$. Proceeding in this way we can construct the entire periodic table.

It is evident when we try to determine the consequences of the Pauli principle for the conduction electrons of a metal that we must first set up a proper system of quantum numbers for the problem, a system which will specify the state of the conduction electrons in the same way as the set of quantum numbers n, l, m_l, m_s specify the state of the electrons in the problem of the free atom.

For the present purpose the most important fact about the free electron is that there is a wave associated with it, of wavelength

$$(5.25) \qquad\qquad \lambda = \frac{h}{p},$$

where h is Planck's constant and p is the momentum mv of the electron, considered to be in free space. This is the celebrated de Broglie relation. The wave nature of the electron has been demonstrated by many experiments, in the first instance the electron diffraction experiments of Davisson and Germer and of G. P. Thomson. In these experiments one detects a beam of electrons diffracted on reflection from the surface of a crystal or diffracted in passing through a polycrystalline foil; the angles at which diffracted electron beams are found are just the angles satisfying the Bragg condition $2d \sin \theta = n\lambda$, where the wavelength in the Bragg equation is to be calculated from the foregoing de Broglie relation. The electron momentum p is related to the accelerating voltage applied to the electron beam by

$$p = (2mE)^{\frac{1}{2}},$$

where E is the energy of the electrons. A convenient practical relation for electrons is

$$\lambda \text{ (A)} \cong \left(\frac{150}{V}\right)^{\frac{1}{2}},$$

where λ is given in angstrom units (10^{-8} cm) and V is the accelerating

voltage in volts. We see that the wavelength of a 150-volt electron
is 1 A; of a 1.5-volt electron, 10 A.

The Schrödinger wave equation

$$(5.26) \qquad \left(-\frac{\hbar^2}{2m}\nabla^2 + V(\mathbf{r}) \right)\psi = E\psi$$

is in effect a generalization of the de Broglie relation to situations where
the potential energy $V(\mathbf{r})$ of the electron is a function of the position $\mathbf{r}$.
In this equation

$$\nabla^2 \equiv \frac{\partial^2}{\partial x^2} + \frac{\partial^2}{\partial y^2} + \frac{\partial^2}{\partial z^2};$$

$\hbar = h/2\pi$ and E is the total energy, which is constant. The function
ψ is the wave function or eigenfunction, and has the significance that,
when properly normalized, $\psi^*\psi \, dx \, dy \, dz$ is the probability of finding
the electron in the volume element $dx \, dy \, dz$. Here ψ^* denotes the
complex conjugate function to ψ.

We can see a connection of the Schrödinger equation with the de
Broglie relation by considering an electron in free space, with $V(\mathbf{r}) = 0$.
The wave equation becomes

$$(5.27) \qquad -\frac{\hbar^2}{2m}\nabla^2\psi = E\psi.$$

We may obtain a solution of this equation with E constant on taking
$\psi \sim e^{i\mathbf{k}\cdot\mathbf{r}}$. We could also take $\psi \sim \sin \mathbf{k}\cdot\mathbf{r}$ or $\cos \mathbf{k}\cdot\mathbf{r}$, or any linear
combination of these solutions. We see that

$$\nabla^2\psi = -k^2\psi,$$

and so ψ is a solution when $\mathbf{k}$ and E are related by

$$(5.28) \qquad E = \frac{\hbar^2}{2m}k^2.$$

Now $\mathbf{k}$, the wave vector, has the significance for free electrons that

$$(5.29) \qquad k = |\mathbf{k}| = \frac{2\pi}{\lambda},$$

where λ is the wavelength. On substitution back in (5.28), we have

$$(5.30) \qquad E = \frac{\hbar^2}{2m}\left(\frac{2\pi}{\lambda}\right)^2 = \frac{1}{2m}\left(\frac{h}{\lambda}\right)^2.$$

If the momentum and wavelength are connected by the de Broglie relation $\lambda = h/p$, we have on substitution

$$E = \frac{1}{2m} p^2 = \frac{1}{2} mv^2,$$

which is exactly the classical energy for a free particle of mass m. We see that for a free particle that the wave equation leads to the same connection between energy and wavelength as does the de Broglie relation.

In the approximation that the conduction electrons are entirely free we may take their wave functions to have the form

(5.31) $\psi \sim e^{i\mathbf{k}\cdot\mathbf{r}}.$

We must do two things to this function before it can be an acceptable solution to the problem. We must normalize it so that the integral of the probability density $\psi^*\psi$ over the allowed region of space is unity:

(5.32) $\int \psi^*\psi \, dV = 1.$

We accomplish this by setting

(5.33) $\psi = \left(\frac{1}{V}\right)^{\frac{1}{2}} e^{i\mathbf{k}\cdot\mathbf{r}};$

here V is the volume of the solid within which the electron is confined. We also want the wave function to satisfy reasonable boundary conditions on the surface of the solid. For example, we can require the wave function to go to zero on the surface.

The boundary conditions introduce a type of quantization into the problem. Consider an electron confined to a line of length L, as in Fig. 5.1. If we require that $\psi(0) = 0$ and $\psi(L) = 0$, then the solutions of the wave equation in one dimension must be of the form

(5.34) $\psi_n = \left(\frac{2}{L}\right)^{\frac{1}{2}} \sin \frac{n\pi x}{L}.$

We obtain the energy by substituting ψ_n in Eq. (5.27), finding

(5.35) $E_n = \frac{\hbar^2}{2m} \left(\frac{\pi}{L}\right)^2 n^2, \qquad (n = 1, 2, 3, \cdots).$

The allowed energy levels are quantized in this way, other values of the energy being excluded as the corresponding ψ's do not satisfy the boundary conditions.

It is often convenient, particularly in three dimensions, to introduce

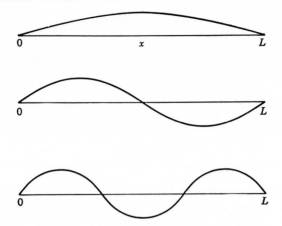

FIG. 5.1. First three wave functions for electron constrained to move on a line of length L.

the boundary conditions in a different way. The method of periodic boundary conditions was introduced in Chapter 3 in connection with lattice vibrations. We quantize the electrons in a cube of side L and require the wave functions to be periodic in x, y, z with period L. We require, for example, that

$$(5.36) \qquad \psi(x + L, y, z) = \psi(x, y, z),$$

with similar relations for the y and z coordinates. Free particle wave functions satisfying the periodicity requirement will be of the form

$$(5.37) \qquad \psi_{\mathbf{n}} = \left(\frac{1}{L}\right)^{3/2} e^{i\frac{2\pi}{L}(n_x x + n_y y + n_z z)}$$

where

$$n_x = 0, \pm 1, \pm 2, \cdots \ ;$$
$$n_y = 0, \pm 1, \pm 2, \cdots \ ;$$
$$n_z = 0, \pm 1, \pm 2, \cdots \ .$$

It is easy to see that this function is satisfactory, for

$$\psi_{\mathbf{n}}(x + L, y, z) = \left(\frac{1}{L}\right)^{3/2} e^{i\frac{2\pi}{L}[n_x(x+L) + n_y y + n_z z]}$$

$$= \left(\frac{1}{L}\right)^{3/2} e^{i\frac{2\pi}{L}(n_x x + n_y y + n_z z)}$$

$$= \psi_{\mathbf{n}}(x, y, z),$$

as required.   Here **n** denotes the triplet of integers (n_x, n_y, n_z).   The
energy corresponding to the solution (5.37) is easily seen to be

$$(5.38) \qquad E_{\mathbf{n}} = \frac{\hbar^2}{2m} \left(\frac{2\pi}{L}\right)^2 (n_x{}^2 + n_y{}^2 + n_z{}^2) = \frac{h^2 n^2}{2m V^{2/3}};$$

here the volume $V = L^3$ and $n^2 = n_x{}^2 + n_y{}^2 + n_z{}^2$.   We note that
the allowed values of the wave vector are given by

$$(5.39) \qquad\qquad\qquad \mathbf{k} = \frac{2\pi}{L} n.$$

We see that the two types of boundary conditions are associated with
two different types of wave functions.   The solutions (5.34) for the
condition $\psi = 0$ at the boundaries are of the form of standing waves
and have the property that the probability density

$$(5.40) \qquad\qquad\qquad \psi^*\psi = \frac{2}{L} \sin^2 \frac{n\pi x}{L}$$

is a periodic function of x.   However, the solutions (5.37) for periodic
boundary conditions are of the form of traveling waves and give a
uniform probability density, as

$$(5.41) \qquad\qquad\qquad \psi^*\psi = \frac{1}{V}.$$

These differences are not significant in the free electron problem, but
it turns out that when the interaction with the crystal lattice is taken
into account the traveling wave solutions have more direct physical
importance than the standing wave solutions.   We shall work with
traveling waves.

It will be evident that we may take, as the quantum numbers appropriate to the free electron problem, the three components of either **k**
or **n**, as connected by (5.39), together with the spin quantum number
$m_s = \pm\frac{1}{2}$ according to whether the electron spin is pointing up or
down.   That is, the state of an electron is specified when we are given
the values of n_x, n_y, n_z, m_s, or, alternatively, k_x, k_y, k_z, m_s.   We must
now consider the effects of the Pauli exclusion principle on the energy
distribution of the conduction electrons.

We see from (5.38) that the energy of an electron depends on $n^2 \equiv
n_x{}^2 + n_y{}^2 + n_z{}^2$, where the n_x, n_y, n_z are positive or negative integers.
The ground energy level of the system may be taken as $n_x = n_y =
n_z = 0$.   We may put two electrons into this level, one for each of the
two possible spin orientations, $m_s = \pm\frac{1}{2}$.   The next electron added to

the system will have to go into a higher energy level, as the exclusion principle prevents it from going into either of the two ground states already occupied. The next energy level above the ground level will have $n^2 = 1$ and may be attained in the following twelve ways:

n_x	n_y	n_z	m_s
1	0	0	$\frac{1}{2}$
1	0	0	$-\frac{1}{2}$
−1	0	0	$\frac{1}{2}$
−1	0	0	$-\frac{1}{2}$
0	1	0	$\frac{1}{2}$
0	1	0	$-\frac{1}{2}$
0	−1	0	$\frac{1}{2}$
0	−1	0	$-\frac{1}{2}$
0	0	1	$\frac{1}{2}$
0	0	1	$-\frac{1}{2}$
0	0	−1	$\frac{1}{2}$
0	0	−1	$-\frac{1}{2}$

The first excited energy level of the system represents twelve independent states, and it will accommodate twelve electrons, according to the Pauli principle.

The ground level and the first excited level can hold a maximum of $2 + 12 = 14$ electrons, and at absolute zero the 14 states will be occupied by 14 electrons. The fifteenth electron to be added to the system then will have to go into another level: the level of lowest energy available to it will have $n^2 = 2$. The reader may confirm for himself that the level $n^2 = 2$ can hold a maximum of 24 electrons. Proceeding in this way we gradually move up the energy levels of the system until all the available electrons are accommodated. At absolute zero all the levels below a certain level will be filled with electrons, and all levels above it will be empty of electrons. The level which divides the filled and vacant levels is known as the Fermi level at absolute zero and is denoted by $E_F(0)$.

There is considerable interest in knowing the value of the Fermi level as a function of the electron concentration N. The number of states having n less than a certain value n_F is simply $2 \times (4\pi/3)n_F^3$, as there are two independent states (of different spin orientation) per unit volume in $\mathbf{n}$ space, each integral triplet n_x, n_y, n_z giving two states. To hold NL^3 electrons at absolute zero, all $\mathbf{n}$ values must then be filled up to

(5.42)
$$\frac{8\pi}{3} n_F^3 = NL^3,$$

TABLE 5.3

CALCULATED FERMI LEVEL VALUES ON THE FREE ELECTRON MODEL

	Li	Na	K	Rb
E_F (ev)	4.72	3.12	2.14	1.82
T_F (deg)	55,000	37,000	24,000	21,000
u_F (cm/sec)	1.31×10^8	1.07×10^8	0.85×10^8	0.80×10^8
	Cs	Cu	Ag	Au
E_F (ev)	1.53	7.04	5.51	5.51
T_F (deg)	18,000	82,000	64,000	64,000
u_F (cm/sec)	0.75×10^8	1.58×10^8	1.40×10^8	1.40×10^8

and so

$$(5.43) \qquad \left(\frac{n_F}{L}\right)^2 = \left(\frac{3N}{8\pi}\right)^{2/3}.$$

The energy corresponding to n_F is

$$(5.44) \qquad E_F(0) = \frac{\hbar^2}{2m}\left(\frac{2\pi}{L}\right)^2 n_F^2 = \frac{\hbar^2}{2m}(3\pi^2 N)^{2/3},$$

on combining (5.38) and (5.43).

The order of magnitude of $E_F(0)$ is about 5 ev; that is, at absolute zero the conduction electrons in a metal are not all condensed into a state of zero energy as on classical mechanics, but rather they fill all allowed energy levels over a range of some 5 ev above the ground state. Values of the Fermi energy on the free electron model are given in Table 5.3, together with values of the effective Fermi temperature T_F defined by

$$(5.45) \qquad T_F = \frac{E_F(0)}{k}.$$

The electron velocity u_F at the Fermi level is defined by

$$(5.46) \qquad \tfrac{1}{2}m u_F^2 = E_F(0).$$

It is interesting to find the density of states, defined as the number of states per unit energy range as a function of the energy. Denoting the density of states by $g(E)$, we know that

$$(5.47) \qquad \int g(E) \, dE = NV = \frac{V}{3\pi^2}\left(\frac{2mE}{\hbar^2}\right)^{3/2},$$

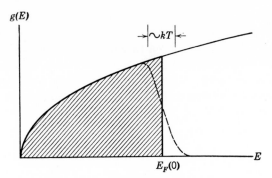

FIG. 5.2.   Plot of density of states $g(E)$ as a function of energy.   At absolute zero the states up to $E_F(0)$ are filled.   The dotted curve indicates the density of filled states at a temperature $T \ll E_F/k$.

using (5.44).   Thus

$$(5.48) \qquad\qquad g(E) = \frac{V}{2\pi^2}\left(\frac{2m}{\hbar^2}\right)^{3/2} E^{1/2}.$$

A plot is given in Fig. 5.2.

Let us now consider the effect of warming up the electrons from absolute zero to temperature T.   In classical mechanics the general effect is to increase the energy of each particle by an amount of the order of kT, which at room temperature is of the order of 0.02 ev. We have seen that the energy distribution in the conduction electron problem extends over several electron volts even at absolute zero.   It is very unlikely that an electron in this distribution will be excited at room temperature if it lies more than 0.1 ev below the Fermi level, as the states within an energy range of kT of such an electron are almost entirely filled, and it is generally not very probable that the electron will gain the $5kT \approx 0.1$ ev necessary to excite it into an otherwise unoccupied state above the Fermi level.

We can say then that the Pauli exclusion principle has a considerable effect on the thermal behavior of the conduction electrons.   On heating from absolute zero every electron does not gain an energy $\sim kT$ as happens classically, but only those electrons already within an energy range of the order of kT of the Fermi level can be excited thermally; these electrons gain an energy which is itself of the order of kT, as sketched in Fig. 5.2.

This drastic modification of the thermal properties of the conduction electrons as compared with classical behavior gives an immediate qualitative solution to the problem of the heat capacity of the conduction electron gas. If N is the total number of electrons, only a fraction of the order of T/T_F can be excited thermally at temperature T, because only these lie within an energy range of the order of kT of the top of the energy distribution. These NT/T_F electrons have each gained a thermal energy of the order of kT, and so the total electronic thermal energy U is of the order of

$$\frac{NT}{T_F} kT = \frac{RT^2}{T_F} \text{ per mole.}$$

The electronic heat capacity is given by

$$C_v = \frac{\partial U}{\partial T} \approx \frac{RT}{T_F},$$

which is proportional to T, in concord with the experimental data discussed in Chapter 3; at room temperature C_v is smaller than $\frac{3}{2}R$, the classical value, by a factor of the order of 0.01 or less. We recall $T_F \sim 5 \times 10^4$ deg.

We now go on to discuss quantitatively the effect of the exclusion principle on the thermal equilibrium distribution of the conduction electrons.

FERMI-DIRAC DISTRIBUTION LAW[8]

From the elementary kinetic theory of gases we are familiar with the Maxwell-Boltzmann distribution law. This law is a result of classical theory and is valid under the ordinary conditions of molecules in a gas. Electrons are much lighter than molecules; also, in a metal the concentration of valence electrons is 10^4 higher than the concentration of molecules in a gas at STP. Under these conditions classical statistics is no longer a valid approximation to the correct quantum statistics. The classical distribution is a good approximation to the true state of affairs only when the average spacing between particles is large in comparison with the de Broglie wavelength (5.25) calculated using the thermal velocity of the particles.

As applied to electrons, quantum statistics requires that we treat all electrons as *indistinguishable* and that each state of the system may be occupied by at most one electron. A one-particle state of the free particle system is determined by a specification of the values of the quantum numbers n_x, n_y, n_z, and the spin quantum number $m_z = \pm\frac{1}{2}$ of the electron. If we can have only one electron in a state, it follows,

---

[8] For an elementary exposition of quantum statistics, see M. Born, *Atomic physics*, Hafner, New York, 5th ed., 1951, Chapter VIII.

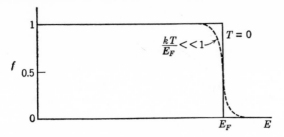

FIG. 5.3. Sketch of the Fermi-Dirac distribution function for absolute zero and for a low temperature. The region over which the distribution is affected by temperature is of the order of kT in width.

when we are dealing with large numbers of electrons, that even in the lowest state of the total system many high quantum number states of the individual electrons will be occupied. This is very different from the Maxwell-Boltzmann case where any number of particles can have the identical energy and momentum. In the lowest state of a classical system all particles can have zero energy and momentum.

Thus at absolute zero the Fermi-Dirac distribution law requires that the probability $f(E)$, for a single particle state at energy E to be occupied by an electron, have the value 1 or 0. The probability will be 1 if E_i is less than the energy $E_F(0)$, up to which the energy levels are filled at absolute zero. In Fig. 5.3 we plot the distribution function f as a function of energy at absolute zero and also at a low temperature such that $kT \ll E_F$. Our task now is to derive an expression for f as a function of E, T, and the number of particles.

Complete derivations of the Fermi-Dirac distribution are found in the standard textbooks on statistical mechanics and on atomic physics. We derive the distribution here by a neat and brief subterfuge. We consider the inelastic collisions of an electron gas with a simple two-level impurity atom with which the electron gas may be imagined to interact. The impurity atom has two energy states 0 and ϵ, as indicated in Fig. 5.4; the occupation probabilities of the two levels will be written as $p(0)$ and $p(\epsilon)$. There are many distinct collision processes involving this impurity atom, but we focus our attention first on those inelastic processes which connect one electron state $\mathbf{k}$ at electron energy E with a state $\mathbf{k}'$ at electron energy $E + \epsilon$.

The transition rate starting at $\mathbf{k}$ and ending at $\mathbf{k}'$ will be proportional to

$$f(E)p(\epsilon)[1 - f(E + \epsilon)],$$

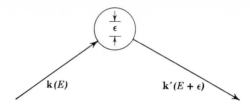

FIG. 5.4.   The sketch indicates that an electron in a state **k** of energy E collides inelastically with an impurity atom having energy ϵ.   In the particular final state shown the electron is in a state **k'** with energy $E + \epsilon$.   In such collisions the atom loses energy ϵ.

where $f(E)$ is the probability that the initial state at **k** is occupied; $p(\epsilon)$ is the probability the impurity atom is in the state ϵ so that it can give up its energy to the electron, and $1 - f(E + \epsilon)$ is the probability that the state **k'** at $E + \epsilon$ is vacant, which it must be if the scattering event is to take place; this is the special feature introduced by the Pauli principle.   Now the transition rate for the reverse process $\mathbf{k'}(E + \epsilon) \rightarrow \mathbf{k}(E)$ is proportional to

$$f(E + \epsilon)p(0)[1 - f(E)],$$

just reversing the steps in Fig. 5.4 and in the preceding argument. The constants of proportionality in the direct and inverse processes are exactly equal by the principle of detailed balance, which follows directly from quantum theory.   Now in thermal equilibrium the actual transition rates $\mathbf{k} \rightarrow \mathbf{k'}$ and $\mathbf{k'} \rightarrow \mathbf{k}$ must be equal, so that the two population factors must be equal:

$$(5.49) \quad \langle f(E) \rangle \langle p(\epsilon) \rangle [1 - \langle f(E + \epsilon) \rangle] = \langle f(E + \epsilon) \rangle \langle p(0) \rangle [1 - \langle f(E) \rangle],$$

where the angular brackets indicate averages in thermal equilibrium at a common temperature T.   By the Boltzmann distribution

$$(5.50) \qquad \frac{\langle p(\epsilon) \rangle}{\langle p(0) \rangle} = e^{-\epsilon/kT},$$

so that

$$(5.51) \qquad \frac{\langle f(E + \epsilon) \rangle}{\langle 1 - f(E + \epsilon) \rangle} \frac{\langle 1 - f(E) \rangle}{\langle f(E) \rangle} = e^{-\epsilon/kT}.$$

This functional equation is easily seen to have a solution for all T if

$$(5.52) \qquad \frac{\langle 1 - f(E) \rangle}{\langle f(E) \rangle} = e^{(E-\mu)/kT},$$

where μ is a constant independent of E, so that we have

$$(5.53) \qquad \langle f(E) \rangle = \frac{1}{e^{(E-\mu)/kT} + 1}.$$

The constant μ is usually written as E_F and is called the Fermi energy. Dropping the angular brackets, we write the Fermi-Dirac distribution law as

$$(5.54) \qquad f = \frac{1}{e^{(E-E_F)/kT} + 1}.$$

At $T = 0°K$, $f = 1$ for $E < E_F$, and $f = 0$ for $E > E_F$. Thus at absolute zero E_F has the significance of a cut-off energy; all states with energy less than E_F are completely filled, and all states with energy greater than E_F are vacant. As T increases, the distribution rounds off as shown in Fig. 5.3, states within about kT below E_F being partly depopulated and states within about kT above E_F being partly populated. The value of E_F is determined by the condition that the total number of particles should be constant; the condition depends on the temperature, but for $kT/E_F \ll 1$ it can be shown that $E_F(T)$ is closely equal to its value at $0°K$. At any temperature, f has the value $\frac{1}{2}$ for $E = E_F$. The distribution is called *degenerate* when $kT \ll E_F$, and *nondegenerate* when $kT \gg E_F$ (classical limit).

In thermal equilibrium the number of free electrons dn with energy between E and $E + dE$ is given by [using (5.48) and the Fermi-Dirac distribution function (5.54)]

$$(5.55) \qquad dn = fg(E)\, dE = \frac{V}{2\pi^2} \left(\frac{2m}{\hbar^2} \right)^{3/2} \frac{E^{1/2}\, dE}{e^{(E-E_F)/kT} + 1}.$$

It is often handy to write

$$(5.56) \qquad C = \frac{V}{2\pi^2} \left(\frac{2m}{\hbar^2} \right)^{3/2},$$

and so

$$(5.57) \qquad dn = \frac{CE^{1/2}\, dE}{e^{(E-E_F)/kT} + 1},$$

and E_F is determined by setting the integral of dn equal to the number of particles.

We now consider several limiting cases.

ABSOLUTE ZERO

Here f is unity for E less than $E_F(0)$, the value of E_F at $0°K$, and is zero for greater values. Thus all states are filled up to E_F, and the value of E_F is determined in terms of the number of electrons per unit volume N by

$$(5.58) \qquad NV = C \int_0^{E_F} (0)E^{1/2}\, dE = \frac{2}{3}\, C[E_F(0)]^{3/2},$$

so that

$$(5.59) \qquad E_F(0) = \frac{h^2}{2m}\, (3\pi^2 N)^{2/3},$$

in agreement with the earlier result (5.44). Calculated energy values are given in Table 5.3.

Example. The kinetic energy of the Fermi gas at $0°K$ is

$$(5.60) \qquad U_0 = \tfrac{3}{5}NE_F(0).$$

This result follows because $E_k \propto k^2$, and the average of k^2 over the filled Fermi sphere is

$$\langle k^2 \rangle = \int_0^{k_F} k^4\, dk \Big/ \int_0^{k_F} k^2\, dk = \frac{3}{5}\, k_F{}^2;$$

thus $\langle E \rangle = \tfrac{3}{5}E_F(0)$. This energy is all kinetic, as we have not considered the electrostatic interactions of the electrons among themselves and with the ion cores.

QUANTUM THEORY OF THE HEAT CAPACITY
OF THE ELECTRON GAS

We have given earlier a qualitative discussion of the electronic heat capacity; we now discuss the problem quantitatively. Our qualitative argument following (5.48) indicates that the change ΔU in the internal energy on heating from 0 to a temperature T will be proportional to T^2/E_F. Thus if we work to order T^2 we do not have to consider changes in E_F with temperature.

The increase in internal energy on heating is given by, with $g(E)$ the density of states,

$$(5.61) \qquad \Delta U = \int_0^\infty Eg(E)[f(E,T) - f(E,0)]\, dE,$$

or, because the term in square brackets is peaked around E_F,

$$(5.62) \qquad \Delta U \cong g(E_F) \int_0^\infty \frac{2\epsilon}{e^{\epsilon/\tau}+1} \, d\epsilon,$$

where $\epsilon = E - E_F$; we have used the fact that

$$[f(E,T) - f(E,0)] = \begin{cases} -(1 + e^{-\epsilon/\tau})^{-1} & \text{for } \epsilon < 0; \\ (1 + e^{\epsilon/\tau})^{-1} & \text{for } \epsilon > 0; \end{cases}$$

so that the contributions to the integral in (5.61) are symmetrical about $\epsilon = 0$. Thus

$$(5.63) \qquad \Delta U = 2(k_B T)^2 g(E_F) \int_0^\infty \frac{x}{e^x + 1} \, dx$$

$$= \frac{\pi^2}{6} (k_B T)^2 g(E_F);$$

the value of the definite integral is given in standard tables (Dwight 862.3) as $\pi^2/12$. The heat capacity is

$$(5.64) \qquad C_v = \frac{d \, \Delta U}{dT} = \frac{\pi^2}{3} k_B^2 T g(E_F).$$

For free electrons we have from (5.46) and (5.48)

$$(5.65) \qquad g(E_F) = \frac{3}{2} \frac{NV}{E_F} = \frac{3}{2} \frac{NV}{k_B T_F},$$

so that the electronic contribution to the heat capacity is

$$(5.66) \qquad C_v = \frac{\pi^2}{2} (NV) k_B \left(\frac{T}{T_F} \right),$$

where NV is the number of conduction electrons in the specimen. The classical heat capacity is thus reduced by $\sim T/T_F$. One often writes $C_v = \gamma T$; values of γ are given in Table 5.4.

For metals for which the free electron model might be applicable we may expect the molar electronic heat capacity to be of the order of $10^{-4}T$ cal/mole-deg. The observed values are often larger than this, which suggests, apart from specific failures of the independent particle model, that the density of states $g(E_F)$ is greater than calculated for free electrons. The discrepancy is particularly marked for transition metals, and we discuss this question in terms of energy band theory in the next chapter.

TABLE 5.4
COEFFICIENT γ OF THE LINEAR TERM γT IN THE MOLAR HEAT CAPACITY
OF METALS

(For superconducting metals, γ refers to the normal state.   The significance
of the column m^*/m will be discussed in the next chapter.   To convert a
value in 10^{-4} cal/mole-deg^2 to millijoule/mole-deg^2, multiply by 0.418.)
Reference: J. G. Daunt, *Progress in low temperature physics*, C. J. Gorter,
editor, North-Holland, Amsterdam, 1955, Chapter XI.

Metal	$\gamma \times 10^4$ cal/mole-deg^2	Valence	Apparent m^*/m
Na	4.3	1	0.6
Cu	1.73–1.80	1	1.5
Ag	1.54–1.6	1	0.95–1.0
Au	1.8		
Be	0.54	2	0.46
Mg	3.25	2	1.33
Zn	1.25–1.42	2	0.8–0.9
Cd	1.7	2	1.75
Hg	4.5–5.3	2	1.8–2.2
Al	3.48	3	1.6
In	4.0–4.33	3	1.3–1.4
Tl	3.65	3	1.15
La	16	3	4.3
Sn (white)	4.0	4	1.2
Pb	7.5	4	2.1
Bi	0.11		
Ti	8		
V	15–22		
Cr	3.80		
α-Mn	33		
α-Fe	12	2.1	12
Co	12	1.6	14
Ni	17.4	0.6	28
Zr	3.9–6.9		
Nb	21		
Mo	5.1		
Pd	26–31	0.5	27
Ta	13–19		
W	3.5		
Pt	16.0–16.5	0.6	13

QUANTUM THEORY OF SPIN PARAMAGNETISM*

In most metals the conduction electrons have a small temperature-independent paramagnetic volume susceptibility, of the order of 10^{-6}, in striking disagreement with the Langevin formula which predicts a susceptibility of the order of 10^{-4} at room temperature and varying as $1/T$. Pauli[9] showed that the application of Fermi-Dirac statistics would correct the theory as required.

The Langevin equation (4.28) as applied to a magnetic moment tells us that the probability that an atom will be lined up parallel to the field H exceeds the probability of the antiparallel orientation by a factor $\sim \mu H/kT$. For N atoms, this gives a net magnetic moment $\sim N H \mu^2/kT$, which is the classical result. For electrons in a metal, however, most of them have zero probability of turning over when a field is applied, because the states with parallel spin are already occupied, at least if they are within the energy $2\mu H$ of the given antiparallel state. As only the electrons within $\sim kT$ of the top of the Fermi distribution have a chance to turn over in the field, only the fraction $\sim T/T_F$ of the total number of electrons should be counted as contributing to the susceptibility. Hence $\chi \sim (N\mu^2/kT) \times (T/T_F) = N\mu^2/kT_F$, which is independent of temperature and of the correct order of magnitude, as T_F is of the order of 10^4 to $10^{5}°$K. This argument supposes that $\mu H \ll kT$, which is true at room temperature as the strongest field yet obtained, 10^6 oersteds, corresponds to a temperature of only $\sim 100°$K.

We now calculate the expression for the paramagnetic susceptibility of a free electron gas. Following the notation of (5.48) and the method of calculation suggested by Fig. 5.5, we have for the net magnetization M

$$MV = \mu_B \int [\tfrac{1}{2}g(E + \mu_B H) - \tfrac{1}{2}g(E - \mu_B H)]f(E)\, dE,$$

where E is the total energy, kinetic plus magnetic, of an electron. For small H, by series expansion,

$$(5.67) \qquad MV \cong \mu_B^2 H \int g'(E)f(E)\, dE \cong \mu_B^2 H g[E_F(0)],$$

$$(5.68) \qquad \chi = \frac{M}{H} = \frac{\mu_B^2 g[E_F(0)]}{V} = \frac{3N\mu_B^2}{2k_B T_F},$$

---

* Paramagnetism is discussed in Chapter 8.
[9] W. Pauli, Z. Physik **41**, 81 (1927).

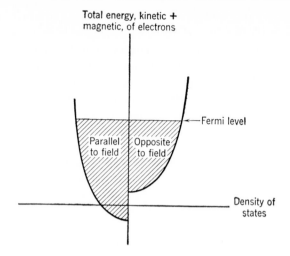

FIG. 5.5. Pauli paramagnetism at $0°K$; the levels in the shaded regions are occupied. At higher temperatures the electrons near the Fermi level will spread out.

the Pauli result. This is the form suggested by our qualitative argument.

In deriving the paramagnetic susceptibility we have supposed that the spatial motion of the electrons is not affected on applying the magnetic field. Actually the running wave functions (5.37) are modified by the magnetic field, and Landau has shown that there is from this cause a diamagnetic moment which for free electrons is equal to $-\frac{1}{3}$ of the paramagnetic moment, and so the total susceptibility of a free electron gas is

$$(5.69) \qquad \chi_T = \frac{N\mu_B{}^2}{k_B T_F};$$

In comparing this with the observed bulk susceptibility, a correction must be applied for the diamagnetism of the ionic cores.

EFFECT OF FERMI-DIRAC DISTRIBUTION ON THE ELECTRICAL CONDUCTIVITY

It is a somewhat surprising fact that the introduction of the Fermi-Dirac distribution in place of the classical Maxwell-Boltzmann distribution usually has little influence on the electrical conductivity, often only changing the kind of average involved in the specification of the relaxation time. One might have expected at first sight to find a more drastic change because with the Fermi-Dirac distribution only those electrons near the Fermi surface can participate in collision processes. This results as all collisions either conserve electron energy or change it by no more than $\sim k_B T$, the thermal energy of a lattice wave.

Using the classical distribution we found earlier in this chapter the expression (5.13) for the conductivity:

$$\sigma = \frac{Ne^2\tau}{m},$$

where N is the electron concentration and τ the relaxation time. It is instructive to give a qualitative classical derivation of this equation from a new point of view, using Fig. 5.6. The figure is drawn for a

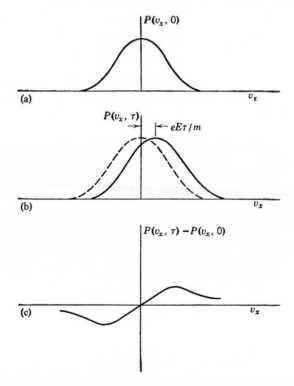

FIG. 5.6. Maxwellian velocity distribution in one dimension. $P(v_x)\,dv_x$ is the fraction of the total number of particles having velocity in dv_x at v_x. (a) Equilibrium velocity distribution. (b) Distribution shifted by electric field applied for time τ. (c) Difference between steady-state distribution and equilibrium distribution.

one-dimensional gas, in the interest of simplicity.   In (a) we show the classical distribution of velocities in thermal equilibrium; in (b) the distribution is shifted to the right by $eE\tau/m$ as a result of the application of an electric field E for a time τ.   If τ is the relaxation time, the shifted distribution will represent the steady-state distribution in the presence of the electric field.   The difference between the steady-state and equilibrium distributions is indicated in (c); by Taylor's theorem the difference is given, to first order in the electric field, by $-(eE\tau/m) \times (dP/dv_x)_{t=0}$.   We assume the distribution function P is normalized to unity: $\int P \, dv_x = 1$.   The average velocity taken over the steady-state distribution,

$$(5.70) \qquad P(v_x, \tau) \cong P(v_x, 0) - \frac{eE\tau}{m}\left(\frac{dP}{dv_x}\right)_{t=0}$$

is given by

$$(5.71) \qquad \bar{v}_x = -\frac{eE\tau}{m}\int v_x\left(\frac{dP}{dv_x}\right)_0 dv_x ;$$

the term in $P(v_x, 0)$ is symmetrical in v_x and does not contribute to $\bar{v}_x$.   That is, the drift velocity is zero in thermal equilibrium.   On integrating by parts,

$$\int v_x\left(\frac{dP}{dv_x}\right)_0 dv_x = -\int P_0 \, dv_x = -1,$$

as

$$[v_x P_0]_{-\infty}^{\infty} = 0,$$

where P_0 denotes $P(v_x, 0)$.   From (5.71),

$$(5.72) \qquad v_D = \bar{v}_x = \frac{eE\tau}{m},$$

and so

$$(5.73) \qquad j = Nev_D = \frac{Ne^2E\tau}{m},$$

or

$$(5.74) \qquad \sigma = \frac{Ne^2\tau}{m},$$

in agreement with the earlier result.

The corresponding situation with the Fermi-Dirac distribution is shown in Fig. 5.7.   The exclusion principle has no effect on the response of the distribution to the electric field, because each electron

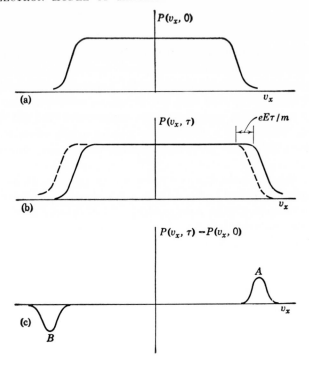

FIG. 5.7. Fermi-Dirac velocity distribution in one dimension. (a) Equilibrium velocity distribution. (b) Distribution shifted by electric field applied for time τ. (c) Difference between steady-state distribution and equilibrium distribution.

in the distribution suffers the same velocity change $eE\tau/m$. There is always a vacant state ready to receive an electron which is changing its state under the action of the electric field, the vacancy being created by the simultaneous change of the state of another electron. The relaxation effects are a little deceptive, as it would seem that many possible collision processes are forbidden by the exclusion principle because the final states are already occupied. But relaxation requires only that the excess electrons, those in A in part (c) of Fig. 5.7, should be able to get back by collisions to B, where there is an electron deficiency. The states in B are vacant, and so the required collisions may take place. That is, the exclusion principle does prevent many collisions, but it does allow those collisions needed to restore equilibrium. We can then carry over without change the derivation leading to the result (5.74): $\sigma = Ne^2\tau/m$. It should just be noted that τ refers to electrons of different velocities in the two cases.

PLASMA FREQUENCY

In recent discussions of the theory of the electron gas, particularly in the work of Bohm and Pines[10] in which electrostatic interactions in the gas are considered approximately, we encounter the concept of the plasma frequency and also the Debye or screening length. The plasma frequency was first discussed in connection with gas discharge problems. It refers to a situation in which initially there is a gas of equal concentrations of positive and negative charges, contained in a flat slab.

Let the charge concentrations of each type be Ne. If the positive gas is displaced normal to the slab by a distance x, the surface charge density developed will be $\pm Nex$, which in esu is equivalent to a uniform volume polarization $P = Nex$. The depolarization field associated with this polarization is

$$(5.75) \qquad \text{(esu)} \qquad E = -4\pi P = -4\pi Nex,$$

and the equation of motion of an undamped particle of mass m is

$$(5.76) \qquad \text{(esu)} \qquad m\ddot{x} = -4\pi Ne^2 x,$$

or, for $x \sim e^{i\omega_p t}$,

$$(5.77) \qquad \text{(esu)} \qquad \omega_p{}^2 = \frac{4\pi Ne^2}{m}.$$

This equation defines the plasma frequency ω_p. For $N \sim 10^{23}$ cm^{-3} as for the conduction electrons in an ordinary metal, and $m \sim 10^{-27}$ gram, $\omega_p \approx 4 \times 10^{16}$ sec^{-1}, which falls in the ultraviolet.[11]

A polarization wave of the form $x \sim e^{i(\omega_p t - kx)}$ in a plasma is called a plasma wave, and the unit of excitation $\hbar\omega_p$ is called a *plasmon*.

If the electrons in the plasma have an rms velocity $\bar{v}$, there is a characteristic length

$$(5.78) \qquad \Lambda_D \approx \frac{\bar{v}}{\omega_p}$$

associated with the plasma; this length is often referred to as a Debye length. For conduction electrons in a metal the Fermi velocity may be $\sim 10^8$ cm/sec, so that $\Lambda_D \sim \frac{1}{4} \times 10^{-8}$ cm.

The Debye length is associated with electrostatic screening of charge fluctuations in the plasma, as may be seen by considering

[10] See the review by D. Pines in F. Seitz and D. Turnbull, editors, *Solid state physics*, Academic Press, New York, vol. 1, 1955.

[11] For observations of the plasma resonance in semiconductors, see Dresselhaus, Kip, and Kittel, *Phys. Rev.* **100**, 618 (1955).

the work done in a thermal fluctuation of the plasma, say a fluctuation which separates all charges of opposite sign by x. The work done is $\int 4\pi Ne^2x \, dx = 2\pi ne^2x^2$ and must be equal to k_BT, the thermal energy of this particular plasma oscillation. Then

$$(5.79) \qquad 2\pi Ne^2x^2 = k_BT = \tfrac{1}{2}mv^2,$$

so that

$$(5.80) \qquad x = \frac{\bar{v}}{\left(\dfrac{4\pi Ne^2}{m}\right)^{1/2}} = \frac{\bar{v}}{\omega_p} = \Lambda_D.$$

This result suggests that charge fluctuations on a scale larger than Λ_D tend to be smoothed out by electrostatic interactions. For a Fermi gas, $\bar{v}$ will be of the order of the velocity v_F at the Fermi surface.

TRANSPARENCY OF ALKALI METALS IN THE ULTRAVIOLET

We mention here one interesting feature of the optical properties of the alkali metals, their transparency in the ultraviolet; the effect was discovered by Wood[12] and explained by Zener.[13] The reflection of light in the infrared is the basis of Problem 5.8.

For good conductors the relaxation time τ is long in comparison with the period $1/\omega$ of light in the visible part of the spectrum, and so to a fair approximation we may omit the resistance term in the equation of motion and write simply, for an electric field vector parallel to the surface,

$$(5.81) \qquad m\ddot{x} = eE,$$

which reduces for a periodic field to

$$(5.82) \qquad x = -\frac{eE}{m\omega^2}.$$

As the polarization is $P = Nex$, the complex refractive index n is given by

$$(5.83) \qquad \epsilon = n^2 = 1 + 4\pi\frac{P}{E} = 1 - \frac{4\pi Ne^2}{m\omega^2} = 1 - \frac{\omega_p{}^2}{\omega^2},$$

where ω_p is defined by (5.77).

[12] R. W. Wood, *Phys. Rev.* **44**, 353 (1933); R. W. Wood and C. Lukens, *Phys. Rev.* **54**, 332 (1938); H. E. Ives and H. B. Briggs, *J. Opt. Soc. Am.* **26**, 238 (1936); **27**, 181 (1937). For a review of the optical properties of metals, see the review by M. P. Givens in F. Seitz and D. Turnbull, ed., *Solid state physics*, Academic Press, New York, vol. 6, 1958.

[13] C. Zener, *Nature* **132**, 968 (1933).

TABLE 5.5

ULTRAVIOLET TRANSMISSION OF ALKALIS

	Li	Na	K	Rb	Cs
λ_0 (calculated, free electrons, mass m) (A)	1550	2090	2870	3220	3620
Effective mass ratio m^*/m, according to Brooks (see Chapter 6)	1.40	0.98	0.94	0.87	0.83
λ_0 (calculated for m^*) (A)	1840	2070	2750	3000	3300
λ_0 observed (A)	1550	2100	3150	3400	

If $\omega_p{}^2/\omega^2$ is less than unity (short wavelengths), the refractive index is real and the metal is transparent to light at normal incidence.

If $\omega_p{}^2/\omega^2$ is greater than unity, n is imaginary, and total reflection may be shown to occur.

The critical wavelength is then, setting $\epsilon = 0$,

$$(5.84) \qquad \lambda_0 = 2\pi \left(\frac{mc^2}{4\pi Ne^2} \right)^{1/2}.$$

The agreement with observation is quite good, as shown in Table 5.5, although the experimental determinations of λ_0 are not too definite because of the width of the cut-off region. Calculated values are also given in the table, using effective masses m^*. The concept of an effective mass is discussed in the next chapter.

THERMIONIC EMISSION EQUATION

We now calculate the Richardson-Dushman equation for the saturation electron current density evaporated from a metal, using the free electron model. We suppose, following Fig. 5.8, that E_0 is the work necessary to remove to infinity an electron from the lowest free electron state in the metal. If the electron is taken from the Fermi level, the work is

$$(5.85) \qquad \phi = E_0 - E_F;$$

this is the definition of the *work function* ϕ.

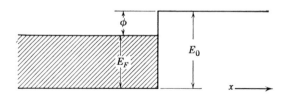

FIG. 5.8.   Model for calculation of thermionic emission.

The rate at which electrons in the momentum range between $\mathbf{p}$ and $\mathbf{p} + d\mathbf{p}$ strike unit area of the surface is

$$(5.86) \qquad v_x n(\mathbf{p})\, d\mathbf{p} = \frac{\partial E}{\partial p_x}\, n(\mathbf{p})\, d\mathbf{p} = n(\mathbf{p})\, dE\, dp_y\, dp_z,$$

as E is the kinetic energy; here $n(\mathbf{p})$ is the number of electrons per unit volume of phase space and is given by

$$(5.87) \qquad n(\mathbf{p}) = \frac{2}{h^3} f,$$

in terms of the Fermi-Dirac distribution function f. The electronic charge e times the rate at which electrons having

$$\frac{p_x^2}{2m} > \phi + E_F$$

strike unit area of the surface will be the emission current density j, apart from a factor representing quantum reflection effects which we neglect. Then

$$(5.88) \qquad j = \frac{2e}{h^3} \int_{-\infty}^{\infty} \int_{-\infty}^{\infty} \int_{\phi + E_F}^{\infty} \frac{dp_y\, dp_z\, dE}{e^{(E - E_F)/kT} + 1}$$

$$= \frac{2kTe}{h^3} \int_{-\infty}^{\infty} \int_{-\infty}^{\infty} \log\left(1 + e^{-\theta}\right)\, dp_y\, dp_z,$$

where

$$\theta = \frac{1}{kT}\left[\phi + \left(\frac{p_y^2 + p_z^2}{2m}\right)\right].$$

For ordinary conditions $\theta \gg 1$, so that we may expand the logarithm and retain only the first term:

$$(5.89) \qquad j = \frac{2kTe}{h^3} e^{-\phi/kT} \iint e^{-(p_y^2 + p_z^2)/2mkT}\, dp_y\, dp_z$$

$$= 4\pi me(kT)^2 h^{-3} e^{-\phi/kT}.$$

This is the Richardson-Dushman equation. We may write the result as

$$(5.90) \qquad j = A T^2 e^{-\phi/kT},$$

where

$$(5.91) \qquad A = 4\pi mek^2 h^{-3} = 120 \text{ amp/cm}^2\text{-deg}^2.$$

TABLE 5.6

REPRESENTATIVE THERMIONIC EMISSION DATA

Metal	A (amp/cm²-deg²)	ϕ (ev)
W	~75	4.5
Ta	55	4.2
Ni	30	4.6
Ag	. . . . . .	4.8
Cs	160	1.8
Pt	32	5.3
Ba on W	1.5	1.56
Cs on W	3.2	1.36
Cr	48	4.60
Cu	. . . . . .	4.45

A plot of $\log j/T^2$ versus $1/T$ is called a Richardson plot and helps determine ϕ.

Experimental values of A and ϕ are given in Table 5.6. The values are sensitive to surface conditions, particularly to surface films and nonuniform surfaces.[14]   Positive ions adsorbed on the surface of the filament will, by attracting conduction electrons, form an electric double layer (dipole layer) at the surface. The sense of the electric field within such a double layer will reduce the work function of the metal. Thus the work function of tungsten is 4.5 ev, whereas tungsten with adsorbed barium has a work function of only 1.36 ev. Work functions from photoelectric data are given in Table 5.7, obtained from the minimum photon energy which will eject a photoelectron.

TABLE 5.7

WORK FUNCTIONS FROM PHOTOELECTRIC DATA

Metal	ϕ (ev)
Na	2.3
K	2.26
Cr	4.37
Zn	4.24
W	4.49
Pt	6.2

[14] For a careful discussion of the data, see C. Herring and M. H. Nichols, *Revs. Modern Phys.* **21**, 185 (1949).

PROBLEMS

5.1. (a) Using the boundary condition $\psi = 0$ on the surfaces of a cube of side L, find all the wave functions for the first four distinct energy levels. (b) Give the energy of each level. (c) What is the degeneracy of each level? That is, what is the number of independent wave functions having the same energy?

5.2. Repeat the work of Problem 5.1, but use periodic boundary conditions.

5.3. We may obtain time-dependent wave functions by multiplying a solution of the wave equation of energy E by the factor $e^{-iEt/\hbar}$. The factor $E/\hbar$ has the dimensions of a frequency. (a) Show that

$$\psi(x,t) \sim e^{-i[(E/\hbar)t - kx]}$$

represents a wave traveling in the positive x direction with phase velocity $E/\hbar k$. (b) What is the group velocity? According to the de Broglie relation, what momentum is associated with the wave? Note that $v_g = \delta\omega/\delta k$, where $\omega = E/\hbar$.

5.4. Using conventional valencies, show that for sodium, potassium, and aluminum the values of $E_F(0)$ are 3.1, 2.1, and 11.7 ev, respectively.

5.5. By qualitative reasoning, show that on the free electron model the electronic paramagnetic susceptibility of a metal at low temperatures under the conditions

$$kT \ll \mu H \ll kT_F$$

is

$$\chi \sim \frac{N\mu^2}{kT_F},$$

of the same form as under the usual conditions $\mu H \ll kT \ll kT_F$.

5.6. An infinite plane metal surface with the normal in the z direction has a work function ϕ and temperature T. The electrons inside the metal obey Fermi-Dirac statistics with Fermi energy E_F.

(a) Write down the integral expression for the number of electrons per unit volume with an x component of velocity between v_x and $v_x + dv_x$ inside the metal.

(b) Write down the integral expression for the flux of electrons escaping with an x component of velocity between v_x and $v_x + dv_x$ after escape.

(c) Similarly for those with a z component of velocity between v_z and $v_z + dv_z$ after escape.

(d) Neglecting the one in the denominator of the distribution function with respect to the exponential function, calculate the average square of the velocity in the x direction and the average square of the velocity in the z direction of the escaping electrons *after* escape.

5.7. Derive an equation connecting the pressure and volume of a Fermi electron gas at $0°K$.

5.8. Show that the complex refractive index of a metal at long wavelengths is given by

$$\text{(gaussian)} \qquad (n + ik)^2 = \frac{1 + 4\pi i\sigma_0}{\omega},$$

where σ_0 is the conductivity for static fields. We define a complex dielectric constant by writing the appropriate Maxwell equation in the conductor as

$$\text{(gaussian)} \qquad \text{curl } \mathbf{H} = \frac{\epsilon}{c} \frac{\partial \mathbf{E}}{\partial t}.$$

Using the relation

$$R = \frac{(n-1)^2 + k^2}{(n+1)^2 + k^2}$$

for the reflection coefficient at normal incidence, show that

$$R \cong 1 - \left(\frac{2\omega}{\pi\sigma_0}\right)^{1/2}.$$

This is the Hagen-Rubens relation. Show that the condition for the validity of the derivation of the results is that $\omega \ll 1/\tau$, where τ is the relaxation time of the electrons. Estimate τ for sodium at room temperature using the observed conductivity.

REFERENCES

R. Becker, *Theorie der Elektrizität*, B. Teubner, Leipzig, 1933, Vol. II.

F. Bloch, *Elektronentheorie der Metalle*, Handbuch der Radiologie, **6.1**, 226–278 (1933).

G. Borelius, *Physikalische Eigenschaften der Metalle*, Handbuch der Metallphysik, Akademische Verlagsgesellschaft, Leipzig, **1**, 181–485 (1935).

L. Brillouin, *Die Quantenstatistik*, Springer, Berlin, 1931.

H. Fröhlich, *Elektronentheorie der Metalle*, Springer, Berlin, 1936.

W. Hume-Rothery, *Electrons, atoms, metals and alloys*, Iliffe, London, 1955.

N. F. Mott and H. Jones, *Theory of the properties of metals and alloys*, Clarendon Press, Oxford, 1936. (Dover paperback reprint.)

R. Peierls, *Quantum theory of solids*, Clarendon Press, Oxford, 1955.

F. O. Rice and E. Teller, *Structure of matter*, John Wiley and Sons, New York, 1949.

F. Seitz, *Modern theory of solids*, McGraw-Hill Book Co., New York, 1940.

J. C. Slater, *Quantum theory of matter*, McGraw-Hill Book Co., New York, 1951.

A. Sommerfeld and H. Bethe, *Elektronentheorie der Metalle*, Handbuch der Physik, Springer, Berlin, **24/2**, 333–622 (1933).

G. H. Wannier, *Elements of solid state theory*, Cambridge University Press, Cambridge, 1959.

A. H. Wilson, *Theory of metals*, Cambridge University Press, Cambridge, 1953, 2nd ed.

J. M. Ziman, *Electrons and phonons*, Clarendon Press, Oxford, 1960.

6 Band theory of solids; Brillouin zones

This chapter is not the easiest one in the book, but it is the most important. It introduces all the important new concepts associated with the quantum theory of solids: energy bands, Brillouin zones, effective mass, and holes.

The free electron model of metals developed in the preceding chapter gives us considerable insight into several of the electronic properties of metals, yet there are other electronic properties of solids for which the free electron model is quite uninstructive. The model cannot help us understand why some chemical elements crystallize to form good conductors of electricity and others to form insulators; still others are semiconductors, with electrical properties varying markedly with temperature. Yet the distinction between the resistivity values of conductors, superconductivity apart, and insulators is striking: the resistivity of a pure metal at low temperatures may be of the order of 10^{-8} ohm-cm, and the resistivity of a good insulator may be as high as 10^{22} ohm-cm, provided precautions are taken to dry the surface of the specimen. It has been remarked by E. M. McMillan that this observed range of 10^{30} in resistivity may be the widest range of any common physical property of solids.

At first thought it is natural to try to ascribe the difference between conductors and insulators to differences in chemical bonding between the metallic bond on the one hand and the covalent and ionic bonds on the other. Electrical conductivity involves two factors: the concentration of available electrons and their electrical mobility $\mu = v_{drift}/E$. Now many nominal insulators have high mobilities. Several, including silicon and germanium, have mobilities much higher than good metallic conductors. Some insulators, particularly ionic crystals and transition element oxides, have low mobilities—often, we believe, because the charge carriers polarize their surroundings strongly by electrostatic interaction and effectively dig themselves a hole in the crystal. The metallic bond generally is associated with fairly high mobility because the high concentration of conduction electrons reduces by electrostatic screening, as just discussed in Chapter 5, the tendency of the conduction electrons to polarize bodily the ion cores. This is another way in which a high conduction electron concentration favors high conductivity.

Every solid has electrons; the important question is under what circumstances a proportion of the electrons act as if they were more or less free. We shall see how to answer this: electrons in crystals are arranged in energy bands (Fig. 6.1), and there are sometimes regions in energy for which no electron energy states are allowed; such forbidden regions are called *energy gaps*. If the number of electrons in a crystal is such that the allowed energy bands which are occupied at all are occupied entirely, then there are no free electrons and the crystal will behave as an insulator. If one or more bands are partly filled (say 10 to 90 percent filled) the crystal will act as a metal. If all bands are entirely filled except for one or two bands which are slightly filled or slightly empty, we say that the crystal is a semiconductor or, perhaps, a semimetal.

If the height in energy of the slightly filled band in the semiconductor in Fig. 6.1c or of the slightly empty band in Fig. 6.1d is $\gg kT$, the electron gas will behave like the Fermi gas treated in the last chapter, in the approximation $kT \ll E_F$. Such a Fermi gas is said to be degenerate. If the width of the region is comparable with kT, the gas will behave classically—we say it is nondegenerate.

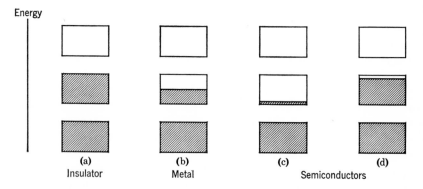

FIG. 6.1. Schematic electron occupancy of allowed energy bands for an insulator, metal, and two semiconductors. The vertical extent of the boxes indicates the allowed energy regions; the cross-hatched areas indicate the regions filled with electrons.

Is it possible to tell whether or not a substance has metallic conductivity just by looking at it? Not always: all metals will indeed have broad band reflectivity in the visible region of the spectrum, the type of reflectivity we call metallic. But any insulator with an energy gap between filled and empty bands of less than 1.5 or 2 ev will also give a more or less metallic reflection. This just means that there are empty allowed energy states in the crystal to which an electron in a filled band may be raised by absorption of a photon of visible light. Thus, for example, pure silicon with an energy gap of 1.10 ev reflects all the way through the visible and gives to the eye a clean silvery metallic impression; pure silicon is not a bad insulator below room temperature.

We can gain some insight into the nature of the difference between insulators and conductors only by extending the free electron model to take account of the interaction of electrons with the periodic lattice of the solid. We shall encounter some quite remarkable properties possessed by electrons in crystals: we shall see that they may respond to applied electric or magnetic fields as if the electrons are endowed with an effective mass m^*, which may be larger or smaller than the free electron mass, or may even be negative.   Further, there are situations in which it is convenient to attribute to the charge carriers in crystals a positive charge $+|e|$; we denote such carriers as *holes*, in contrast to electrons which behave with their normal negative charge $-|e|$.

On the free electron model the allowed energy values are distributed quasi-continuously from zero to infinity. We saw in the preceding chapter that

$$E = \frac{\hbar^2}{2m} (k_x^2 + k_y^2 + k_z^2),$$

where, for a cube of side L,

$$k_x,\ k_y,\ k_z = \frac{2\pi}{L} (0,\ \pm 1,\ \pm 2,\ \pm 3,\ \cdot\ \cdot\ \cdot).$$

The free electron wave functions are of the form

$$\psi \sim e^{i\mathbf{k}\cdot\mathbf{r}}$$

and represent running waves carrying momentum $\mathbf{p} = \hbar\mathbf{k}$, according to the de Broglie relation.

We have seen in the earlier discussion of x-ray propagation in crystals that Bragg reflection is an important and characteristic feature of wave propagation in periodic structures, including periodic electri-

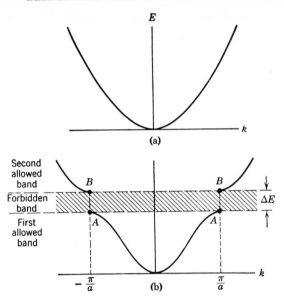

FIG. 6.2. (a) Plot of energy versus wave vector for a free electron. (b) Plot of energy versus wave vector for a monatomic linear lattice of lattice constant a. The energy gap shown is associated with the first Bragg reflection at $k = \pm\pi/a$.

cal circuits. Bragg reflection occurs also for electron waves in crystals. The observations of Davisson and Germer on the wave nature of the electron were observations of the Bragg reflection of an electron beam from the crystal surface. The most important consequence of Bragg reflection for our present discussion is that it leads to the existence of an energy gap in the distribution in energy of the states of the conduction electrons. That is, there may arise a substantial region of energy in which solutions of the wave equation do not exist. Such energy gaps or forbidden energy bands, as they are also called, are of decisive significance in determining whether a solid is to be an insulator or a conductor.

BRILLOUIN ZONE IN ONE DIMENSION

Let us try to understand physically the reasons for the existence of a forbidden band, considering first the simple problem of a monatomic one-dimensional lattice. The low energy portions of the band structure are shown qualitatively in Fig. 6.2, in (a) for entirely free electrons and (b) for electrons which are nearly free, but which have an energy discontinuity at $k = \pm\pi/a$, giving rise to a forbidden energy band.   In one dimension the Bragg equation $2d \sin \theta = n\lambda$ becomes

(6.1)
$$k = \frac{n\pi}{a}.$$

The first reflections occur at $k = \pm\pi/a$, and the first energy gap also occurs at these points.   Other energy gaps occur for the other positive and negative integral values of n.   The reflection at $k = \pm\pi/a$ arises because the wave reflected from the $(p \pm 1)$st atom interferes constructively with the original wave at the pth atom, the difference in phase being just $\pm 2\pi$ for these particular values of k.   The region in k space between $-\pi/a$ and π/a is referred to in this instance as the first Brillouin zone.   The energy is quasi-continuous within a Brillouin zone and may be discontinuous on the boundaries of a zone.   The energy is quasi-continuous rather than continuous within a zone because of the imposition of boundary conditions on the problem.

At $k = \pm\pi/a$ the stationary state wave functions are not traveling waves as for the free electron model, but the solutions at these particular k values are made up equally of waves traveling to the right and to the left: they are standing waves.   It is really obvious that the solutions when the Bragg condition is satisfied cannot be in the form of traveling waves, for a wave traveling in one sense is soon Bragg-reflected and then travels in the opposite sense.   The next Bragg reflection reverses the direction of travel again.   The only stationary situation is that represented by standing waves.   In the lowest approximation we have at $k = \pm\pi/a$ the two independent standing wave solutions

(6.2)
$$\psi_1 \sim \frac{\sin \pi x}{a} \sim (e^{i\pi x/a} - e^{-i\pi x/a});$$

$$\psi_2 \sim \frac{\cos \pi x}{a} \sim (e^{i\pi x/a} + e^{-i\pi x/a}).$$

Both these solutions hold equally at $k = +\pi/a$ and also at $k = -\pi/a$. The solutions are both made up, as can be seen from the right-hand forms, of equal parts of waves $e^{i\pi x/a}$ and $e^{-i\pi x/a}$ traveling in opposite directions.

We now must show that the two solutions ψ_1, ψ_2 correspond to different values of the energy, even though the functions have the same values of the wave vector.   We recall that in quantum mechanics the probability density of a particle is $|\psi|^2$.   In Fig. 6.3a we have indicated the general nature of the variation of the electrostatic potential energy of a conduction electron in the field of the positive ion cores of

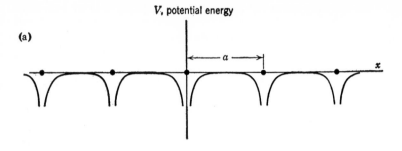

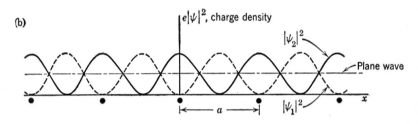

FIG. 6.3. (a) Variation of potential energy of a conduction electron in the field of the positive ion cores of a monatomic linear lattice. (b) Distribution of probability density in the lattice for $|\psi_1|^2 \sim \sin^2 \pi x/a$; $|\psi_2|^2 \sim \cos^2 \pi x/a$ and for a plane traveling wave.

a monatomic linear lattice. We expect the ion cores to bear a positive charge, as each has lost one or more valence electrons in forming the metal. In (b) we sketched the distribution of charge density corresponding to the standing waves ψ_1, ψ_2 and to a plane traveling wave. We note the traveling wave $\sim e^{ikx}$ distributes electronic charge uniformly over the line with the origin as shown, the standing wave $\psi_1 \sim \sin \pi x/a$ distributes charge preferentially midway between ion cores; and the standing wave $\psi_2 \sim \cos \pi x/a$ distributes charge preferentially on the ion cores, where the potential energy is a minimum. On calculating average values of the potential energy over the three charge distributions, we expect to find the potential energy ψ_2 less than that of a plane wave, whereas the potential energy of ψ_1 is greater than that of a plane wave. If the potential energies of ψ_1 and ψ_2 differ by an amount ΔE we have, referring to Fig. 6.2b, an energy gap of width ΔE. The wave function at points A will be ψ_2, and the wave function above the energy gap at points B will be ψ_1.

Let us recount briefly how the forbidden band came about. If the wave functions at values k far removed from the Brillouin zone boundaries $\pm \pi/a$ may be represented by plane waves e^{ikx}, then in forming a solution of the wave equation as the boundaries are approached and Bragg reflection becomes imminent the wave e^{ikx} gradually is supplemented by an increasing admixture of the wave $e^{i[k-(2\pi/a)]x}$, until at the zone boundary $k = \pm \pi/a$ the solution is $e^{i\pi x/a} \pm e^{-i\pi x/a}$. The evolution of the standing wave solution is traced through in detail in Appendix A. What is important at present is that the solutions for $k = \pm \pi/a$ combine to give standing waves of different energies, the energies being different not through the kinetic term but through the potential energy of interaction with the ion cores. The two wave functions distribute the electronic charge in distinctly different ways with respect to the positive ion core field. The difference in potential energy leads to a splitting of the energy bands at $k = \pm \pi/a$.

It is useful also to look at the formation of allowed and forbidden bands in another way, starting from the energy levels of the neutral separated atoms and watching the changes in the levels as the charge distributions of adjacent atoms overlap when the atoms are brought together to form the metal. We can understand the origin of the splitting of free atom energy levels into bands as the atoms are brought together by considering two hydrogen atoms,[1] each with its electron in the 1s (ground) state. In Fig. 6.4 the wave functions ψ_A, ψ_B on the separated atoms are shown in (a). As the atoms are brought closer together and their wave functions overlap, we are led to consider the two combinations $\psi_A \pm \psi_B$. Each combination preserves the equality of electron distribution between the two protons, but an electron in the state $\psi_A + \psi_B$ will have a somewhat lower energy than in the state $\psi_A - \psi_B$. In the former state shown in (b) the electron spends part of the time in the region midway between the two protons, and in this region it is under the influence of the attractive potential of both protons at once, thereby increasing the binding energy. In the state $\psi_A - \psi_B$ shown in (c) the probability density vanishes midway between the nuclei, and the extra contribution to the binding does not appear. Thus as two atoms are brought together two separated energy levels are formed for each level of the isolated atom. For N atoms, N levels are formed for each level of the isolated atom, and these N levels will be associated with one or more bands.

The results for six hydrogen atoms in a line are sketched in Fig. 6.5. As the free atoms are brought together the Coulomb interaction between the atom cores and the overlapping parts of the electron dis-

[1] For a detailed treatment of the binding of the hydrogen molecule-ion, see L. Pauling and E. B. Wilson, *Introduction to quantum mechanics*, McGraw-Hill, New York, 1935, Chapter XII.

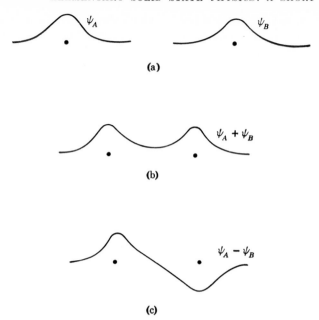

FIG. 6.4. (a) Wave functions of electrons on two hydrogen atoms at large separation. (b) Ground state combination at closer separation. (c) Excited state combination.

tribution splits the energy levels of the combined system, spreading the levels out into bands. Each level ns of the free atom is spread out in the metal into a band of energies. Here n denotes the principal quantum number, and s indicates zero orbital angular momentum. The width of the band is proportional to the strength of the interaction or overlap between neighboring atoms, each in the state ns. There will be bands formed as well from p, d, $\cdots$ states ($l = 1, 2, \cdots$) of the free atoms. Each of the $(2l + 1)$ levels degenerate in the free atom will form a band, and one of these bands will not have in general the same energy as any other band over any substantial proportion of the range of the wave vector. Two or more bands may coincide in energy at certain special positions in the Brillouin zone.

The approximation which starts out from the wave functions of the free atoms is known as the tight binding approximation; a simple example of its use appears in Appendix B. The tight binding approximation is generally thought to be quite good for the inner electrons of atoms, but it is probably not often a good description of the conduction electrons themselves. It is often used to describe approximately the d bands of transition metals. The tight binding approximation does show clearly the connection between number of atoms and number of states in the band.

It turns out that the special k values for which energy discontinuities occur do not depend on the particular approximation used to calculate the wave functions or the energies, but are a general property of the space group of the crystal structure. Returning for the moment to our monatomic linear lattice, we recall that the first allowed energy band extends from $-(\pi/a) \leq k \leq (\pi/a)$. In this range k has the values $(2\pi/L)[0, \pm 1, \pm 2, \cdots \pm (L/2a)]$. Now L/a is just equal to the number of atoms, as a is the lattice constant and L the length of the region over which the periodic boundary conditions are applied. Recalling that the state at $k = +\pi/a$ is not independent of the state at $k = -\pi/a$, but is identical with it, we see that there are a total of

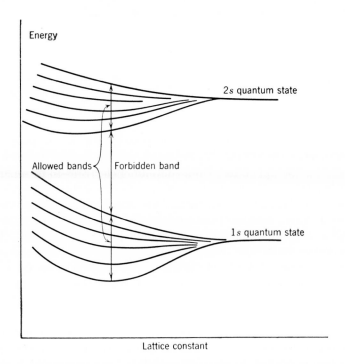

FIG. 6.5. Dependence of energy levels upon lattice constant, for a line of 6 hydrogen atoms, showing the incipient formation of allowed and forbidden energy bands. As the atoms are moved closer together the coupling between atoms increases, splitting the energy levels as shown here. The problem is similar to that of a line of coupled electrical or mechanical oscillators.

L/a independent values of k. Furthermore, for each value of k there are two values of m_s, the spin quantum number.

We have the important result that a band formed from L/a primitive cells contains $2L/a$ states. If there is one atom per cell and each atom contributes one valence electron to the band, the band will be half full and the solid will possess the characteristic properties of a metal. If each atom contributes two valence electrons, the band will be exactly full provided no other bands overlap it in energy. If there are no overlapping bands, the band of interest will not contribute to electrical conductivity. All states in the band being full, an applied electric field cannot cause the electrons in the band to change their state, and therefore they cannot be accelerated. Thus the bands formed from the filled inner electronic shells of an atom do not normally lead to conductivity. These bands are narrow because the inner wave functions of the separate atoms do not overlap very much in the metal. The narrow low-lying bands do not overlap in energy the outer vacant or partly filled bands. As a closed shell always contains an even number of electrons, the corresponding energy bands will be filled.

A solid with one valence electron per atom must then be a metal if there is only one atom per primitive cell, that is, if the atoms form a Bravais lattice. If there are two atoms (each having one valence electron) per primitive cell the solid will be an insulator if the energy bands do not overlap.

For a solid to be an insulator it is necessary for it to contain an even number of electrons per atom or per primitive cell, and furthermore it is necessary for the uppermost band containing electrons to be separated from other bands above by an energy gap $\gg kT$ at the temperature of interest. The alkaline earth metals are not insulators even though they are divalent, because bands overlap, as indicated in Fig. 6.6. In this way a band which might be exactly filled in the absence of overlap is not entirely filled, and a band which might be vacant in the absence of overlap is partly filled. The alkali metals and the noble metals are good conductors because they are monovalent and the conduction band is only half filled. Solid hydrogen is an insulator: the crystal is formed of molecules H_2 having an even number of electrons. Diamond is an insulator because it has four valence electrons and the relevant bands are separated by some 5 ev. Silicon and germanium have the same valence and crystal structure as diamond, but are semiconductors: the band separations are of the order of 1 ev. Sodium chloride is an insulator; the group $NaCl$ associated with each lattice point has twenty-eight electrons, an even number. The essential differences between insulators and metallic conductors may be attributed in this way to

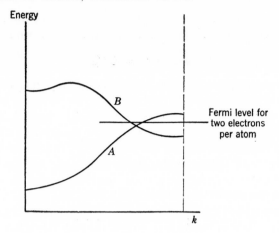

FIG. 6.6. Sketch showing how overlapping bands, A and B, make it possible for a crystal of a divalent element to show metallic conductivity. The bands are filled up to the Fermi level as shown, so that A is nearly filled and B is slightly filled. The overlap need not be in the same direction in $\mathbf{k}$ space for both bands.

differences in valency and sometimes also to differences in the energy relationships of the various bands.

WAVE FUNCTIONS IN A PERIODIC LATTICE

Bloch[2] has proved the important theorem that the solutions of the Schrödinger equation with a periodic potential are of the form

$$(6.3) \qquad \psi_{\mathbf{k}} = u_{\mathbf{k}}(\mathbf{r})e^{i\mathbf{k}\cdot\mathbf{r}},$$

where $u_{\mathbf{k}}(\mathbf{r})$ is a function, depending in general on the wave vector $\mathbf{k}$, which is periodic in x, y, z with the periodicity of the potential; that is, with the period of the lattice. We see that the plane wave $e^{i\mathbf{k}\cdot\mathbf{r}}$ is modulated with the period of the lattice. The solutions (6.3) are known as Bloch functions.

A standard proof of the Bloch result is given in the book by Mott and Jones, pp. 57–59. Bloch gives a rather neater proof based on elementary group theory. We give here an abbreviated and somewhat incomplete argument. We consider N lattice points on a ring of length Na, and suppose that the potential is periodic in a, so that

$$(6.4) \qquad V(x) = V(x + ga),$$

[2] F. Bloch, Z. Physik **52**, 555 (1928); the result was known earlier to mathematicians as Floquet's theorem.

where g is an integer. Because of the symmetry of the ring we look for eigenfunctions ψ such that under the translation we have

$$(6.5) \qquad \psi(x + a) = C\psi(x),$$

where C is a complex constant of unit amplitude. Then

$$(6.6) \qquad \psi(x + ga) = C^g\psi(x);$$

and, if the eigenfunction is to be single-valued,

$$(6.7) \qquad \psi(x + Na) = \psi(x) = C^N\psi(x),$$

so that C is one of the N roots of unity, or

$$(6.8) \qquad C = e^{i2\pi g/N}; \quad g = 0, 1, 2, \cdots, N - 1.$$

We have then

$$(6.9) \qquad \psi(x) = e^{i2\pi xg/Na}u_g(x)$$

as a satisfactory solution, where $u_g(x)$ has periodicity a. Letting

$$(6.10) \qquad k = \frac{2\pi g}{Na},$$

we have

$$(6.11) \qquad \psi_{\mathbf{k}} = e^{ikx}u_k(x),$$

which is the Bloch result.

We say that we know the band structure of a solid when we know the energy $E_{\mathbf{nk}}$ as a function of the wave vector $\mathbf{k}$ written within each energy band $\mathbf{n}$.

WAVE FUNCTIONS FOR ZERO WAVE VECTOR

It may appear to the reader that there is a certain inconsistency between the discussion of the preceding chapter, in which we emphasized the usefulness of the free electron model as applied to the monovalent metals, and the discussion of the present chapter emphasizing the importance of the states of the isolated atom and also the interaction between the conduction electron and the ion cores. It fortunately turns out that in the monovalent metals the inconsistency is sometimes only apparent. It is possible for the energy over most of a band to depend on the wave vector in approximately the same way as for a free electron, whereas at the same time the wave function may be quite unlike a plane wave but may pile up charge on the positive ion cores much as in the isolated atom.

In the last chapter the important result of the free electron model was the relation

(6.12) $$E_{\mathbf{k}} = \frac{\hbar^2}{2m} k^2.$$

We can broaden the scope of the treatment by observing that the really important part of the result is the quadratic dependence of the energy on the wave vector. We can carry over all the results even if the constant of proportionality is changed, with

(6.13) $$E_{\mathbf{k}} = \frac{\hbar^2}{2m^*} k^2,$$

where m^* is called the effective mass. We may then simply substitute m^* for m in the expressions for the Fermi energy, heat capacity, susceptibility, and conductivity, among others.

Let us first see how it can happen that we have $E_{\mathbf{k}} \cong (\hbar^2/2m)k^2$ while the wave functions are not like plane waves. Suppose that we have solved the wave equation in the periodic potential for $\mathbf{k} = 0$, obtaining the solution $\psi = u_0(\mathbf{r})$, where $u_0(\mathbf{r})$ will have the periodicity of the lattice and will naturally reflect in its shape the variation of the potential energy near the ion cores. We construct next the function

(6.14) $$\psi = u_0(\mathbf{r})e^{i\mathbf{k}\cdot\mathbf{r}}.$$

This function is of the Bloch form (6.3), but will not be in general an exact solution of the wave equation because we have suppressed the dependence of u on $\mathbf{k}$. However, it is obvious that the function is likely to be a much better approximation than a plane wave to the correct wave function. The energy of the approximate solution still depends on $\mathbf{k}$ as $(\hbar^2/2m)k^2$, exactly as for the plane wave, even though the modulation represented by $u_0(\mathbf{r})$ may be very strong. We calculate the average value of the energy as follows: we have from the prescription for taking averages in quantum mechanics

(6.15) $$\bar{E} = \int u_0{}^*(\mathbf{r})e^{-i\mathbf{k}\cdot\mathbf{r}}\left[-\frac{\hbar^2}{2m}\nabla^2 + V(\mathbf{r}) \right] e^{i\mathbf{k}\cdot\mathbf{r}}u_0(\mathbf{r})\, d\tau.$$

Now

$$\nabla e^{i\mathbf{k}\cdot\mathbf{r}}u_0(\mathbf{r}) = i\mathbf{k}e^{i\mathbf{k}\cdot\mathbf{r}}u_0(\mathbf{r}) + e^{i\mathbf{k}\cdot\mathbf{r}}\nabla u_0(\mathbf{r});$$

$$\nabla^2 e^{i\mathbf{k}\cdot\mathbf{r}}u_0(\mathbf{r}) = -k^2 e^{i\mathbf{k}\cdot\mathbf{r}}u_0(\mathbf{r}) + 2i\mathbf{k}e^{i\mathbf{k}\cdot\mathbf{r}}\nabla u_0(\mathbf{r}) + e^{i\mathbf{k}\cdot\mathbf{r}}\nabla^2 u_0(\mathbf{r});$$

and so

$$(6.16) \quad \bar{E} = \frac{\hbar^2}{2m} k^2 + \int u_0{}^*(\mathbf{r}) \left[-\frac{\hbar^2}{2m} \nabla^2 + V(\mathbf{r}) \right] u_0(\mathbf{r}) \, d\tau$$

$$= \frac{\hbar^2}{2m} k^2 + E_0.$$

The term in $\int u_0{}^*(\mathbf{r}) \nabla u_0(\mathbf{r}) \, d\tau$ is zero by symmetry: it can be shown that for the $\mathbf{k} = 0$ state u_0 must be either an even or an odd function of $\mathbf{r}$.   We therefore have the desired result in (6.16).

There is then considerable interest in obtaining reliable calculations of $u_0(\mathbf{r})$, as this function often will give us a good picture of the distribution of charge within a unit cell.   Wigner and Seitz developed a simple and fairly accurate method of calculating $u_0(\mathbf{r})$ if the field of the free ion is known, and there have been many developments in the calculation of wave functions in solids since their work; this, however, is not the place to discuss them.

In Fig. 6.7 is shown the Wigner-Seitz wave function of lowest state in the conduction (3s) band of metallic sodium.   It may be noted that the function is practically constant over 90 percent of the atomic volume.   To the extent that the solutions for higher $\mathbf{k}$ may be approximated by $e^{i\mathbf{k}\cdot\mathbf{r}}u_0(\mathbf{r})$, as in (6.14), it will be true that the wave functions in the conduction band are similar to plane waves over most of the atomic volume, but oscillate and increase markedly in the region of the ion core.

It is often of some importance to take some account of the $\mathbf{k}$ dependence of the part $u_\mathbf{k}(\mathbf{r})$ of the Bloch function, rather than to approximate

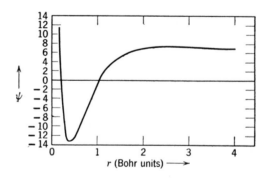

FIG. 6.7.   The lowest wave function of metallic sodium.   A Bohr unit of length is 0.529×10^{-8} cm.

it by $u_0(\mathbf{r})$. By applying the Hamiltonian operator

$$- \frac{\hbar^2}{2m} \nabla^2 + V(\mathbf{r})$$

to the Bloch function $e^{i\mathbf{k}\cdot\mathbf{r}}u_{\mathbf{k}}(\mathbf{r})$, it is a simple matter for the reader to verify that $u_{\mathbf{k}}(\mathbf{r})$ must satisfy the differential equation

$$(6.17) \quad \left[-\frac{\hbar^2}{2m}\nabla^2 - \frac{i\hbar^2}{m}\mathbf{k}\cdot\nabla + V(\mathbf{r}) \right] u_{\mathbf{k}}(\mathbf{r}) = \left(E_{\mathbf{k}} - \frac{\hbar^2 k^2}{2m} \right) u_{\mathbf{k}}(\mathbf{r}).$$

The term in $\mathbf{k}\cdot\nabla$ is often treated as a perturbation. To the second order in k^2, the energy turns out to be, for a cubic crystal and a band which is not degenerate at $\mathbf{k} = 0$, of the form

$$(6.18) \qquad\qquad E_{\mathbf{k}} = E_0 + \frac{\hbar^2 k^2}{2m^*},$$

where m^* is not in general equal to the free electron mass. Values of m^*/m of alkali metals, as calculated by Brooks, are:

	Li	Na	K	Rb	Cs
$\dfrac{m^*}{m} =$	1.40	0.98	0.94	0.87	0.83

EFFECTIVE MASS OF ELECTRONS IN CRYSTALS

The relation (6.18) suggests that an electron in a crystal may behave as if it had a mass different from the free electron mass. This is surprising but true: we know of crystals in which the effective mass may be larger or smaller than m; the effective mass may be anisotropic, and it may even be negative. Masses less than $0.01m$ have been observed. The crystal does not weigh any less if m^* is smaller than m, nor is Newton's second law violated for the crystal taken as a whole. The important point is that an electron in a periodic potential is accelerated (relative to the crystal) in an applied electric or magnetic field as if its mass were equal to the effective mass, which we now define.

We shall consider the concept of an effective mass from several points of view. We first look at the motion of a wave packet in an applied electric field $\mathcal{E}$. We suppose that the wave packet is made up of states near a particular k value in a single band.

The general expression for the group velocity v_g is

$$(6.19) \qquad\qquad v_g = \frac{d\omega}{dk}.$$

This is a familiar result in physical optics. Now the frequency associated with a wave function of energy E is given by $\omega = E/\hbar$, and so

$$(6.20) \qquad\qquad v_g = \hbar^{-1} \frac{dE}{dk}.$$

The work δE done on the electron by the electric field $\mathcal{E}$ in the time interval δt is

$$(6.21) \qquad\qquad \delta E = e\mathcal{E}v_g\,\delta t.$$

We observe, however

$$(6.22) \qquad\qquad \delta E = \frac{dE}{dk}\,\delta k = \hbar v_g\,\delta k,$$

using (6.20). Thus on comparing (6.21) with (6.22) we have

$$(6.23) \qquad\qquad \delta k = \frac{e\mathcal{E}}{\hbar}\,\delta t,$$

or

$$(6.24) \qquad\qquad \frac{\hbar\,dk}{dt} = e\mathcal{E}.$$

This is an important relation, showing that in a crystal $\hbar\,dk/dt$ is equal to the external force on the electron, whereas in free space it is, of course, $m\,dv/dt$ that is equal to the force. We are not overthrowing Newton's second law of motion; the point is that the electron in the crystal is subject to forces from the crystal lattice as well as from external sources. If we choose to express the motion in terms of the external force alone, it is not surprising that the resulting equation of motion is not simply $F = ma$. It is surprising that any good at all comes out of an approach in terms of external forces alone, but we shall see that the effective mass is a most useful quantity.

From (6.20) we have

$$(6.25) \qquad\qquad \frac{dv_g}{dt} = \hbar^{-1}\frac{d^2E}{dk\,dt} = \hbar^{-1}\left(\frac{d^2E}{dk^2}\frac{dk}{dt}\right).$$

Using (6.24) for dk/dt, we have

$$(6.26) \qquad\qquad \frac{dv_g}{dt} = \frac{d^2E}{dk^2}\frac{e\mathcal{E}}{\hbar^2}.$$

It appears on comparison with the classical equation $dv/dt = e\mathcal{E}/m$ that $\hbar^2/(d^2E/dk^2)$ plays the role of a mass, and we call this quantity the *effective mass* m^*:

$$(6.27) \qquad\qquad m^* = \frac{\hbar^2}{d^2E/dk^2}.$$

We note that, if the energy is given by $E = (\hbar^2/2m^*)k^2$, then m^* here is consistent with (6.27).

It is easy to generalize (6.27) to take account of an anisotropic energy surface. We find for the components of the effective mass tensor

$$(6.28) \qquad \left(\frac{m}{m^*}\right)_{ij} = \frac{m}{\hbar^2} \frac{d^2 E_{\mathbf{k}}}{dk_i \, dk_j},$$

where i, j are Cartesian coordinates.

PHYSICAL BASIS OF EFFECTIVE MASSES

We now attempt to shed some light on how it is that an electron of mass m when put into a crystal may respond to applied fields as if the mass were m^*. The interaction with the lattice is responsible for the difference between m and m^*. It is helpful in this connection to think of the process of Bragg reflection of electron waves in a lattice.

Consider the physical implications with reference to the familiar weak binding approximation (Appendix A) in one dimension with a perturbation $V = 2V_0 \cos Gx$, representing the interaction of the electron with the lattice. The band structure is shown in Fig. 6.8. At a point A near the bottom of the lower band the state is represented quite adequately by a plane wave e^{ikx}; the reflected component is small and increases only slowly as k is increased, and so in this region $m^* \cong m$. An increase in the reflected component represents momentum transfer between the lattice and the electron. At B the reflected component $e^{i(k-G)x}$ is quite large; it is larger still at C and becomes

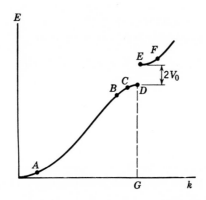

FIG. 6.8. Band structure arising from the perturbation $2V_0 \cos Gx$. The eigenfunctions ψ_k may be written approximately as linear combinations of e^{ikx} and $e^{i(k-G)x}$, with relative amplitudes depending on k.

equal in amplitude to e^{ikx} at D, at which point (as at E also) the eigen-functions are standing waves, rather than running waves. It is thus not surprising to find in the region B to D negative values for m^*. A negative m^* means only that on going from state k to state $k + \Delta k$ the momentum transfer to the lattice is opposite to and larger than the momentum transfer to the electron. Although k is increased by Δk by the applied electric field, the consequent Bragg reflections result in an over-all decrease in the momentum of the electron, so that the effective mass may be described as being negative. As we proceed from E towards F, the amplitude of $e^{i(k-G)x}$ decreases and m^* assumes a small positive value; that is, the increase in electron velocity result-ing from a given impulse is larger than that which a free electron would experience. The lattice makes up the difference through the recoil that it experiences when the amplitude of $e^{i(k-G)x}$ is diminished. A pictorial discussion of this argument is given in Fig. 6.9. The most direct experimental determination of the effective mass is by means of cyclotron resonance experiments, as will be discussed in the chapter on the physics of semiconductors.

We suppose for simplicity that in the portion of a band of interest all the states may be described by the same value of the effective mass m^*. From Chapter 5,

$$E_F(0) = \frac{\hbar^2}{2m^*} (3\pi^2 N)^{2/3},$$

and so the Fermi energy E_F and the Fermi temperature T_F of a degen-erate electron gas are inversely proportional to m^*; we may then introduce m^* consistently in the theory in place of m. In this fashion we may transcribe various results of the free electron theory.

We find for the electronic heat capacity that

(6.29) $C_v \propto m^*.$

For the Pauli spin susceptibility

(6.30) $\chi_s \propto m^*.$

The proportionality of the heat capacity and spin susceptibility to m^* reflects directly the proportionality of the density of states at the top of the Fermi distribution to the effective masses. We note further from Chapter 5 that the electrical conductivity and mobility are pro-portional to $1/m^*$, so that

(6.31) $\sigma = \frac{Ne^2\tau}{m^*},$

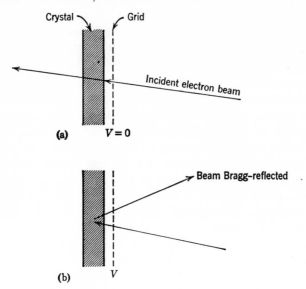

FIG. 6.9.   Explanation of light effective masses near a Brillouin zone boundary. In (a) the energy of the electron beam incident on a thin crystal is slightly too low or too high to satisfy the condition for Bragg reflection and the beam is transmitted through the crystal.   The application of a small voltage across the grid may, as in (b), cause the Bragg condition to be satisfied, and the electron beam will then be reflected from the appropriate set of crystal planes.   Thus a small change in the energy of the electron beam has caused a very large change in the momentum of the beam; this situation corresponds to a light effective mass.   The effective mass may be positive or negative in this experiment, according to whether the initial energy was above or below the Bragg energy.   The crystal itself experiences the usual classical recoil when the beam is reflected.

and the mobility

$$(6.32) \qquad\qquad \mu = \frac{e\tau}{m^*}.$$

We may draw several qualitative conclusions from this discussion. The metals of the transition groups of the periodic table are known to have unfilled inner shells, and the corresponding bands may be unfilled. As the overlap of inner shells on adjacent atoms is likely to be relatively small, the bands will be quite narrow in energy, and the density of states will be high.   We therefore expect the transition metals to have values of $m^*/m \gg 1$, and to have high electronic heat capacities and high paramagnetic susceptibilities.   High diamagnetic susceptibilities will occur when $m^* \ll 1$, according to the Landau theory.

TABLE 6.1

COMPILATION OF VALUES OF THE MAGNETIC SUSCEPTIBILITY OF TRANSITION
ELEMENTS AT ROOM TEMPERATURE

[Selected by C. J. Kriessman and H. B. Callen, *Phys. Rev.* **94**, 837 (1954)]

Element	χ (emu/gram) $\times 10^6$	Element	χ (emu/gram) $\times 10^6$
Ti	3.2	Mn	9.7
Zr	1.3	Re	0.37
Hf	0.42	Ru	0.43
V	5.0	Os	0.05
Nb	2.24	Rh	0.99
Ta	0.84	Ir	0.18
Cr	3.3	Pd	5.23
Mo	0.94	Pt	0.97
W	0.30		

The observations are in agreement with this idea. Reference to Table 6.1 shows that many of the transition metals, including cobalt, iron, manganese, niobium, nickel, palladium, and platinum, have unusually large electronic heat capacities, suggesting the effective mass ratio m^*/m is of the order of 10 or more. A compilation of values of the magnetic susceptibility of transition elements is given in Table 6.1.

According to the theory we may expect values of the effective mass ratio $m^*/m \ll 1$ for states near a small energy discontinuity, and H. Jones has explained on this basis the strong diamagnetism of bismuth and gamma-brass, which have diamagnetic susceptibilities ~ 5 to 10 times larger than normal. In certain directions in the bismuth crystal values of m^*/m of the order of 10^{-2} are required to explain the susceptibility and its anisotropy.

HOLES: POSITIVE CHARGE CARRIERS

A single electron in an energy band may have positive or negative effective mass: the positive effective mass states occur near the bottom of a band because positive effective mass means that the band has upward curvature ($\partial^2 E/\partial k^2$ is positive). Negative effective mass states occur near the top of a band; a single electron in a negative mass state is not stable thermodynamically and will tend to drop down in energy to a positive mass state. In both situations the electron behaves as if the charge were negative, as appropriate for an electron.

The situation is different when most of the states in a band are filled, with the only vacant states having negative mass ($\partial^2 E/\partial k^2$ negative).

The vacant states, or holes, act as if they had positive charge and positive effective mass. To start with we should recall that a filled band can carry no current—there are no vacant states in the band for an electron to jump into, and thus nothing happens when electric or magnetic fields are applied, provided these are not strong enough to deform or destroy the band structure.

MOTION OF HOLES

The fact that vacant states near the top of an otherwise filled band behave in every way as particles of positive charge $+|e|$ is one of the most interesting features of the band theory of solids. It is also a feature of considerable practical importance, as the operation of transistors depends directly on the coexistence of holes and electrons within semiconducting crystals. The first experimental evidence for holes came from the occurrence of positive values of the Hall coefficient, as in the following discussion. It has been established by means of cyclotron resonance experiments[3] with circularly polarized radiation that holes and electrons rotate in opposite senses in a magnetic field, just as one would expect for charges of opposite sign.

It is not difficult to understand[4] the reason for the behavior of holes. We now consider in detail the motion of a hole in an applied electric field. We treat the one-dimensional example illustrated by Fig. 6.10. Initially the band is filled except for the single vacant state F at the top of the band. An electric field $\mathcal{E}_x$ is now applied in the $+x$ direction. The resulting motion of the electrons in the band is governed by the equation

$$(6.33) \qquad \hbar \dot{k}_x = F = -|e|\mathcal{E}_x,$$

and each electron changes its k_x value at the same rate. The equation of motion tells us that Δk_x is negative for the situation illustrated. The vacant state initially at F is displaced first to E and at a later time moves to D. That is, the hole moves along with the electrons in the direction of decreasing k_x.

For the portion of the energy surface to the left of F the slope $\partial E/\partial k_x$ is positive; from (6.20) the group velocity is

$$(6.34) \qquad v_g = \hbar^{-1}\frac{\partial E}{\partial k_x},$$

so that we have a positive velocity. We see then that the velocity of

[3] Dresselhaus, Kip, and Kittel, *Phys. Rev.* **98**, 368 (1955).
[4] W. Shockley, *Holes and electrons in semiconductors*, Van Nostrand, Princeton, New Jersey, 1950.

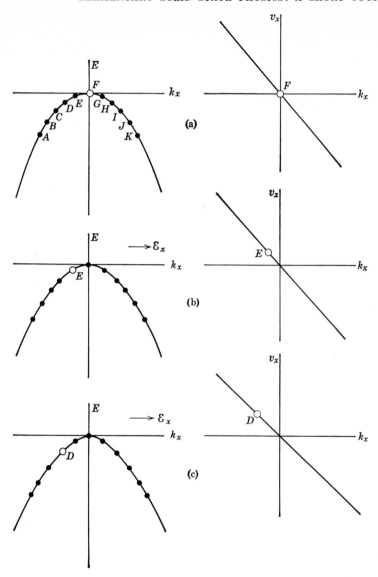

FIG. 6.10. (a) At $t = 0$ all states are filled except F at the top of the band; the velocity v_x is zero at F because $\partial E/\partial k_x = 0$. (b) An electric field $\mathcal{E}_x$ is applied in the $+x$ direction. The force on the electrons is in the $-k_x$ direction and all electrons make transitions together in the $-k_x$ direction, moving the hole to E. (c) After a further interval the electrons move farther along and the hole is now at D. In this way the hole has moved to decreasing k_x values, corresponding to higher positive velocities. The increasing positive velocity is consistent with a positive charge.

the hole increases in the direction of the electric field. This fact alone would be compatible with the assignment to the hole of either a positive charge and positive mass or negative charge and negative mass. The following consideration shows that only the positive possibility is correct. We have to establish the connection between the sense of the charge flow and the sense of the particle flow.

If the band were entirely filled, the total velocity summed over every electron in the band would be zero: a filled band cannot carry current. The contribution of a single electron in the state D to the velocity sum is positive. Now, if the band is filled except for the state D, the rest of the electrons in the band must have a negative net velocity

$$\bar{v}_x = -\hbar^{-1} \frac{\partial E}{\partial k_x}$$

in order for the total velocity to be zero for the band when completely filled. As the hole is accelerated the electrons are accelerated in the opposite direction, in effect transporting negative charge to the left as drawn; but the hole is moved to the right and in effect transports positive charge to the right. We must therefore assign the hole a positive charge. But to be consistent with the rate of change of velocity we must then assign the hole a positive effective mass

$$(6.35) \qquad m^* \text{ (hole)} = \frac{-\hbar^2}{\partial^2 E / \partial k_x^2}$$

It is useful to summarize the equations which govern the motion of a *hole* in an otherwise filled band:

$$(6.36) \qquad \hbar \dot{\mathbf{k}}_h = -|e| \left(\boldsymbol{\varepsilon} + \frac{1}{c} \mathbf{v}_h \times \mathbf{H} \right)$$

$$(6.37) \qquad \hbar \bar{\mathbf{v}}_h = \nabla_{\mathbf{k}} E \qquad \qquad \text{holes}$$

$$(6.38) \qquad \left(\frac{1}{m_h^*} \right)_{ij} = -\frac{1}{\hbar^2} \frac{\partial^2 E}{\partial k_i \, \partial k_j}$$

We should emphasize that all problems can be solved by considering the notion of electrons alone, but if the band is nearly filled, it is more convenient to deal with the vacant states or holes. We note that, if $E = E_0 - (\hbar^2/2m^*)k^2$, then $\bar{\mathbf{v}}_h = -\hbar \mathbf{k}/m^*$ and $m^* \dot{\mathbf{v}}_h = +|e| \left(\boldsymbol{\varepsilon} + \frac{1}{c} \mathbf{v}_h \times \mathbf{H} \right).$

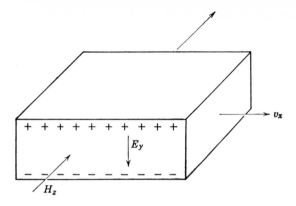

FIG. 6.11.   Hall effect.   Electrons flowing in the x direction in the presence of the magnetic field H_z are deflected toward the lower face of the specimen, which then charges up until the resulting electric field cancels the effect of the magnetic field.

HALL EFFECT

The most striking experimental evidence leading us to introduce the concept of positive current carriers or holes in crystals is furnished by the Hall effect.   When a conductor is placed in a magnetic field perpendicular to the direction of current flow, a voltage is developed across the specimen in the direction perpendicular to both the current and the magnetic field, as shown in Fig. 6.11.   The voltage is called the Hall voltage.   It is developed because the moving charges making up the current are forced to one side by the magnetic field.   The charges accumulate on a face of the specimen until the electric field associated with the accumulated charge is large enough to cancel the force exerted by the magnetic field.   The Hall effect is an important tool, especially in semiconductor research, as in simple situations the effect provides a direct estimate of the concentration of charge carriers.

It is usually assumed in calculating the Hall voltage that the specimen is in the form of a thin plane slab and the voltage is developed across the narrow dimension, as in Fig. 6.11.   The Lorentz force on a charge carrier is

$$(6.39) \qquad \mathbf{F} = e\left(\mathbf{E} + \frac{1}{c}\mathbf{v} \times \mathbf{H}\right).$$

The Hall electric field in the y direction is given by the condition

$$(6.40) \qquad F_y = 0 = e\left(E_y - \frac{1}{c}v_x H_z\right),$$

for the geometry shown. Thus

$$(6.41) \qquad E_y = \frac{v_x H_z}{c} = \frac{j_x H_z}{Nec},$$

where j_x is the current density and N is the carrier concentration. The ratio

$$(6.42) \qquad R_H = \frac{E_y}{j_x H_z} = \frac{1}{Nec}$$

is called the Hall constant and is negative for free electrons. The value of the Hall coefficient in electrostatic units statvolt-cm/statamp-oersted is of the magnitude 10^{-24} for normal metals; it will be much larger in semiconductors, as N is much smaller. The value of the Hall coefficient in practical units volt-cm/amp-oersted is 9×10^{11} times the value in electrostatic units.

It is often convenient to consider the Hall angle

$$(6.43) \qquad \phi = \frac{E_y}{E_x} = \frac{\sigma H_z}{Nec}$$

$$= \frac{e\tau H}{m^* c} = \frac{\mu H}{c},$$

using (6.31) and (6.32). We note from Problem 6.2 that eH/m^*c is just the cyclotron angular frequency ω_c for a free particle of mass m^* in a magnetic field H; thus

$$\phi = \omega_c \tau,$$

where τ is the relaxation time. The Hall angle is equal to the average number of radians (usually fractional) traversed by a particle between collisions.

Observed values of the Hall constant for several metals are compared in Table 6.2 with values calculated directly from the concentration of valence electrons. For the monovalent metals the agreement between observed and calculated values is quite satisfactory. However, the sign of the effect in beryllium, zinc, and cadmium is opposite to that predicted for electrons. This situation represented a famous unsolved problem until clarified by band theory. A positive Hall constant implies that the current is carried by positive charges. We have seen that vacant states near the top of an otherwise filled energy band behave as if endowed with a positive charge. The anomalous large value of the constant for bismuth is interpreted on band theory as caused by a low concentration of electrons outside nearly filled bands.

TABLE 6.2
COMPARISON OF OBSERVED HALL CONSTANTS WITH THOSE CALCULATED ON FREE ELECTRON THEORY

$R_H \times 10^{13}$ (volt-cm/amp-oersted) at Room Temperature

Metal	Observed	Calculated
Li	-17.0	-13.1
Na	-25.0	-24.4
K	-42	-47
Cs	-78	-73
Cu	$- 5.5$	$- 7.4$
Ag	$- 8.4$	-10.4
Au	$- 7.2$	-10.5
Be	$+24.4$	$- 2.5$
Zn	$+ 3.3$	$- 4.6$
Cd	$+ 6.0$	$- 6.5$
Al	$- 4$	......
Bi	~ -1000	$- 4.1$

ELECTRICAL CONDUCTIVITY OF METALS

The electrical conductivity of a metal is limited only by deviations from the perfect lattice—the deviations may be caused by lattice vibrations or by static imperfections such as lattice vacancies and impurities. If the lattice were perfect, the electron waves ψ_k would pass through the lattice unscattered, without resistance, just as light passes through a perfect crystal without scattering or alternation. The thermal motion of the lattice causes the conductivity of a pure specimen at high temperatures $(T > \Theta)$ to vary as T^{-1}, whereas at low temperatures $(T \ll \Theta)$ the variation (Fig. 6.12) may be proportional to T^{-5}. Here Θ is the Debye temperature. In disordered (random) alloys the structural irregularities may dominate the resistance even at room temperature, but in very pure metals the thermal motion is dominant above liquid hydrogen temperatures.

The calculation of the resistivity is simpler at high temperatures than at low temperatures, and we can quite easily make a significant estimate if we treat the lattice motion on the Einstein model of individual oscillators of frequency $\omega_E = k\Theta/\hbar$.

The departure of the lattice from the perfect array is measured at each lattice site by the amplitude d of the thermal oscillations. At $T > \Theta$,

$$\tfrac{1}{2}M\omega_E{}^2 d^2 = \tfrac{1}{2}kT, \qquad \text{or} \qquad \tfrac{1}{2}Md^2\left(\frac{k\Theta}{\hbar}\right)^2 = \tfrac{1}{2}kT,$$

so that

$$(6.44) \qquad\qquad d^2 = \frac{\hbar^2 T}{Mk\Theta^2},$$

where M is the mass of the ion core. It is reasonable to view d^2 as a rough measure of the effective scattering cross section for electrons in a metal, so that the mean free path is

$$(6.45) \qquad\qquad \Lambda \approx \frac{1}{Nd^2},$$

where N is the concentration of ions. Thus the electron relaxation

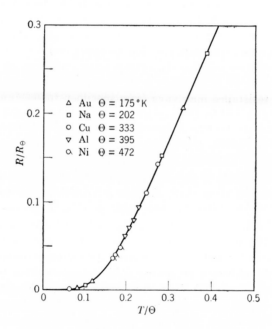

FIG. 6.12. Theoretical (Grüneisen) temperature variation of electrical resistance, and experimental values for various metals. (After Bardeen.)

time is, taking v_F as the velocity at the Fermi surface,

$$(6.46) \qquad \tau = \frac{\Lambda}{v_F} \approx \frac{1}{v_F N d^2},$$

and the electrical conductivity is, for electron concentration N,

$$(6.47) \qquad \sigma = \frac{Ne^2\tau}{m} \approx \frac{e^2}{mv_F d^2} \approx \frac{M}{m}\frac{e^2k}{\hbar^2 v_F} \cdot \frac{\Theta^2}{T}.$$

For $M/m \approx 10^5$; $v_F = 10^8$ cm/sec; $\Theta \approx T \approx 300°$K, we estimate $\sigma \approx 10^{18}$ esu, corresponding to a resistivity of the order of 1 μohm-cm. This is of the correct order of magnitude, and the temperature dependence is correct for the high temperature limit.

RESIDUAL RESISTANCE

The resistivity of a metal containing impurity atoms may usually be written in the form

$$(6.48) \qquad \rho = \rho_i + \rho_L,$$

where ρ_L is the resistivity caused by thermal motion of the lattice, and ρ_i is the resistivity caused by scattering of the electron waves by impurity atoms which disturb the periodicity of the lattice. If the concentration of impurity atoms is small, ρ_i is independent of temperature; this statement is known as *Matthiessen's rule*.

The residual resistance is the extrapolated resistivity at $0°$K and is equivalent to ρ_i, as ρ_L vanishes as $T \to 0$. Measurements show that the residual resistance may vary from specimen to specimen, whereas the resistivity caused by thermal motion is independent of the specimen.

BRILLOUIN ZONES

We now apply band theory in a descriptive and qualitative way to account for a number of physical properties of metals and alloys. We shall be concerned in the main with the relationship between the Fermi surface and the boundary of the Brillouin zone. As the number of conduction electrons is varied by alloying constituents of valency different from that of the solute matrix, the relative positions of the Fermi surface and zone boundary are altered. In certain circumstances this alteration may induce a crystallographic transformation in the alloy, or there may be marked changes in other properties, such as lattice parameters, elastic constants, magnetic susceptibility, and a number of effective conduction electrons. The magnetic properties of transition metals are particularly sensitive indicators of the effects of alloying.

We have seen from (6.1) that the energy discontinuities in the mon-

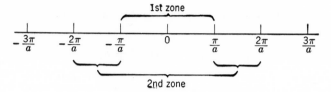

FIG. 6.13.   Brillouin zones of a linear monatomic lattice with lattice constant a.

atomic one-dimensional lattice occur when the wave number satisfies

$$(6.49) \qquad\qquad k = \frac{n\pi}{a},$$

where n is any positive or negative integer.   Thus it is the value of the wave number which is important for the energy discontinuities. In three dimensions the wave vector $\mathbf{k}$ plays the same role, as we see from the Bragg equation.   The position of the energy discontinuities which occur will naturally depend on the type of the crystal lattice.

In the one-dimensional monatomic lattice a line representing the value of k is divided up by the energy discontinuities into segments of length π/a, as shown in Fig. 6.13.   The line segments are known as *Brillouin zones;* the segment $-\pi/a < k < \pi/a$ is the first Brillouin zone; the two segments $-2\pi/a < k < -\pi/a$ and $\pi/a < k < 2\pi/a$ form the second Brillouin zone, etc.   The zone description was introduced by Brillouin, who pointed out that many important and characteristic features of electron propagation in periodic structures could be described by considering the positions in $\mathbf{k}$-space of the boundaries of the zones; these positions are independent of the details of the electron-lattice interaction, being determined instead by the geometry of the crystal structure.   Energy discontinuities occur on the zone boundaries.

The Brillouin zones may be found most directly from the Bragg equation in the form

$$(6.50) \qquad\qquad 2\mathbf{k} \cdot \mathbf{G} + G^2 = 0,$$

where $\mathbf{G}$ is 2π times a reciprocal lattice vector.   As an example of the connection of the Bragg equation with Brillouin zones, we consider the simple square lattice in two dimensions.   The reciprocal lattice vectors are of the form $(n_1/a)\mathbf{i} + (n_2/a)\mathbf{j}$, for lattice constant a; here n_1, n_2 are integers.   We have then

$$\mathbf{G} = \frac{2\pi}{a}\,(n_1\mathbf{i} + n_2\mathbf{j}).$$

The Bragg equation (6.50) for reflection of a wave by a periodic lattice becomes

$$(6.51) \qquad k_x n_1 + k_y n_2 = \frac{\pi(n_1^2 + n_2^2)}{a}.$$

We find the boundaries of the first zone by first setting $n_1 = \pm 1$, $n_2 = 0$, obtaining

$$(6.52) \qquad k_x = \frac{\pm \pi}{a},$$

and then setting $n_1 = 0$, $n_2 = \pm 1$, obtaining

$$(6.53) \qquad k_y = \frac{\pm \pi}{a}.$$

The four lines (6.52) and (6.53) determine the boundary of the first zone, forming a square, as shown in Fig. 6.14.

The outer boundary of the second zone is determined by setting $n_1 = \pm 1$, $n_2 = \pm 1$, obtaining the equations of the four lines

$$(6.54) \qquad \pm k_x \pm k_y = \frac{2\pi}{a},$$

where the signs are independent.

The extension to the sc, bcc, and fcc lattices follows directly. The first Brillouin zone of the simple cubic lattice is a cube of edge $2\pi/a$.

The first zones of the bcc and fcc lattices are shown in Fig. 6.15, and a discussion in detail follows.

It turns out to be possible to restrict consideration to the first Brillouin zone in all problems, as the wave vector $\mathbf{k}$ can always be reduced by subtracting 2π times an appropriate reciprocal lattice vector to give a $\mathbf{k}'$ lying in the first zone while still preserving the Bloch form of the wave function

$$(6.55) \qquad \psi_{\mathbf{k}} = e^{i\mathbf{k}\cdot\mathbf{r}} u_{\mathbf{k}}(\mathbf{r}) = e^{i(\mathbf{k}-\mathbf{G})\cdot\mathbf{r}} u_{\mathbf{k}}(\mathbf{r}) e^{i\mathbf{G}\cdot\mathbf{r}}$$

$$= e^{i\mathbf{k}'\cdot\mathbf{r}} u_{\mathbf{k}'}'(\mathbf{r}) = \psi_{\mathbf{k}'},$$

as $e^{i\mathbf{G}\cdot\mathbf{r}}$ is periodic in the lattice and may be combined with $u_{\mathbf{k}}(\mathbf{r})$. The scheme in which all $\mathbf{k}'$s are considered to lie in the first zone is known as the *reduced zone scheme*.

The zone boundaries are determined by

$$2\mathbf{k} \cdot \mathbf{G} + G^2 = 0,$$

where $\mathbf{G}$ is 2π times a reciprocal lattice vector. It is seen that each

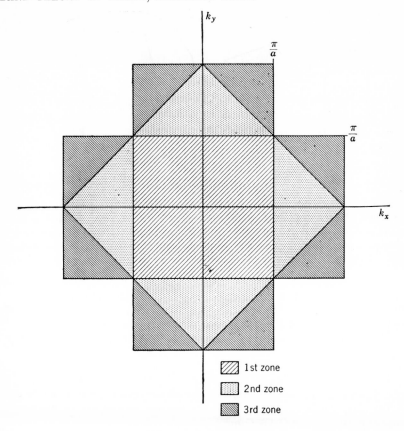

FIG. 6.14. Brillouin zones of a simple square lattice in two dimensions. The first three zones are marked.

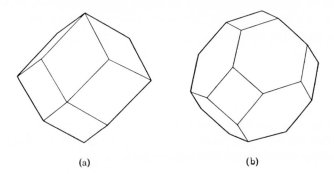

(a)   (b)

FIG. 6.15. The first Brillouin zone in (a) the body-centered cubic lattice and (b) the face-centered cubic lattice.

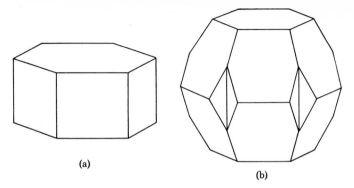

(a)

(b)

FIG. 6.16.   First and second Brillouin zones for the hexagonal close-packed structure.   There is no discontinuity in energy across the top and bottom faces of the first zone if the structure is hexagonal close-packed; so we often encounter a composite zone called the first Jones zone made up of the side faces of (a) with all parts of the second zone (b) above and below the lines of interception with (a).

zone boundary is normal to a $\mathbf{G}$ at its midpoint.   We must first find the form of $\mathbf{G}$, using the definitions of a reciprocal lattice vector.

The primitive translation vectors of the bcc lattice as shown in Fig. 6.16 may be taken as

$$\mathbf{a} = \frac{a}{2}(\mathbf{i} + \mathbf{j} + \mathbf{k});$$

(6.56)
$$\mathbf{b} = \frac{a}{2}(-\mathbf{i} + \mathbf{j} + \mathbf{k});$$

$$\mathbf{c} = \frac{a}{2}(-\mathbf{i} - \mathbf{j} + \mathbf{k}),$$

where a is the side of the conventional unit cube and $\mathbf{i}, \mathbf{j}, \mathbf{k}$ are orthogonal unit vectors parallel to the cube edges.   The volume of the primitive cell is

(6.57) $$V = \mathbf{a} \cdot \mathbf{b} \times \mathbf{c} = \tfrac{1}{2}a^3;$$

we see that this is correct because the unit cube of volume a^3 contains two lattice points.   The primitive translations $\mathbf{a}^*, \mathbf{b}^*, \mathbf{c}^*$ of the reciprocal lattice are given by relations of the form

(6.58) $$\mathbf{a}^* = \frac{\mathbf{b} \times \mathbf{c}}{\mathbf{a} \cdot \mathbf{b} \times \mathbf{c}}.$$

Thus, using (6.56), we have

$$\mathbf{a}^* = \frac{1}{a}(\mathbf{i} + \mathbf{k});$$

(6.59)
$$\mathbf{b}^* = \frac{1}{a}(-\mathbf{i} + \mathbf{j});$$

$$\mathbf{c}^* = \frac{1}{a}(-\mathbf{j} + \mathbf{k}).$$

These are the primitive vectors of a fcc lattice. If h, k, l are integers,

(6.60)
$$\mathbf{G} = 2\pi(h\mathbf{a}^* + k\mathbf{b}^* + l\mathbf{c}^*)$$

$$= \frac{2\pi}{a}[(h - k)\mathbf{i} + (k - l)\mathbf{j} + (h + l)\mathbf{k}].$$

The shortest nonzero $\mathbf{G}$'s are the twelve vectors

(6.61)
$$\frac{2\pi}{a}(\pm\mathbf{i} \pm \mathbf{j}); \frac{2\pi}{a}(\pm\mathbf{j} \pm \mathbf{k}); \frac{2\pi}{a}(\pm\mathbf{i} \pm \mathbf{k}).$$

The zone boundaries determined by (6.50) are planes normal to each $\mathbf{G}$ at the midpoint. The first Brillouin zone will be formed from the shortets $\mathbf{G}$'s, of which there are twelve given by (6.61). The zone is therefore the rhombic dodecahedron shown in Fig. 6.15a. Note that the rhombic dodecahedron constructed in this fashion is a possible choice for the primitive cell of the fcc lattice, as the figures fill all space and each figure contains one lattice point. We have then for the volume of the zone in $\mathbf{k}$ space $\frac{1}{4}(4\pi/a)^3 = 2(2\pi/a)^3$. The number of states per unit volume of $\mathbf{k}$ space is $2/(2\pi)^3$ per unit volume of the crystal, so that there are $4/a^3$ states in the zone per unit volume of crystal. A bcc crystal contains $2/a^3$ atoms per unit volume; thus there are two states in the zone per atom, one state for each spin orientation. This result agrees with our earlier statement that an energy band contains two states for every atom in the crystal.

There are several further points of interest about the first zone of the bcc lattice. The radius k_i of a sphere inscribed in the zone is $k_i = \sqrt{2}\,\pi/a$, so that the volume of the sphere is $(4\pi/3)2^{3/2}\pi^3/a^3$, which is $\pi/3(2)^{1/2} = 0.74$ of the volume of the zone. If the Fermi surface is spherical it will just contact the zone boundary for a conduction electron concentration of $2 \times 0.74 = 1.48$ per atom. The matter of con-

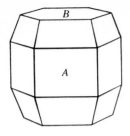

FIG. 6.17. The composite zone for the hexagonal close-packed structure. [After H. Jones, *Proc. Roy. Soc.* (*London*) **A147**, 396 (1934).]

tact with the zone boundary is important in the theory of alloys, as in the following discussion.

FACE-CENTERED CUBIC LATTICE

The primitive translation vectors of the fcc lattice as shown in Fig. 6.17 may be taken as

$$(6.62) \quad \begin{aligned} \mathbf{a} &= \frac{a}{2}(\mathbf{i} + \mathbf{j}); \\ \mathbf{b} &= \frac{a}{2}(\mathbf{i} + \mathbf{k}); \\ \mathbf{c} &= \frac{a}{2}(\mathbf{j} + \mathbf{k}). \end{aligned}$$

The volume of the primitive cell is $\mathbf{a} \cdot \mathbf{b} \times \mathbf{c} = \frac{1}{4}a^3$. Using (6.58) the primitive translations of the reciprocal lattice are found to be

$$(6.63) \quad \begin{aligned} \mathbf{a}^* &= \frac{1}{a}(-\mathbf{i} - \mathbf{j} + \mathbf{k}); \\ \mathbf{b}^* &= \frac{1}{a}(-\mathbf{i} + \mathbf{j} - \mathbf{k}); \\ \mathbf{c}^* &= \frac{1}{a}(\mathbf{i} - \mathbf{j} - \mathbf{k}). \end{aligned}$$

These are the primitive translations of a bcc lattice. We have now

$$(6.64) \quad \mathbf{G} = \frac{2\pi}{a}[(-h - k + l)\mathbf{i} + (-h + k - l)\mathbf{j} + (h - k - l)\mathbf{k}].$$

The shortest nonzero G's are the eight vectors

$$(6.65) \quad \frac{2\pi}{a}(\pm\mathbf{i} \pm \mathbf{j} \pm \mathbf{k}).$$

The zone boundaries are determined for the most part by the eight planes normal to these vectors at their midpoints, but it may be seen that the corners of the octahedron thus formed are truncated by the planes which are the perpendicular bisectors of the six vectors

$$(6.66) \quad \frac{2\pi}{a}(\pm 2\mathbf{i}); \frac{2\pi}{a}(\pm 2\mathbf{j}); \frac{2\pi}{a}(\pm 2\mathbf{k}).$$

The first zone is then the truncated octahedron shown in Fig. 6.15*b*.

The zone is a possible choice of the primitive cell of a bcc lattice, and so the volume is $\frac{1}{2}(4\pi/a)^3 = 4(2\pi/a)^3$. There are then $8/a^3$ states in the zone per unit volume of crystal. A fcc crystal contains $4/a^3$ atoms per unit volume, and so we have again two states per atom.

The radius of the inscribed sphere is $k_i = \sqrt{3}\,\pi/a$; the volume of the sphere is $(4\pi/3)3^{3/2}\pi^3/a^3$, which is $3^{1/2}\pi/8 = 0.68$ of the volume of the zone. If the Fermi surface is spherical, it will contact the zone boundary when the electron concentration is $2 \times 0.68 = 1.36$ electrons per atom.

HEXAGONAL CLOSE-PACKED STRUCTURE

The primitive translation vectors of the hexagonal space lattice as shown in Fig. 6.18 may be taken as

$$\mathbf{a} = \frac{a}{2}\mathbf{i} + \left(\frac{3^{1/2}a}{2}\right)\mathbf{j};$$

$$(6.67) \qquad \mathbf{b} = -\frac{a}{2}\mathbf{i} + \left(\frac{3^{1/2}a}{2}\right)\mathbf{j};$$

$$\mathbf{c} = c\mathbf{k}.$$

The volume of the primitive cell is $(3^{1/2}a/2)a^2c$. The basis of the hcp structure contains two atoms. Note that hcp is a structure and not a space lattice; the space lattice is the hexagonal space lattice. The

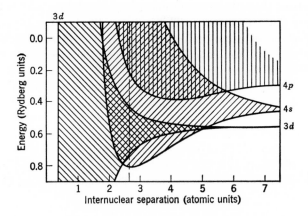

FIG. 6.18.   Energy bands in copper as a function of internuclear separation. [After H. M. Krutter, *Phys. Rev.* **48**, 664 (1935).]

primitive translations of the reciprocal lattice are

$$\mathbf{a}^* = \frac{1}{a}\mathbf{i} + \left(\frac{1}{3^{1/2}a}\right)\mathbf{j};$$

(6.68) $$\mathbf{b}^* = -\frac{1}{a}\mathbf{i} + \left(\frac{1}{3^{1/2}a}\right)\mathbf{j};$$

$$\mathbf{c}^* = \frac{1}{c}\mathbf{k};$$

thus the lattice is its own reciprocal. This may be verified by comput-
ing $\mathbf{a} \cdot \mathbf{a}^*$, etc. We have

(6.69) $$\mathbf{G} = 2\pi\left[\frac{1}{a}(h-k)\mathbf{i} + \left(\frac{1}{3^{1/2}a}\right)(h+k)\mathbf{j} + \frac{1}{c}l\mathbf{k}\right].$$

The shortest nonzero $\mathbf{G}$'s are the eight vectors

$$\frac{2\pi}{a}\left[\pm\mathbf{i} \pm \left(\frac{1}{3^{1/2}}\right)\mathbf{j}\right];$$

(6.70) $$\frac{2\pi}{a}\left[\pm\left(\frac{2}{3^{1/2}}\right)\mathbf{j}\right];$$

$$\frac{2\pi}{c}\pm\mathbf{k}.$$

The first zone shown in Fig. 6.16a is formed by the planes normal to
these vectors at their midpoints. It can be shown for the basis of the
hcp structure there is no large energy discontinuity across the horizontal faces of the first zone. This is essentially because the reflections
from the plane of atoms midway between the planes bounding the
primitive cell will just cancel in phase the reflections from the basal
plane. We are therefore led to consider the second Brillouin zone.
The second zone is shown in Fig. 6.16b and may be found directly by
the methods employed above. The conclusions just stated are modified by inclusion of the spin-orbit interaction; this provides a small
energy gap across most of the horizontal face of the first zone.

The first zone contains two states per primitive cell or one state
per atom; the combined first and second zones contain four states per
primitive cell or two states per atom. The composite zone (Fig. 6.17)
contains

(6.71) $$n = 2 - \frac{3}{4}\left(\frac{a}{c}\right)^2\left[1 - \frac{1}{4}\left(\frac{a}{c}\right)^2\right]$$

states per atom.   This zone is the smallest region bounded by planes of energy discontinuity.   Such a zone is sometimes called a Jones zone, after H. Jones who introduced it.

In Fig. 6.17, we note the $\mathbf{k}$-value at A is $2\pi/3^{\frac{1}{2}}a$ and at B the $\mathbf{k}$ value is $2\pi/c$.   For the ideal close-packed arrangement $c/a = (\frac{8}{3})^{\frac{1}{2}} = 1.63$, and so $k_A/k_B = (\frac{8}{9})^{\frac{1}{2}}$ and the ratio of the free electron energies at the two points is $E_A/E_B = \frac{8}{9}$.   We therefore expect contact of the Fermi surface with the zone boundary to be established first at point A.   The axial ratios of zinc and cadmium depart considerably from the ideal ratio; for zinc $c/a = 1.86$, and so $k_A/k_B = 1.07$; $E_A/E_B = 1.15$; and contact with the zone boundary may be established first at point B.

BAND STRUCTURE OF METALS

ALKALI METALS

The alkali atoms have one s valence electron on each atom: $2s$ in lithium, $3s$ in sodium, $4s$ in potassium, $5s$ in rubidium, and $6s$ in cesium. In the alkali metals, the s levels are spread out into a wide band and in some respects the conduction electrons act as if they were free.   The crystal structures are all body-centered cubic at room temperature. The s band is half-filled, and so if the Fermi surface is spherical it should lie comfortably within the first Brillouin zone.   We have seen previously that the sphere inscribed in the first zone holds 1.48 electrons per atom.   For lithium there is some theoretical evidence that the Fermi surface does not depart much from a sphere: Kohn and Rostoker have calculated the energies on the Fermi surface in the [100] and [111] directions, finding that the energies differ by only 3 percent. However, the effective mass is calculated to be $1.4m$.

NOBLE METALS

Copper, silver, and gold are monovalent metals, but they differ from the alkali metals by having a d shell in the free atoms filled just at these points in the periodic system.   The crystal structures are all face-centered cubic.   Although the alkali metals have a small ion embedded in a large atomic volume, the noble metals have their filled d shells nearly in contact and acting as rigid spheres.   The nearest neighbor distance in sodium is 3.71 A, and the ionic diameter of Na^+ is 1.9 A, giving a clearance of 1.8 A.   In copper, the nearest neighbor distance is 2.55 A and the ionic diameter of Cu^+ is 1.92 A, giving a clearance of 0.63 A.   The clearance in silver is 0.36 A, and in gold 0.14 A.   The compressibility of the alkali metals are 50 to 100 times higher than those of the corresponding noble metals; the cohesive energies are four

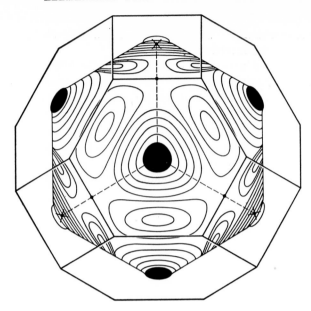

FIG. 6.19.   The Fermi surface of copper, according to Pippard.

to five times lower in the alkalies.   The low compressibility of the, noble metals is an effect of the exclusion principle: the high electron density in the d shells resists interpenetration.   The cohesive energies are thought to be high because of interactions between the d shells.

The d band is believed to overlap the s band, as shown in Fig. 6.18. Calculations by Howarth for copper suggest that the $3d$ band is 3.46 ev in width and the Fermi surface lying in the $4s$ band is 3.7 ev above the top of the $3d$ band.   The Fermi surface is estimated on a free electron model to be 7.1 ev above the bottom of the $4s$ band.   In pure copper the Fermi surface is known to touch the zone boundary, as shown in Fig. 6.19, at the centers of the hexagonal faces.

It is believed that the average effective masses of the electrons in the noble metals are close to the free electron mass.   Calculations by Kambe give the values as tabulated.   The electronic heat capacity

	Cu	Ag	Au
$\dfrac{m^*}{m}$	1.012	0.992	0.994

of silver is in close agreement with the calculated value, assuming $m^* = m$; for copper the heat capacity suggests $m^* \cong 1.4m$.   There are, however, various corrections to the independent electron model which may change the effective density of states at the Fermi surface and thus may change the electronic heat capacity. We do not know how to calculate these changes with confidence, and so it would be cautious at present not to push too hard the interpretation of the experimental data.

DIVALENT METALS

The metals Be, Mg, Ca, Zn, Sr, Cd, Ba, and Hg are characterized by an outer s^2 configuration; that is, there are two valence electrons in the s state of the free atom. The crystal structures are: hcp (Be, Mg, Ca, Zn, Cd); fcc (Ca, Sr); bcc (Ba); complex (Hg). The divalent metals have an even number of valence electrons and would be insulators were it not for the presumed overlap of higher bands with the s band. Be, Zn, and Cd are known to have positive Hall constants, suggesting that the major contribution to the conductivity arises from holes at the top of the s band, the holes being left by the electron overspill into the next band. It is likely that the overlap of the Fermi surface is particularly small for beryllium, which may be not far from an insulator. The large Hall constant suggests that perhaps only ~10 percent of the total number of valence electrons are effective in conductivity.

TRIVALENT METALS

The trivalent metals are B, Al, Ga, In, and Tl; the electronic configuration is s^2p. Of these, only aluminum can be considered to be a typical metal (Fig. 6.20). Boron is a semiconductor and has a com-

FIG. 6.20. Fermi surface of aluminum.

plicated crystal structure. Aluminum has a higher ratio of electrical conductivity to density than does copper; the crystal structure of aluminum is fcc. Gallium melts at 30°C; the crystal structure is orthorhombic. Indium has a face-centered tetragonal structure: it may be thought of as a face-centered cubic lattice distorted by an 8 percent elongation parallel to a cube edge. Thallium occurs in hcp and bcc modifications.

BINARY ALLOYS

We are now concerned primarily with substitutional solid solutions of one metal in another. We are going to examine some aspects of the changes in physical properties consequent to the addition of atoms A to a metal B. We suppose that the A atoms enter the metal in a random fashion in lattice positions equivalent to those occupied by the B atoms. The distinct effects that occur when the A atoms enter the structure in a regular, rather than random, fashion are considered briefly at the end of this chapter under the heading of the order-disorder transformation.

Hume-Rothery[5] has discussed the general requirements for solid solutions to occur. He suggests that the solid solution range is very restricted if the atomic diameters of solvent and solute differ by more than 15 percent. The atomic diameter for this purpose is usually taken as the closest distance of approach in the crystal structure of the element (Table 1.2). Thus the size factor is favorable in the Cu (2.55 A) − Zn (2.66 A) system, and zinc dissolves in copper as a fcc solid solution up to 38 atomic percent zinc. The size factor is somewhat unfavorable in the Cu (2.55 A) − Cd (2.97 A) system and only 1.7 atomic percent cadmium is soluble in copper. The size factors expressed as percentages referred to copper are 4 percent for Zn in Cu and 16.5 percent for Cd in Cu.

Although the size factor may be favorable, solid solutions will not form if there is a strong tendency to form stable intermediate compounds. Thus if the solvent is strongly electronegative and the solute element strongly electropositive (or vice versa), it is likely that intermediate compounds will precipitate out of solution. Although the size factor is favorable (2 percent) for As in Cu, only 6 percent As is soluble. The size factor is favorable (9 percent) for Sb in Mg, yet the solubility of Sb in Mg is very small.

In the following sections we discuss various aspects of the electronic structure of alloys. The discussions are phrased in terms of the average number of nominal conduction electrons per atom: for example, the

[5] See the books by Hume-Rothery cited at the end of the chapter.

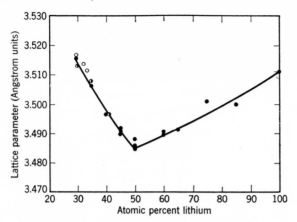

FIG. 6.21. Lattice parameter of body-centered cubic magnesium-lithium alloys. [After D. W. Levinson, *Acta Met* **3**, 294 (1955).]

electron concentration n in the alloy 50 Cu-50 Zn is 1.50; in 50 Cu-50 Al, $n = 2.00$. We assume that the energy surfaces are spherical and that the principal effect of alloying elements of different valency is simply to change the electron concentration. The consequences of these assumptions are often in remarkable agreement with experiment, to the astonishment of the theoretical physicist.

Measurements of the lattice parameter of Li-Mg alloys are shown in Fig. 6.21. In the range shown the structure is bcc. The lattice contracts during the initial stages of the addition of Mg to Li. When the lithium content drops below 50 atomic percent, corresponding to an average electron concentration increasing above 1.5 per atom, the lattice starts to expand. We have seen earlier for a spherical Fermi surface that contact with the zone boundary is established at $n = 1.48$ electrons per atom, for a bcc lattice. It therefore appears that the expansion of the lattice is associated with the onset of overlap across the zone boundary. This is one type of effect relating to electron concentration and the Brillouin zone boundary.

HUME-ROTHERY RULES FOR ALLOY PHASES

Hume-Rothery first drew attention to the importance of the average valence electron/atom ratio as a kind of universal parameter in the description of the properties of alloys. He was originally concerned with the occurrence of certain alloy structures at a definite electron per atom ratio. The phase diagram of the copper-zinc system is shown

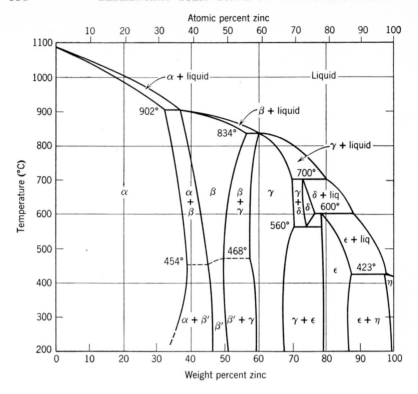

FIG. 6.22.   Equilibrium diagram of the copper-zinc system.

in Fig. 6.22.   The phases of interest are: α (fcc), β (bcc), γ (complex cubic cell of 52 atoms), and ϵ (hcp).

The α-phase of pure copper ($n = 1$) persists until an electron concentration of about 1.38.   The β-phase has a minimum electron concentration of about 1.48.   The γ-phase exists for the approximate range of n between 1.58 and 1.66, and the ϵ-phase occurs near 1.75. The term electron compound denotes in an alloy system an intermediate phase where crystal structure is determined by the establishment of a certain electron/atom ratio.   The empirical values usually quoted as the Hume-Rothery rules are: $\frac{3}{2}(= 1.50)$ for the β-phase, $\frac{21}{13}(= 1.62)$ for the γ-phase, and $\frac{7}{4}(= 1.75)$ for the ϵ-phase.   Representative experimental data are collected in Table 6.3, based on the usual chemical valency assignments.

The Hume-Rothery rules find a simple explanation on band theory in the approximation of nearly free electrons.   Jones pointed out that the observed limit of the α-phase (fcc) occurs very close to the electron concentration of 1.36 for which the inscribed Fermi sphere makes contact with the Brillouin zone surface for the fcc lattice. In pure copper it is known (Fig. 6.19) that the actual Fermi surface contacts the boundary at the hexagonal faces; it is possible that a further contact at the square faces is made for $n \simeq 1.4$ and that it is this contact which forces the $\alpha \rightarrow \beta$ transformation. The observed electron concentration of the β-phase (bcc) is close to the concentration 1.48 for which the inscribed Fermi sphere makes contact with the Brillouin zone surface for the bcc lattice. Contact of the Fermi sphere with the zone boundary for the γ-phase is at the concentration 1.54, according to Jones. Contact for the ϵ-phase (hcp) is at the concentration 1.69 for the ideal c/a ratio.

It is apparent that there is an intimate connection between the electron concentration at which a new phase appears and the electron concentration at which the Fermi surface makes contact with the Brillouin zone boundary. The general explanation of the association is that it is expensive energetically to add further electrons once the filled states contact the zone boundary. Additional electrons can be accommodated only in states above the energy gap characterizing the boundary or in the states near the corners of the first zone. The number of states near the corners falls off markedly as a function of energy. In this circumstance it is often energetically favorable for the crystal structure to change, the final structure being one which contains a larger Fermi

TABLE 6.3

ELECTRON/ATOM RATIOS OF ELECTRON COMPOUNDS

	α-Phase	β-Phase	Minimum γ-Phase	ϵ-Phase
Alloy	Boundary	Boundary	Boundaries	Boundaries
Cu-Zn	1.38	1.48	1.58–1.66	1.78–1.87
Cu-Al	1.41	1.48	1.63–1.77	
Cu-Ga	1.41			
Cu-Si	1.42	1.49		
Cu-Ge	1.36			
Cu-Sn	1.27	1.49	1.60–1.63	1.73–1.75
Ag-Zn	1.38		1.58–1.63	1.67–1.90
Ag-Cd	1.42	1.50	1.59–1.63	1.65–1.82
Ag-Al	1.41			1.55–1.80

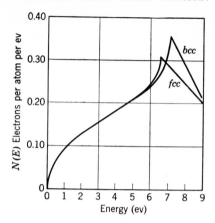

FIG. 6.23. $N(E)$, number of states per unit energy range for face-centered cubic and body-centered cubic lattices, as a function of energy.

surface. In this way the sequence α (1.36), β (1.48), γ (1.54), ϵ (1.69) is made plausible, where the numbers in parentheses refer to the electron concentrations at which contact occurs.

The transformation from fcc to bcc is illustrated by Fig. 6.23, which shows the number of states per unit energy range as a function of energy for the fcc and bcc structures. It is seen that as the number of electrons is increased a point is reached above which it is easier to accommodate additional electrons in the bcc lattice.

There are numerous applications to other structures of reasoning similar to those mentioned in the more recent metallurgical literature.

TRANSITION ELEMENTS

We list for convenience the elements of the three groups of transition metals.

Sc	Ti	V	Cr	Mn	Fe	Co	Ni
Y	Zr	Nb	Mo	Tc	Ru	Rh	Pd
La	Hf	Ta	W	Re	Os	Ir	Pt

It is thought that the transition metals have partly filled d shells in the metallic state. The shells concerned are $3d$, $4d$, and $5d$ for the respective groups. Despite intensive effort and uninhibited speculation, little is actually known about the electronic structure of the metals. More is known perhaps about Fe, Co, Ni, Pd, and Pt than about the other transition metals because the five mentioned have been studied magnetically in some detail.

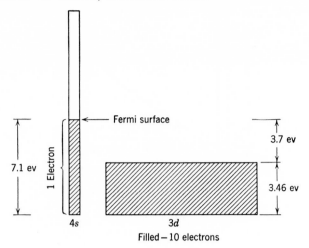

FIG. 6.24. Schematic relationship of 4s and 3d bands in metallic copper. The 3d band holds ten electrons per atom and is filled in copper. The 4s band can hold two electrons per atom; it is shown half-filled, as copper has one valence electron outside the filled 3d shell. The energies shown are from calculations by Howarth; it is coincidental that the bottoms of both bands fall nearly at the same energy.

Several of the characteristic properties of the transition metals are believed to arise from the overlap of the s conduction band with the d band immediately below in energy. In the transition metals the d band is not normally filled entirely; let us, however, first consider the relationship of the bands in copper which has a filled d band. Figure 6.24 is drawn according to the discussion of copper earlier in this chapter. There is a considerable energy gap between the top of the d band and the Fermi surface lying in the s band. It is useful for later applications to show the bands divided in two halves, one-half for each orientation of the electron spin. In Fig. 6.25 we show the d band of copper divided into two sub-bands, one for electrons having spin up, the other for spin down. Each sub-band holds five electrons.

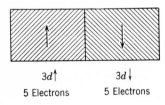

FIG. 6.25. The filled 3d band of copper shown as two separate sub-bands of opposite electron spin orientation, each band holding five electrons. With both sub-bands filled as shown, the net spin (and hence the net magnetization) of the d band is zero.

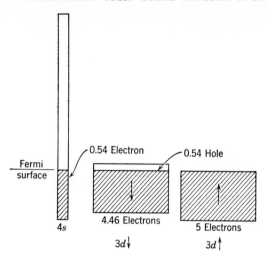

FIG. 6.26. Schematic relationship of bands in nickel at absolute zero. The energies of the $3d \uparrow$ and $3d \downarrow$ sub-bands are separated by an exchange interaction. The $3d \downarrow$ band is filled; the $3d \downarrow$ band contains 4.46 electrons and 0.54 hole. The $4s$ band is usually thought to contain approximately equal numbers of electrons in both spin directions, and so we have not troubled to divide it into sub-bands. The net magnetic moment of 0.54 μ_B per atom arises from the excess population of the $3d \uparrow$ band over the $3d \downarrow$ band. It is often convenient to speak of the magnetization as arising from the 0.54 hole in the $3d \downarrow$ band.

Let us now consider nickel, having one less electron than copper. Nickel is ferromagnetic and has at absolute zero a saturation magnetic moment of 0.60 Bohr magnetons per atom. After an appropriate correction for a small contribution from orbital electronic motion, we have in nickel at saturation an excess of 0.54 electron per atom having spin preferentially oriented in one direction. Stoner showed how one can interpret nonintegral values of the saturation magneton number in terms of the energy band model. For nickel we have to accommodate 10 electrons outside the filled inner shells. If we distribute the 10 electrons as shown in Fig. 6.26, we can account for the observed saturation moment in a natural way. This assumption takes care of the magnetic moment and leaves 0.54 electron for the $4s$ band. The separation in energy between the $3d$ sub-bands is a result of the exchange interaction discussed in Chapter 8. When the metal is heated above the Curie temperature, the holes distribute themselves equally in the two sub-bands, the exchange interaction is dominated by thermal effects, and the saturation moment disappears. The situation in nickel above the Curie temperature is shown in Fig. 6.27.

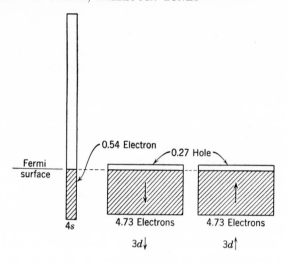

FIG. 6.27. Band relationships in nickel over the Curie temperature. The net magnetic moment is zero, as there are equal numbers of holes in both $3d \downarrow$ and $3d \uparrow$ bands.

There is a certain arbitrariness in the distribution of Fig. 6.26, as we can transfer electrons from both d sub-bands to the s band provided we take 0.54 more from one sub-band than from the other. Evidence that our particular choice may correspond to reality is provided by Fig. 6.28, which gives the effective number of unpaired electrons on

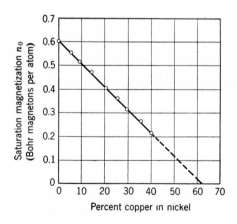

FIG. 6.28. Bohr magneton numbers of nickel-copper alloys.

alloying copper in nickel.   As we add copper we are adding one extra electron per copper atom.   The density of states in the d band is believed to be over ten times greater than that in the s band, so that the extra electron goes at least 90 percent into the d band and less than 10 percent into the s band.   The magneton number is observed to go to zero at about 60 atomic percent copper according to Fig. 6.28. Let us try to understand the effect of adding copper.   At this concentration we have added about 0.54 electron to the d band and about 0.06 electron to the s band.   But 0.54 electron added to the d band in Fig. 6.26 will just fill both d sub-bands and will bring the magnetization to zero, in excellent agreement with observation.

For simplicity the block drawings shown represent the density of states as uniform in energy.   The actual density may be quite far from uniform: Fig. 6.29 gives the results of a calculation by Koster for nickel. The width of the band is about 2.8 ev.   We see the d band is characterized by a high density of states: there are 10 electrons in about 3 ev, whereas in the s band there is 1 electron in about 7 ev.   The average density of states is of the order of twenty times greater in the d band than in the s band.   This value of the density of states ratio provides a rough indication of the expected enhancement of the electronic heat capacity and the paramagnetic susceptibility in nonferromagnetic transition metals as compared with monovalent metals.

It is believed that palladium may have a distribution of electrons similar to that of nickel.   At room temperature the picture for palladium is like Fig. 6.27 for nickel over the Curie point, except that now we have to deal with a 5s band instead of 4s and 4d instead of 3d. The addition of hydrogen in solution in metallic palladium reduces the

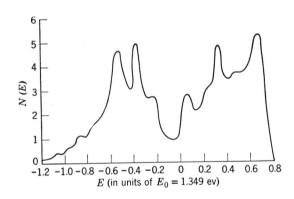

FIG. 6.29.   Density of states $N(E)$ as a function of energy for the d bands in nickel. [According to calculations by G. F. Koster, *Phys. Rev.* **98**, 901 (1955).]

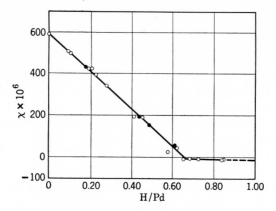

FIG. 6.30. Effect of dissolved hydrogen on the susceptibility of palladium: molar susceptibility versus H/Pd ratio.

susceptibility as shown in Fig. 6.30. When hydrogen goes into solution it is thought to ionize: the electrons join the bands of the palladium just as the valence electron of copper joins the bands of nickel. The bare protons diffuse around in the metal. Proton resonance experiments by Norberg support this model. When 0.6 extra electron per atom have been added, the 4d bands are filled and further addition of hydrogen has no marked effect. The paramagnetic susceptibility can be high only as long as the d bands are not entirely filled, because the d bands have a high density of states.

The average atomic moments of binary alloys of the elements in the iron group are plotted in Fig. 6.31 as a function of electron concentration. What we may call the main sequence of alloys on the right-hand branch follows the simple rule given earlier, but as the electron concentration is decreased a point is reached below which neither of the 3d sub-bands is completely filled.

Let us turn briefly to the question of the electrical conductivity of the transition metals. It might be thought that the availability of the d band as a path for conduction in parallel with the s band would increase the conductivity, but this is not so. We compare below the electrical resistivities in microhm-cm at 18°C of Ni, Pd, and Pt with the noble metals immediately following them in the periodic table:

Ni	Pd	Pt
7.4	10.8	10.5
Cu	Ag	Au
1.7	1.6	2.2

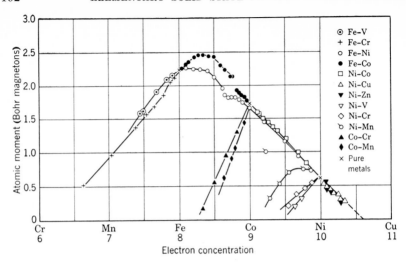

FIG. 6.31.   Average atomic moments of binary alloys of the elements in the iron group.   (After Bozorth.)

It is apparent that the resistivities of the transition metals cited are higher than those of the noble metals by a factor of the order of 5. It is believed the high resistivities of the transition metals are caused by collisions in which an s electron is scattered into the d band, this being an extra scattering mechanism not present when the d band is filled.   The d electrons have heavy effective masses and would not themselves give a high conductivity.

The low compressibilities of the transition metals are believed to arise from the overlapping d shells, but satisfactory quantitative calculations have not been carried out.   Thus although the elements of the first transition group are the mechanical basis of modern civilization, we can explain very little of their properties.

ORDER-DISORDER TRANSFORMATION[6]

Although the topic does not lend itself simply to interpretation in terms of band theory, we are at a convenient point to discuss the ordering of alloys.   The dashed horizontal lines in the phase diagram of the Cu-Zn system (Fig. 6.22) represent the Curie temperature for order in the alloy.   Let us consider a binary alloy AB composed of

[6] For reviews see F. C. Nix and W. Shockley, *Revs. Modern Phys.* **10**, 1 (1938); H. Lipson, *Progress in Metal Physics* **2**, 1–52 (1950); T. Muto and Y. Takagi, *Solid State Phys.* **1**, 194 (1955).

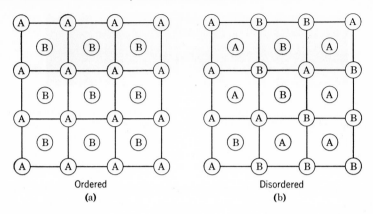

Ordered
(a)

Disordered
(b)

FIG. 6.32. Ordered (a) and disordered (b) arrangements of AB ions in the alloy AB.

equal numbers of two types of metal atoms, A and B. The alloy is said to be *ordered* if the A and B atoms stand in a regular periodic arrangement with respect to one another, as in Fig. 6.32a. The alloy is *disordered* if the A and B atoms are randomly arranged, as in Fig. 6.32b. Many of the properties of an alloy are sensitive to the degree of order. A common ordered arrangement is one in which all the nearest neighbor atoms of a B atom are A atoms, and vice versa; this results when the dominant interaction among the atoms is a strong attraction between AB pairs. If dissimilar atoms avoid each other, a two-phase system is formed.

The system is considered completely ordered at absolute zero; it becomes less ordered as the temperature is increased, until a transition

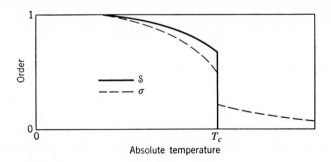

FIG. 6.33. Long range (S) and short range (σ) order versus temperature, for an AB₃ alloy. (After Nix and Shockley.)

FIG. 6.34. X-ray powder photographs of Cu_3Au alloy. (a) Disordered by quenching from $T > T_c$; (b) ordered by annealing at $T < T_c$. (Courtesy of C. S. Barrett.)

temperature is reached above which the disorder is complete. To be more precise, the transition temperature marks the disappearance of *long range order* over many interatomic distances, but some *short range order* or correlation among near neighbors may persist above the transition. A qualitative plot of the equilibrium order is given in Fig. 6.33, and long and short range orders are defined below. If an

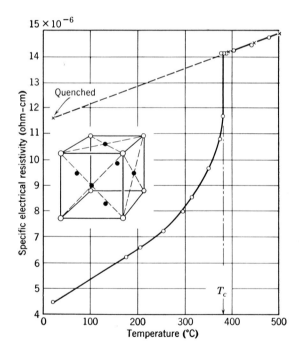

FIG. 6.35. Electrical resistivity versus temperature for Cu_3Au. The alloy was in equilibrium at temperatures above 350°C. (After Nix and Shockley.)

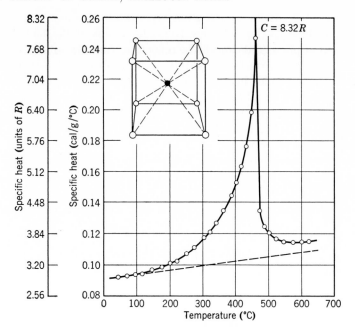

FIG. 6.36. Specific heat versus temperature of CuZn (β-brass) alloy. (After Nix and Shockley.)

alloy is cooled rapidly (quenched) from high temperatures to below the transition temperature, a metastable state may be produced in which a nonequilibrium disorder is "frozen" in the structure. An ordered specimen may be disordered at constant temperature by heavy irradiation with nuclear particles.

The degree of order may be investigated experimentally by several methods, the most powerful being x-ray diffraction (Fig. 6.34). The disordered structure in Fig. 6.32b will have diffraction lines at the same positions as if the lattice points were all occupied by only one type of atom, because the effective scattering power of each plane is equal to the average of the A and B scattering powers. The ordered structure in Fig. 6.32a has extra diffraction lines not possessed by the disordered structure. The extra lines are called superstructure lines, and they characterize the diffraction by the A or B lattices separately. Thus in the ordered CuZn alloy the structure is the cesium chloride structure with atoms on a bcc lattice. This may be thought of as arising from the superposition of two interpenetrating simple cubic lattices, one of copper atoms alone and the other of zinc atoms alone. For example, a bcc lattice of one atom type alone does not have a (100) diffraction line, as the reflection from the atoms at the body centers is 180° out of phase and cancels the reflection from the cube face. This tells us that the form factor $S\{100\}$ = 0, as discussed in Chapter 2. The same result holds in a disordered bcc structure, but in the ordered bcc structure the amplitude of the reflection from the body center will in general differ from the amplitude of the reflection from the cube face; the cancellation now will not be complete, so that we have a (100) superstructure reflection.

The electrical resistivity (Fig. 6.35) is lower in the ordered state than in the disordered state, as expected on the theory of lattice scattering. The heat capacity has an anomaly in the neighborhood of the transition temperature, as shown in Fig. 6.36. The anomaly is associated with the extra internal energy required to disorder the structure. The ferromagnetic properties of alloys may be sensitive to the degree of order; in some cases, as in Ni_3Mn, the disordered alloy is weakly ferromagnetic and the ordered alloy is strongly ferromagnetic.

PROBLEMS

6.1. In an anisotropic crystal the energy may be given in terms of the components of the wave vector by

$$E = \alpha_x k_x{}^2 + \alpha_y k_y{}^2 + \alpha_z k_z{}^2.$$

Find the equations of motion which replace $\mathbf{F} = md^2\mathbf{r}/dt^2$.

6.2. Show that $\omega_c = eH/m^*c$ is the angular frequency of the motion in a magnetic field H of an electron having energy $E_\mathbf{k} = \hbar^2 k^2/2m^*$.

6.3. Derive the form of the first Brillouin zone for a simple cubic lattice.

6.4. Make a plot of the first two Brillouin zones of a primitive rectangular two-dimensional lattice with axes a, $b = 3a$.

6.5. (a) Show for a simple square lattice (two dimensions) that the kinetic energy of a free electron at a corner of the first zone is higher than that of an electron at the midpoint of a side face of the zone by a factor of two.

(b) What is the corresponding factor for a simple cubic lattice (three dimensions)?

(c) What bearing might similar considerations have on the conductivity of divalent metals?

6.6.[1] The cohesion of the alkali metals may be thought of in a *rough* approximation as arising from the Coulomb energy of point positive changes arranged on a bcc lattice and imbedded in a uniform sea of conduction electrons. To a close approximation the Coulomb energy of this model is obtained by calculating the energy of a point charge $+ |e|$ interacting electrostatically with a negative charge $- |e|$ distributed uniformly throughout the volume of the s-sphere. The repulsive part of the energy is given by the electrostatic interaction energy of the electron distribution with itself and also by the kinetic energy of the electron gas.

[1] This problem is fairly long and not elementary; it is also instructive.

(a) Show that the electrostatic energy is $E_c = -9e^2/10r_0$, of which $-3e^2/2r_0$ arises from the interaction of the point charge with the electron distribution and $3e^2/5r_0$ arises from the interaction of the electron distribution with itself.

(b) Show that the average kinetic energy of an electron at 0°K is

$$\bar{E}_0 = \frac{3}{10} \frac{\hbar^2}{m^*} \left(\frac{9\pi}{4}\right)^{2/3} \frac{1}{r_0^2}.$$

(c) The total energy of the system $E = \bar{E}_0 + E_c$ is a function of r_0; minimize E as a function of r_0. Evaluate E and r_0 at equilibrium, taking $m = m^*$, and compare with the observed cohesive energy and lattice parameter of sodium. In making the comparison, add the ionization energy of atomic sodium to the cohesive energy.

(d) Calculate the compressibility.

6.7. Using reference books, give the size factors and limit of solid solution in metal of lower valency for the following alloy systems: Ag-Mg, Ag-Zn, Ag-Al, Cu-Mg, Cu-Al, Cu-Si, Cu-Pb, Cu-Bi.

6.8. Calculate for the composite zone of the ideal hcp structure the electron concentration at which a spherical Fermi surface touches (a) the hexagonal end face; (b) the side face of the first zone at position A in Fig. 6.17.

6.9. Show that, when concentrations N_e of electrons and N_h of holes are present, the Hall coefficient is equal to

$$\frac{1}{ec} \left[\frac{N_e b^2 - N_h}{(N_e b + N_h)^2} \right],$$

where $b = \mu_e/\mu_h$ is the mobility ratio.

6.10. (a) Using Fig. 6.23, estimate the value of the electronic heat capacity of nickel. Compare the result with the observed value.

(b) What value of the average effective mass would describe the estimated value if each atom were supposed for purposes of calculation to contribute 0.6 electron to the band?

6.11. Cu_3Au alloy (75% Cu, 25% Au) has an ordered state below 400°C, in which the gold atoms occupy the 000 positions and the copper atoms the $\frac{1}{2} \frac{1}{2} 0$, $\frac{1}{2} 0 \frac{1}{2}$, and $0 \frac{1}{2} \frac{1}{2}$ positions in a face-centered cubic lattice. Give the indices of the new x-ray reflections which appear when the alloy goes from the disordered to the ordered state. List all new reflections with indices $\leqq 3$. Can you give a general rule for the indices of the additional reflections?

REFERENCES

All the references cited at the end of Chapter 5 are relevant to this chapter; the following references apply to electrical conductivity:

J. Bardeen, "Electrical conductivity of metals," *J. Appl. Phys.* **11**, 88 (1940).

E. Justi, *Leitfähigkeit und Leitungsmechanismus fester Stoffe*, Vandenhoek, Göttingen, 1948.

D. K. C. MacDonald, "Properties of metals at low temperatures," *Progress in Metal Physics*, **3**, 42–57 (1952).

D. K. C. MacDonald and K. Sarginson, "Galvanomagnetic effects in conductors," *Repts. Prog. Phys.* **15**, 249–274 (1952).

R. E. Peierls, *Quantum theory of solids*, Clarendon Press, Oxford, 1955.

W. Shockley, *Electrons and holes in semiconductors*, Van Nostrand, Princeton, New Jersey, 1950.

V. F. Weisskopf, "On the theory of the electric resistance of metals," *Am. J. Phys.* **11**, 1 (1943).

The following references relate to the theory of alloys:

J. Friedel, "Electronic structure of primary solid solutions in metals," *Advances in Physics* **3**, 446 (1954).

W. Hume-Rothery, *Electrons, atoms, metals and alloys*, Iliffe, London, 1955.

W. Hume-Rothery, *Structure of metals and alloys*, Institute of Metals, London, 1947.

W. Hume-Rothery and B. R. Coles, "Transition metals and their alloys," *Advances in Physics* **3**, 149–243 (1954).

M. A. Jaswon, *Theory of cohesion*, Pergamon Press, London, 1954.

N. F. Mott, "Recent advances in the electron theory of metals," *Prog. in Metal Phys.* **3**, 76–114 (1952).

L. Pauling, *Nature of the chemical bond*, Cornell University Press, Ithaca, 1945, Chapter XI.

G. V. Raynor, *Introduction to the electron theory of metals*, Institute of Metals, London, 1949.

G. V. Raynor, "Progress in the theory of alloys," *Progr. in Metal Phys.* **1**, 1–76 (1949).

G. V. Raynor, "The band structure of metals," *Repts. Prog. Phys.* **15**, 173–248 (1952).

7 Semiconductors: physics and devices

Semiconductors are electronic conductors with values of the electrical resistivity at room temperature generally in the range $\sim 10^{-2}$ to $\sim 10^9$ ohm-cm, intermediate between good conductors ($\sim 10^{-6}$ ohm-cm) and insulators ($\sim 10^{14}$ to $\sim 10^{22}$ ohm-cm). At absolute zero a pure and perfect crystal of most semiconductors would behave as an insulator; the characteristic semiconducting properties are usually brought about by thermal agitation, impurities, or lattice defects. Many devices of wide industrial application are based on the properties of semiconductors: they include rectifiers, modulators, detectors, thermistors, photocells, and transistors. We discuss in this chapter the central physical features of semiconductor crystals and the principles of rectification and transistor action. We concern ourselves primarily with the properties of silicon and germanium, as their properties are perhaps generally the best understood at present. Other important semiconducting substances include cuprous oxide, Cu_2O; selenium; lead telluride, $PbTe$; lead sulfide, PbS; silicon carbide, SiC; and indium antimonide, $InAs$.

INTRINSIC CONDUCTIVITY

Except at low temperatures a highly purified semiconductor often exhibits *intrinsic conductivity*, as distinguished from the *impurity conductivity* of less pure specimens. We shall speak of the *intrinsic temperature range* as the temperature range in which the electrical properties of a semiconductor are not essentially modified by impurities in the crystal. The character of the electronic band scheme leading to intrinsic conductivity is given in Fig. 7.1. At absolute zero we postulate a vacant conduction band, separated by an energy gap E_g from a filled valence band. As the temperature is increased, electrons are thermally excited from the valence band to the conduction

199

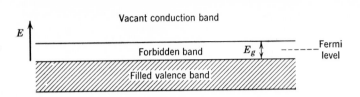

FIG. 7.1.   Band scheme for intrinsic conductivity.   At 0°K the conductivity is zero, all states in the valence band being filled and all states in the conduction band being vacant.   As the temperature is increased, the conductivity increases because electrons are thermally excited up to the conduction band, where they become mobile.

band.   Both the electrons in the conduction band and the vacant states or holes left behind in the valence band will contribute to the electrical conductivity, as shown in Fig. 7.2.   At temperatures below the intrinsic range the electrical properties are controlled by impurities, and here we speak of impurity conductivity or extrinsic conductivity.

To calculate the intrinsic conductivity at temperature T we must find the equilibrium concentration n_e of electrons in the conduction band, which under intrinsic conditions is equal to the equilibrium concentration n_h of holes in the valence band.   We also must know the mobilities (drift velocity/electric field) μ_e for electrons and μ_h for holes.   The conductivity is then given, according to the earlier definitions, by

$$(7.1) \qquad \sigma = |e|(n_e\mu_e + n_h\mu_h).$$

By convention the mobilities of both electrons and holes are taken to be positive, we must remember that the drift velocities are actually opposite, as in Fig. 7.2.

We may anticipate a temperature dependence of the form $e^{-E/kT}$ for the concentration of electrons in the conduction band, and, as it is unlikely that the mobility will depend on temperature in as strong a fashion, we may expect that the intrinsic conductivity may vary as $e^{-E/kT}$, or the resistivity

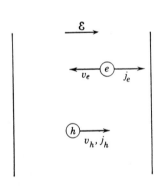

FIG. 7.2.   Motion of electrons (e) and holes (h) in an electric field $\mathcal{E}$; the directions of the velocity (v) and current (j) flows are shown.

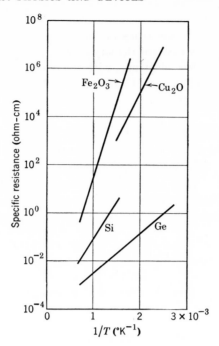

FIG. 7.3.   Plot of log ρ versus $1/T$ for several semiconductors in the intrinsic
range.   (After J. A. Becker.)

ρ as $e^{E/kT}$.   It will turn out that E should be taken as $E_g/2$, where E_g
is the energy gap between bands.   If

(7.2) $$\rho = Ae^{E_g/2kT},$$

then

(7.3) $$\log \rho = \log A + \frac{E_g}{2kT},$$

so that in the intrinsic range log ρ should be approximately a linear
function of $1/T$.   This is observed experimentally, as shown in Fig. 7.3.

We now calculate in terms of the Fermi energy E_F the number of
electrons excited to the conduction band at temperature T.   In semiconductor physics E_F is called the *Fermi level*, or the chemical potential.
We measure the energy E from the top of the valence band, as in Fig.
7.1.   At low temperatures we may suppose $E - E_F \gg kT$, so that the
Fermi-Dirac distribution function reduces to

(7.4) $$f \cong e^{(E_F - E)/kT}.$$

This is the probability that a conduction electron state is occupied. If we suppose that the electrons in the conduction band behave as if they are free, we may take the density of states in the conduction band as equal to that for free electrons, with the energy referred to the bottom of the band. Thus, from (5.48), the number of states with energy between E and $E + dE$ is

$$(7.5) \qquad g_e(E) \, dE = \frac{1}{2\pi^2} \left(\frac{2m_e}{\hbar^2} \right)^{3/2} (E - E_g)^{1/2} \, dE$$

per unit volume, where m_e is the effective mass of an electron in the conduction band. Here all energies are measured relative to the top of the valence band. Combining (7.4) and (7.5), we have for the number of electrons per unit volume in the conduction band

$$(7.6) \qquad N_e = \int_{E_g}^{\infty} g_e(E) f_e(E) \, dE$$

$$= \frac{1}{2\pi^2} \left(\frac{2m_e}{\hbar^2} \right)^{3/2} e^{E_F/kT} \int_{E_g}^{\infty} (E - E_g)^{1/2} e^{-E/kT} \, dE$$

which integrates to

$$(7.7) \qquad N_e = 2 \left(\frac{2\pi m_e kT}{\hbar^2} \right)^{3/2} e^{(E_F - E_g)/kT}.$$

In problems of this character the determination of the Fermi level may sometimes be difficult, but we have not solved the problem until E_F is known. In this instance it is useful to calculate the equilibrium concentration of holes N_h. The distribution function f_h for holes is related to the electron distribution function f_e by

$$(7.8) \qquad f_h = 1 - f_e,$$

because a hole is the absence of an electron. We have

$$(7.9) \quad f_h = 1 - \frac{1}{e^{(E-E_F)/kT} + 1} = \frac{1}{e^{(E_F-E)/kT} + 1} \cong e^{(E-E_F)/kT},$$

if $(E_F - E) \gg kT$. If we suppose that the holes near the top of the valence band behave as free particles with effective mass m_h, the density of hole states is given by

$$(7.10) \qquad g_h(E) \, dE = \frac{1}{2\pi^2} \left(\frac{2m_h}{\hbar^2} \right)^{3/2} (-E)^{1/2} \, dE,$$

recalling that the energy is measured positive upwards from the top of the valence band. Proceeding as before, we find

$$(7.11) \qquad N_h = \int_{-\infty}^{0} g_h(E)f_h(E) \, dE = 2 \left(\frac{2\pi m_h kT}{h^2}\right)^{3/2} e^{-E_F/kT}$$

for the concentration of holes in the valence band.

On multiplying together the expressions for N_e and N_h we have the useful equilibrium relation

$$(7.12) \qquad N_e N_h = np = 4 \left(\frac{2\pi kT}{h^2}\right)^{3} (m_e m_h)^{3/2} e^{-E_g/kT}.$$

Here we have introduced the notation $n \equiv N_e$; $p \equiv N_h$, in conformity with current practice in the field.

We note the important fact from (7.12) that the product of the electron and hole concentrations is a constant in a given material at a given temperature: introducing an impurity to increase n, say, must decrease p, as the product must remain constant. This result is important in practice—we can reduce the total carrier concentration, sometimes enormously, by the deliberate introduction of suitable impurities. The only assumption made is that the distance of the Fermi level E_F from the edge of both bands should be large in comparison with kT.

For an intrinsic semiconductor $n = p$, as the thermal excitation of an electron from the valence band leaves behind a hole. Thus from (7.12) we have, letting the subscript i denote intrinsic,

$$(7.13) \qquad n_i = p_i = 2 \left(\frac{2\pi kT}{h^2}\right)^{3/2} (m_e m_h)^{3/4} e^{-E_g/2kT},$$

showing that the excitation depends exponentially on $E_g/2kT$, where E_g is the width of the forbidden gap. On setting (7.7) and (7.11) equal we have

$$(7.14) \qquad e^{2E_F/kT} = \left(\frac{m_h}{m_e}\right)^{3/2} e^{E_g/kT},$$

or

$$(7.15) \qquad E_F = \tfrac{1}{2}E_g + \tfrac{3}{4}kT \log \frac{m_h}{m_e}.$$

If $m_h = m_e$, $E_F = \tfrac{1}{2}E_g$; that is, the Fermi level is in the middle of the forbidden gap.

From (7.1) and (7.13) the electrical conductivity in the intrinsic region will be

$$(7.16) \qquad \sigma_i = 2|e| \left(\frac{2\pi kT}{h^2}\right)^{3/2} (m_e m_h)^{3/4} e^{-E_g/2kT}(\mu_e + \mu_h).$$

TABLE 7.1

VALUES OF THE ENERGY GAP BETWEEN THE VALENCE AND CONDUCTION
BANDS IN SEMICONDUCTORS, AT ROOM TEMPERATURE

Crystal	E_g(ev)	Crystal	E_g(ev)
Diamond	6	ZnSb	0.56
Si	1.10	GaSb	0.78
Ge	0.68–0.72	PbS	0.34–0.37
Sn (gray)	0.08	PbSe	0.27
InSb	0.18	PbTe	0.30
InAs	0.33	CdS	2.42
InP	1.25	CdSe	1.74
GaAs	1.4	CdTe	1.45
AlSb	1.6–1.7	ZnSe	2.60
InSe	(1)	AgI	2.8
GaP	2.25	Ag_2Te	0.17
α-Mg_3Sb_2	0.82	Cu_2O	2.1
Ca_2Si	0.9	Mg_2Si	0.7
Ca_2Sn	0.9	Mg_2Ge	0.7
Ca_2Pb	0.46	Mg_2Sn	0.3

As the mobilities are likely to depend on temperature only as a simple power law over an appropriate region, the temperature dependence of the conductivity will be dominated by the exponential dependence of the carrier concentration. Values of the energy gap determined for a number of substances are given in Table 7.1. Many of the values were determined from the slope of plots of log σ versus $1/T$; some of the other values were determined from the long wavelength limit of the optical absorption arising from the promotion of an electron from the valence band to the conduction band, accompanied by the absorption of a photon. If for the photon $h\nu \geq E_g$, strong optical absorption may occur; if the photon energy is less then the gap energy the absorption is usually much weaker.

MOBILITY IN THE INTRINSIC REGION

The mobility μ is defined as the drift velocity per unit electric field. In an ideal intrinsic semiconductor the mobility is determined by lattice scattering; that is, by collisions between lattice waves and electron waves. In actual intrinsic specimens there are always some impurity atoms that may dominate the scattering of electrons at low temperatures when the lattice waves are quiescent, but at higher temperatures the lattice scattering is dominant.

Experimental values of the mobility at room temperature are given in Table 7.2. By comparison, the mobility in metallic copper is 35 cm^2/volt-sec at room temperature. In most substances quoted the values are probably representative of lattice scattering. We notice a tendency for crystals with small energy gaps (Table 7.1) to have high values of the electron mobility. This is because small gaps imply small effective masses, which theory suggests should favor high mobilities. The low mobilities generally characteristic of holes in diatomic crystals are believed to be connected with the complex degenerate forms of the energy surfaces in such crystals at the top of the valence band.

IMPURITY OR EXTRINSIC CONDUCTIVITY

Certain types of impurities and imperfections may affect drastically the electrical properties of a semiconductor. For example, the addition of boron to silicon in the proportion of 1 boron atom to 10^5 silicon atoms increases the conductivity of pure silicon by a factor of 10^3 at room temperature. In a compound semiconductor a stoichiometric deficiency of one constituent will act as an impurity; thus semiconductors such as copper oxide or zinc oxide are known as *deficit* semiconductors.

We consider in particular the effect of impurities in silicon and ger-

TABLE 7.2
CARRIER MOBILITIES AT ROOM TEMPERATURE
(Most of the values are probably determined by lattice scattering)

Mobility (cm^2/volt-sec)

Crystal	Electrons	Holes
Diamond	1,800	1200
Si	1,600	400
Ge	3,800	1800
InSb	77,000	1250
InAs	23,000	~100
InP	3,400	650
GaSb	2,500–4,000	650
PbS	600	200
PbSe	900	700
PbTe	17,000	. . . . .
AgCl	50	. . . . .

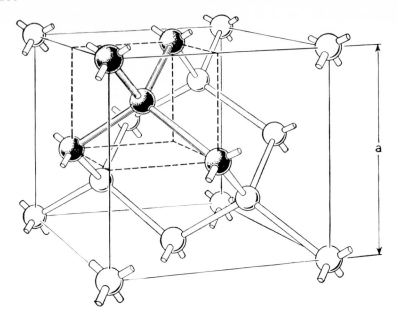

FIG. 7.4.   Crystal structure of diamond, showing the tetrahedral bond arrangement.   Germanium, silicon, and gray tin have the same structure.   Many diatomic semiconductors have the zinc blende (ZnS) structure which may be derived from the diamond structure by decomposing the latter into two fcc lattices, the cations (Zn) populating one fcc lattice and the anions (S) populating the other. (After W. Shockley, *Electrons and holes in semiconductors*.   Copyright 1950. Van Nostrand.)

manium.   These elements crystallize in the diamond structure as shown in Fig. 7.4 with each atom forming four covalent bonds, one with each of its four nearest neighbors, corresponding to the chemical valence four.   The bonds make tetrahedral angles, similar to the arrangement of C-H bonds in methane, CH_4.   If now an impurity atom of valence five, such as phosphorus, arsenic, or antimony, is substituted in the lattice in place of a normal atom, there will be one valence electron from the impurity atom left over after the four covalent bonds are established with the nearest neighbors, that is, after the impurity atom has been accommodated in the structure with as little disturbance as possible.   The situation as shown in Fig. 7.5 is that we have in the structure an excess positive charge from the impurity atom which has lost one electron, and we have also the excess electron.   It is verified by lattice constant studies and by determining the density of carriers that the pentavalent impurities enter the lattice by substitution for normal atoms, rather than by going into interstitial positions. Impurity atoms which may be ionized to give up an electron are called *donors*.

The excess electron moves in the Coulomb potential $e/\epsilon r$ of the impurity ion, where ϵ is the dielectric constant of the medium. The factor $1/\epsilon$ takes account of the reduction in the Coulomb force between charges caused by the electronic polarization of the medium. This treatment is valid for orbits large in comparison with the distance between atoms, and for slow motions of the electron such that the

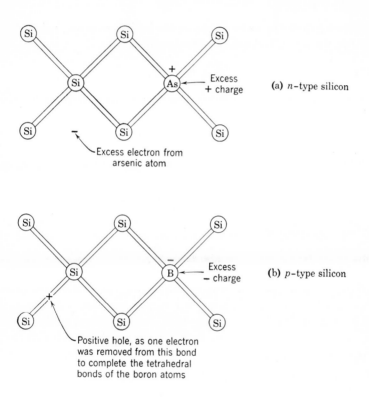

(a) *n*-type silicon

(b) *p*-type silicon

FIG. 7.5. Charges associated with impurity atom in silicon; (a) with arsenic impurity an electron is available for conduction; (b) with boron impurity a positive hole is available. The type designation is *n* for negative carriers and *p* for positive carriers or holes. The arsenic atom is called a *donor* atom because on becoming ionized it gives up an electron to the conduction band. The boron atom is called an *acceptor* atom because on becoming ionized it takes up an electron from the valence band; that is, the ionization of the hole associated with the acceptor corresponds to the addition of an electron to the acceptor, the hole moving to the former state of the valence electron.

208 ELEMENTARY SOLID STATE PHYSICS: A SHORT COURSE

time required to pass an atom is long in comparison with the period of the motion of the inner bound electrons of the atom, conditions satisfied by the extra electron of P, As, Sb, in Ge or Si.

We wish now to estimate the binding energy of the donor impurity. The Bohr theory of the hydrogen atom may readily be modified to take into account both the dielectric constant of the medium and the effective mass of an electron in the periodic potential of the crystal. Formally, we need only replace e^2 by e^2/ϵ and by m^* in the standard results.

IMPURITY STATES

Let us consider the Bohr model of the hydrogen atom, using the old quantum theory. The quantization condition is

$$(7.17) \qquad \oint p \, dq = nh,$$

where n is the principal quantum number; we have thus for a circular orbit

$$(7.18) \qquad (m^*r^2\omega)(2\pi) = nh.$$

The total energy is the sum of the potential and kinetic energies

$$(7.19) \qquad E = -\frac{e^2}{\epsilon r} + \frac{1}{2} m^*r^2\omega^2.$$

The force equation is

$$(7.20) \qquad m^*\omega^2 r = \frac{e^2}{\epsilon r^2},$$

and so the substitution of ω^2 from (7.18) gives

$$(7.21) \qquad r = \frac{\epsilon n^2\hbar^2}{e^2 m^*}$$

for the orbital radius.

Substitution of (7.20) in (7.19) gives

$$(7.22) \qquad E = -\frac{e^2}{2\epsilon r}.$$

Eliminating r with the help of (13.23) we have for the energy

$$(7.23) \qquad E = -\frac{e^4 m^*}{2\epsilon^2\hbar^2 n^2}.$$

These results for E and r are in accord with the prescription stated previously. They are just the Bohr results with m^* written for m, and e^2/ϵ written for e^2.

The application of these formulas to germanium and silicon is complicated by the anisotropic effective mass of the conduction electrons in these crystals, as discussed in a following section under the subject of cyclotron resonance. However, the dielectric constant enters the energy (7.23) as the square, whereas the effective mass enters only as the first power. We may obtain a general impression of the impurity levels by using an average value of the anisotropic effective masses: we shall use $m^* \approx 0.12m$ for electrons in germanium and $m^* \approx 0.25m$ for electrons in silicon. The dielectric constant has the value 15.8 for germanium and 11.7 for silicon; the values apply with fair accuracy from low frequencies up to the frequencies corresponding to the energy gap, so that the values should be applicable to the present problem where the orbital frequencies involved are very much less than the frequency corresponding to the gap.

The ionization potential of the free hydrogen atom is 13.6 ev, corresponding to the use of (7.23) with $\epsilon = 1$; $m^* = m$; $n = 1$. For germanium the ionization potential on the present model should be reduced with respect to hydrogen by the factor $m^*/m\epsilon^2 = 0.12/250 = 4.8 \times 10^{-4}$, giving $(13.6)(4.8 \times 10^{-4}) = 0.0065$ ev, while the corresponding result for silicon is 0.025 ev. Calculations[1] using the correct anisotropic mass tensor give 0.00905 ev for germanium and 0.0298 ev for silicon. Further corrections for silicon have been considered by Luttinger and Kohn. Observed values of the donor ionization energies for pentavalent impurities in germanium and silicon are given in Table 7.3. The values are obtained largely by thermal considerations to be

TABLE 7.3

DONOR IONIZATION ENERGIES OF PENTAVALENT IMPURITIES IN
GERMANIUM AND SILICON, IN EV

	P	As	Sb
Si	0.045	0.049–0.056	0.039
Ge	0.0120	0.0127	0.0096

described; some of the values have also been obtained by direct optical absorption.

We note that the radius of the first Bohr orbit is increased by the factor $\epsilon m/m^*$ over the value 0.53 A for the free hydrogen atom.

[1] J. M. Luttinger and W. Kohn, *Phys. Rev.* **98**, 915 (1955); M. Lampert, *Phys. Rev.* **97**, 352 (1955); C. Kittel and A. H. Mitchell, *Phys. Rev.* **96**, 1488 (1954).

TABLE 7.4
ACCEPTOR IONIZATION ENERGIES OF TRIVALENT IMPURITIES IN
GERMANIUM AND SILICON, IN EV

	B	Al	Ga	In
Si	0.045	0.057–0.067	0.065–0.071	0.16
Ge	0.0104	0.0102	0.0108	0.0112

The corresponding radius is $(132)(0.53) = 70$ A in germanium and $(47)(0.53) = 25$ A in silicon.

Just as an electron may be bound to a pentavalent impurity, a hole may be bound to a trivalent impurity in germanium or silicon. The two situations are compared in Fig. 7.5. Typical trivalent impurities are B, Al, Ga, and In; such impurities are called *acceptors*, because they can take up electrons from the valence band, leaving holes in the band. The acceptor problem is similar in principle to that for electrons, although the initial strain of visualization on the reader is greater. Experimental values of the ionization energies of acceptors in germanium and silicon are given in Table 7.4. It is seen that the ionization energies for acceptors are not unlike those for donors. The equivalent Bohr model carries over in principle for holes just as for electrons, except that in germanium and silicon there is, as we shall see, an orbital degeneracy at the top of the valence band which complicates the theoretical problem enormously.

A glance at Tables 7.3 and 7.4 shows that the donor and acceptor ionization energies may be comparable with kT at room temperature (0.026 ev). We expect then to find the thermal ionization of donor and acceptor impurity atoms to be important in the electrical conductivity of germanium and silicon at room temperature. If donor atoms are present in considerably greater numbers than acceptors, the thermal ionization of donors will cause electrons to be freed in the conduction band. The conductivity of the specimen will be controlled by electrons (negative charges) and the material is said to be *n*-type. If acceptors are dominant, holes will be freed in the valence band and the conductivity of the specimen will be controlled by holes (positive charges): the material is then said to be *p*-type. We recall that in the absence of impurities the numbers of holes and electrons are equal and the material is described as intrinsic. The intrinsic electron concentration n_i at 300°K is 2.5×10^{13} cm^{-3} in germanium and 1.4×10^{10} cm^{-3} in silicon; the electrical resistivity of intrinsic material is 43 ohm-cm for germanium and 2.6×10^5 ohm-cm for sili-

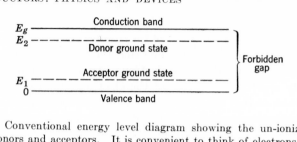

FIG. 7.6. Conventional energy level diagram showing the un-ionized ground states of donors and acceptors. It is convenient to think of electrons as tending to sink and holes as tending to float. The donor ionization energy is $E_g - E_2$; the acceptor ionization energy is E_1.

con. As the lowest impurity concentrations attained at present are of the order of 10^{12} impurity atoms per cubic centimeter, it is evident we may expect to be able to work with germanium intrinsic at room temperature, but not with silicon intrinsic at room temperature. Impurities with no effect on the carrier concentration are probably present in higher proportions.

THERMAL IONIZATION OF IMPURITIES

We now consider the important statistical problem of determining the concentration of ionized donors and acceptors in thermal equilibrium at a temperature T. The energy level diagram is shown in Fig. 7.6, the energies being measured upward from the top of the valence band. We let N_d, N_a denote the concentrations of donor and acceptor atoms, respectively; $N_d{}^0$, $N_a{}^0$ the concentration of neutral (un-ionized) donors and acceptors; $N_d{}^+$, $N_a{}^-$ the concentration of ionized donors and acceptors. Recalling that the Fermi distribution function tells us the fractional occupation by an *electron* of a state at a given energy, we have

$$(7.24) \qquad N_d{}^0 = \frac{N_d}{1 + e^{(E_2 - E_F)/kT}};$$

$$(7.25) \qquad N_d{}^+ = N_d - N_d{}^0 = \frac{N_d}{1 + e^{-(E_2 - E_F)/kT}};$$

$$(7.26) \qquad N_a{}^- = \frac{N_a}{1 + e^{(E_1 - E_F)/kT}}.$$

We introduce the notation

$$(7.27) \qquad n_0 = 2\left(\frac{2\pi m_e kT}{h^2}\right)^{3/2}; \qquad p_0 = 2\left(\frac{2\pi m_h kT}{h^2}\right)^{3/2}.$$

In writing (7.24) we have omitted in the interest of simplicity a factor $\frac{1}{2}$ which is often seen in front of the exponential.   The factor arises when one takes into account the fact that the energy of a spin-degenerate donor level occupied by two electrons, one of each spin orientation, is probably quite high because of the electrostatic interaction of the two electrons, so that the level is usually occupied by at most one electron.   The consequences of our simplification are not serious.

We require electrical neutrality of the system as a whole.   The statement that the number of positive charges must equal the number of negative charges is expressed by the equation

$$(7.28) \qquad p + N_d{}^+ = n + N_a{}^-,$$

where, as before, n and p are the concentrations of electrons in the conduction band and holes in the valence band, respectively.   Using (7.7) and (7.11),

$$(7.29) \quad p_0 e^{-E_F/kT} + \frac{N_d}{1 + e^{-(E_2 - E_F)kT}} = n_0 e^{(E_F - E_g)/kT} + \frac{N_a}{1 + e^{(E_1 - E_F)/kT}}.$$

We now treat the special case of $N_a = 0$; that is, no acceptors are present.   It is convenient to assume further that there are sufficient number of donors present to give enough conduction electrons to suppress p, the hole concentration, to a value much below the intrinsic value (7.13).   The suppression occurs because formula (7.12), which is essentially an expression of the law of mass action, requires the product np to be constant; thus, if n is increased by a certain factor, p is decreased by the reciprocal factor.   Neglecting p is equivalent to saying that

$$(7.30) \qquad e^{(E_F - E_g)/kT} \gg e^{-E_F/kT}.$$

Then (7.29) reduces to

$$(7.31) \qquad \frac{N_d}{1 + e^{-(E_2 - E_F)/kT}} = n_0 e^{(E_F - E_g)/kT}.$$

This may be written as

$$e^{2E_F/kT}[n_0 e^{-(E_2 + E_g)/kT}] + e^{E_F/kT}[n_0 e^{-E_g/kT}] - N_d = 0,$$

and so the Fermi energy is determined by

$$(7.32) \qquad e^{E_F/kT} = \frac{\{-1 + [1 + 4(N_d/n_0)e^{(E_g - E_2)/kT}]^{1/2}\}}{2e^{-E_2/kT}}.$$

We evaluate E_F in two limiting situations. First, we suppose

$$(7.33) \qquad 4 \frac{N_d}{n_0} e^{(E_g - E_2)/kT} \ll 1,$$

corresponding to small N_d or high T. Then

$$e^{E_F/kT} \cong \frac{N_d}{n_0} e^{E_g/kT},$$

and

$$(7.34) \qquad E_F \cong E_g + kT \ln \frac{N_d}{n_0}.$$

and so

$$(7.35) \qquad n = n_0 e^{(E_F - E_g)/kT} \cong N_d,$$

which means that the number of conduction electrons is approximately equal to the number of donors under the foregoing conditions.

In a second limit we suppose

$$(7.36) \qquad 4 \frac{N_d}{n_0} e^{(E_g - E_2)/kT} \gg 1,$$

corresponding to large N_d or low T. Now

$$(7.37) \qquad e^{E_F/kT} \cong \left(\frac{N_d}{n_0} \right)^{1/2} e^{(E_g + E_2)/2kT},$$

giving

$$(7.38) \qquad n = (2N_d)^{1/2} \left(\frac{2\pi kT m_e}{h^2} \right)^{3/4} e^{-E_d/2kT},$$

defining $E_d = E_g - E_2$ as the donor ionization energy. In this limit the electron concentration varies as the square root of the donor concentration. At low temperatures, however, there are usually fewer conduction electrons than there are acceptor atoms present as an unavoidable impurity. A number of donor atoms are ionized in filling up the acceptors, and this process tends to pin down the Fermi level at E_2, rather than as given by (7.37). In this situation n varies as $\exp(-E_d/kT)$ and not as $\exp(-E_d/2kT)$. Identical results hold for acceptors, appropriate changes being made, under the assumption $N_d = 0$. If the donor and acceptor concentrations are of comparable orders of magnitude, affairs are quite complicated, and one usually has to solve (7.29) by graphical methods.

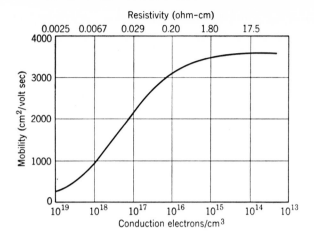

FIG. 7.7.   Calculated curves of mobility versus carrier density and resistivity for n-type germanium at 300°K.   It is assumed that all the donor atoms are ionized and that there are no acceptors.   (After Conwell.)

MOBILITY IN THE PRESENCE OF IMPURITY ATOMS

When relatively few impurity atoms are present, or at high temperatures, lattice scattering will determine the mobility.   At higher impurity concentrations, electron scattering by impurity atoms may be important.   The scattering will depend on whether the impurity is neutral or ionized.   The neutral atom problem is equivalent to the scattering of an electron by a hydrogen atom, but with the dielectric constant correction.   We note that the area of the first Bohr orbit is increased by $(\epsilon m/m^*)^2$, or $(47)^2$ in silicon.   An exact solution for the scattering cross section is quite difficult in the energy range of interest in semiconductors.

The scattering by ionized donors or acceptors has been solved by Conwell and Weisskopf, who utilized the Rutherford scattering formula.   The effect of ionized impurity scattering in reducing the mobility is shown in Fig. 7.7.

ANALYSIS OF EXPERIMENTAL RESULTS

A good general picture of the physical behavior of a semiconductor can be obtained by measuring the electrical conductivity and Hall coefficient as functions of temperature and impurity doping over wide ranges.   We discuss here results obtained by Conwell and Debye[2] on

[2] E. M. Conwell, *Proc. I.R.E.* **40**, 1327 (1952); P. P. Debye and E. M. Conwell, *Phys. Rev.* **93**, 693 (1954).

n-type germanium. These results will convey an impression of the kind of information which can be obtained from a systematic analysis of conductivity and Hall data.

We have seen (Chapter 6) that in a simple metal the Hall coefficient is given by

$$(7.39) \qquad R_H = -\frac{1}{N|e|c},$$

where N is the electron concentration. In semiconductors we often deal with a Maxwellian distribution of velocities, and the connection between R_H and N may vary slightly from (7.39) by a factor close to unity according to the form of the dependence of the mean free path on velocity. Results on carrier concentration deduced from measurements of the Hall voltage for the carrier density versus temperature for a set of germanium crystals doped with arsenic donors are shown in Fig. 7.8. It is seen that for temperatures between liquid air and room temperature the donors are essentially all ionized. Thus crystal 55 has 8×10^{12} excess donors per cm^3, whereas crystal 54 has 7×10^{15} excess donors per cubic centimeter. A little above room temperature crystal 55 becomes intrinsic, and the carrier concentration rises sharply. Below 20 to 50°K the carrier concentration decreases as the donors become un-ionized. From the slope of the plot we estimate the ionization energy to be $\sim$0.01 ev. In crystal 58 the donor concentration ($\sim 10^{18}$ cm^{-3}) is sufficiently high so that neighboring donor states overlap appreciably and the donor ionization energy has apparently vanished: the carrier concentration is independent of temperature.

The temperature dependence of the electrical conductivity of the same set of crystals is shown in Fig. 7.9. The decrease at low temperatures is caused by the decrease in the concentration of conduction electrons. The decrease on going from 78 to 300°K is caused by increased lattice scattering. The sudden increase above 300°K for crystal 55 is caused by the onset of intrinsic conductivity. The slope of the intrinsic region leads to the value 0.7 ev for the energy gap of germanium.

If the current carriers are predominantly of one type only, we may obtain the mobility simply from the product of the conductivity and the Hall coefficient

$$(7.40) \qquad cR_H\sigma = c\left(\frac{1}{N|e|c}\right)\left(\frac{Ne^2\tau}{m^*}\right) = \frac{e\tau}{m^*} = \mu,$$

apart from factors of the order of unity. The temperature dependence

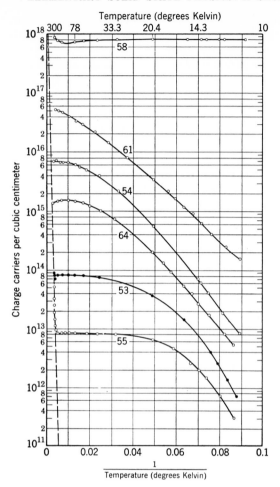

FIG. 7.8. Density of charge carriers versus the reciprocal of absolute temperature for a set of arsenic-doped germanium crystals. The data were taken by Debye. The numbers identify particular samples. The dashed line represents the density of intrinsic carriers. (After Conwell.)

of the mobility as obtained in this way for the set of arsenic-doped germanium crystals is shown in Fig. 7.10. The temperature dependence of the mobility in the purest crystal (55) follows approximately the $T^{-3/2}$ law predicted by the simple theory. For crystal 61 one sees a decrease in mobility at low temperatures thought to be characteristic of scattering by ionized impurity atoms.

LIFETIME AND RECOMBINATION

It is possible in semiconductors to obtain departures from the thermal equilibrium concentrations of electrons and holes in several ways: by injecting carriers into the sample through a metal contact or by the creation of electron-hole pairs by light or by charged particle bombardment. Once disturbed, the system tends to return to equilibrium by recombination of the excess electrons and holes. The recombination rate can be observed by measuring the time variation of the conduct-

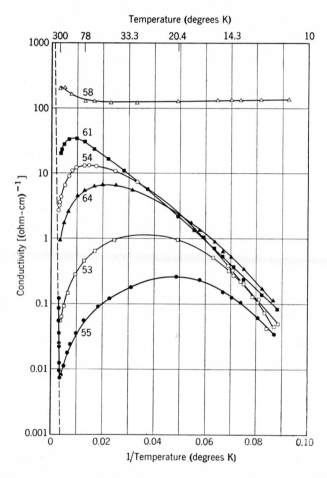

FIG. 7.9. Conductivity versus absolute temperature for the same set of arsenic-doped germanium crystals. The data were taken by Debye. The dashed line represents intrinsic conductivity. (After Conwell.)

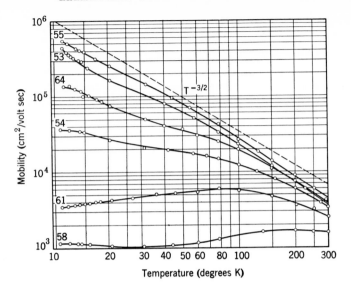

FIG. 7.10.   Mobility versus temperature for the same set of arsenic-doped germanium crystals.   The data were taken by Debye.   The dashed line represents a $-\frac{3}{2}$ slope characteristic of lattice scattering.   (After Conwell.)

ance of the specimen after excitation or by detecting the drift in an electric field of excess carriers produced at one point and detected at another point.

In the simplest case excess electrons and holes are produced in equal numbers and they recombine both at the same rate.   Letting

Δn = excess electron concentration above value at thermal equilibrium;

Δp = excess hole concentration above value at thermal equilibrium;

we have by assumption $\Delta n = \Delta p$.   At small concentrations of excess carriers the decay is usually exponential and characterized by a constant lifetime τ.[3]   We have then

$$(7.41) \qquad \frac{dn}{dt} = -\frac{1}{\tau}\,\Delta n; \qquad \frac{dp}{dt} = -\frac{1}{\tau}\,\Delta p.$$

In practice it is often found that the decay of excess minority carrier concentration proceeds at different rates in n- and p-type material;

[3] It is standard practice, however unfortunate, that the same symbol τ should denote both relaxation time and lifetime.

thus we deal with a lifetime τ_n for excess electrons in p-type material and a lifetime τ_p for excess holes in n-type material.

The recombination mechanisms are still obscure, but it is known that direct radiative recombination of an electron and a hole with emission of a photon is relatively improbable in germanium and silicon. Shockley has calculated minority carrier lifetimes of the order of 1 sec for the radiative process in germanium at room temperature; over-all observed lifetimes are reported to be of the order of 0.01 sec in unusually pure germanium crystals, and are more typically of the order of 100 μsec in commercial material. The emission of radiation accompanying minority carrier injection has been observed experimentally.

It has been found that recombination occurs both in the volume and on the surface of the crystal. The observed lifetime τ is composed of separate lifetimes for volume τ_v and surface τ_s recombination:

$$(7.42) \qquad \frac{1}{\tau} = \frac{1}{\tau_v} + \frac{1}{\tau_s}.$$

The two contributions are usually distinguished by measurements on filaments of varying dimensions and surface treatment. Both lifetimes may vary from crystal to crystal and also vary with temperature. The volume lifetime τ_v is particularly sensitive to small amounts of copper, iron, and nickel: a nickel contamination of 10^{12} atoms/cm^3 may shorten the lifetime observably. The volume lifetime is also sensitive to lattice imperfections: quenching from an elevated temperature, plastic flow, and radiation damage have all been observed to reduce the lifetime drastically, in some instances to under 1 μsec.

The lifetime for surface recombination τ_s is particularly sensitive to the mechanical and chemical treatment of the surface. Because the carriers must diffuse to the surface before they can recombine there, the surface lifetime depends on the dimensions of the specimen. It is useful to deal with the surface velocity of recombination as this quantity does not depend on the specimen dimensions. The surface velocity of recombination s is defined by

$s =$ (recombination rate per unit area)/(excess concentration just
below the surface).

Values of s have been reported for germanium at room temperature between about 15 cm/sec and 10,000 cm/sec. The highest surface recombination velocities are found for sandblasted surfaces; the lowest velocities are found for surfaces polished smooth and then etched with empirical solutions. A certain amount of magic is thought to be involved in a good etch.

Shockley has derived equations relating τ_s, s, and the cross-section dimensions for long rods of rectangular cross section $2B \times 2C$. He finds

$$(7.43) \qquad (s \to \infty) \qquad \frac{1}{\tau_s} = \frac{\pi^2 D}{4}\left(\frac{1}{B^2} + \frac{1}{C^2}\right);$$

$$(7.44) \qquad (s \to 0) \qquad \frac{1}{\tau_s} = s\left(\frac{1}{B} + \frac{1}{C}\right).$$

The first limit means that surface recombination is dominant; the second limit means that volume recombination is dominant. In (7.43) the quantity D is the diffusion constant for the minority carrier. The diffusion constant or diffusivity may be calculated from the mobility by the Einstein relation[4]

$$(7.45) \qquad \mu kT = eD.$$

In germanium at room temperature we have

$$D_n = 93 \text{ cm}^2/\text{sec}; \qquad D_p = 44 \text{ cm}^2/\text{sec}.$$

It will prove useful in connection with the discussion of p-n junctions in the next chapter to derive an expression for the average displacement distance of a carrier during its lifetime, considering for simplicity only volume recombination. In the steady state the general hydrodynamic equation of continuity as written for holes is

$$(7.46) \qquad \frac{\partial p}{\partial t} + \text{div } p\mathbf{v}_p = \text{(generation minus recombination) rate per}$$

unit volume.

Here $\mathbf{v}_p$ is the drift velocity of the holes. Now the diffusion equation is

$$(7.47) \qquad p\mathbf{v}_p = -D_p \text{ grad } p,$$

according to the definition of the diffusivity. Let us consider the steady-state flow of holes from a region in which they are generated

---

[4] This relation is easily proved. Suppose that the particles of charge e are in a constant electric field E. According to the Boltzmann distribution law the concentration of particles $n(x)$ at x is proportional to exp $(-eEx/kT)$. The condition that in equilibrium no net current should flow is

$$\mu nE + D\frac{dn}{dx} = 0,$$

the definition of the diffusivity D being used as the net flux of particles per unit concentration gradient. From this equation we see that $n(x)$ is also proportional to exp $(-\mu Ex/D)$; (7.45) follows on equating the exponents.

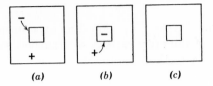

FIG. 7.11. A recombination center captures alternately an electron and a hole and thus catalyzes their recombination, as shown in parts (a), (b), and (c). (After Shockley.)

to a region where they recombine at the rate p/τ_p, according to (7.41). In the steady state $\partial p/\partial t = 0$, and (7.46) and (7.47) reduce in the recombination region to

$$(7.48) \qquad D_p \nabla^2 p - \frac{p}{\tau_p} = 0.$$

For linear geometry we look for a solution of the form, for positive x,

$$(7.49) \qquad p = p_0 e^{-x/L_p};$$

it is supposed that the holes are generated in the region of negative x and recombine in the region of positive x. Substituting (7.49) in (7.48) we find we must have

$$(7.50) \qquad L_p = (D_p \tau_p)^{1/2}.$$

The length L_p is known as the *diffusion length* for holes; it is a measure of the length a hole diffuses in a lifetime. For electrons

$$(7.51) \qquad L_n = (D_n \tau_n)^{1/2}$$

by a parallel argument. In germanium at room temperature a hole with a lifetime of 10^{-3} sec has a diffusion length of

$$(7.52) \qquad L_p = (44 \times 10^{-3})^{1/2} \cong 0.2 \text{ cm.}$$

Shockley has suggested a mechanism whereby imperfections may catalyze recombination. As indicated in Fig. 7.11, an electron and hole are initially free at stage (a); in (b) an electron is captured by the recombination center; a hole is attracted electrostatically by the captured electron, and in (c) the electron has dropped into the hole, leaving the recombination center ready to repeat the process with another electron and hole.

MINORITY CARRIER TRANSPORT AND HOLE INJECTION

Haynes and Shockley have developed an experiment that illustrates the participation of minority carriers in transport processes in solids and that provides a method for the direct measurement of diffusion and drift.

The experimental arrangement is illustrated diagramatically in Fig. 7.12. The germanium is n-type as illustrated and is present as a rod. A sweeping field is applied from end to end of the rod by a battery. This field acts in such a direction as to draw electrons from right to left through the rod. If any holes were introduced in the rod, they would drift from left to right.

When the pulse generator at the left-hand point contact, or emitter point, operates, the emitter point is biased positive and causes holes to be injected into the rod. These holes are then drawn down the rod by the sweeping field. After a time they arrive in the neighborhood of the collector point, which, as the figure shows, is biased negative. It thus tends to attract holes, and some of the holes flow to the collector point and thus contribute to the current flowing in the collector circuit. This current flows through a resistor, and the voltage across the resistor is applied to the vertical plates of a cathode-ray oscilloscope. At time t_1 the switch to the emitter point is closed for a brief moment; the time of closing is indicated by a "pick-up" signal on the face of the oscilloscope. After this nothing happens until time t_2 when some of the holes arrive at the collector point; the concentration of holes builds up for a moment and then decays as the group of holes passes. The spread of time of arrival of the holes is a measure of the diffusion constant; the elapsed time $t_2 - t_1$ is a measure of the mobil-

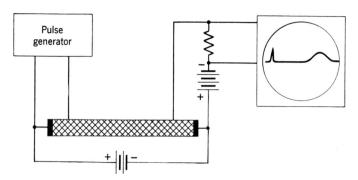

FIG. 7.12. Schematic representation of experiment to observe the drift and diffusion of injected holes in n-type germanium. (After Haynes and Shockley.)

ity, provided the minority carriers are not trapped and then released on the way between the emitter and collector. The evidence is that such trapping is not significant.

The experiment also demonstrates that it is possible to inject holes into a semiconductor at a suitable metal-semiconductor contact. The metal under positive bias voltage takes up electrons from the valence band of the semiconductor, thereby creating holes in the valence band. The process of hole injection is important in semiconductor applications, particularly in the point contact transistor.

CYCLOTRON RESONANCE EXPERIMENTS

In several substances it has proved possible to determine experimentally the form of the energy surfaces of the conduction and valence bands near the band edges; that is, the energy $E(\mathbf{k})$ is determined as a function of the wave vector $\mathbf{k}$. The determination of the energy surface is equivalent to a determination of the effective mass tensor, as we have seen that

$$(7.53) \qquad \left(\frac{1}{m^*}\right)_{ij} = \hbar^{-2}\frac{\partial^2 E}{\partial k_i\, \partial k_j}.$$

The only direct determinations of the effective masses in semiconductors are provided by cyclotron resonance experiments, in which the current carriers in a solid are accelerated in spiral orbits about the axis of a static magnetic field H. The angular rotation frequency ω_c of the carriers is, according to the usual cyclotron equation,[5]

$$(7.54) \qquad \omega_c = \frac{\pm eH}{m^*c},$$

where m^* is an appropriate effective mass. Resonant absorption of energy from an r-f electric field perpendicular to the static magnetic field (Fig. 7.13) occurs when the frequency of the r-f field is equal to the cyclotron frequency $f_c = \omega_c/2\pi$. The $\pm$ choice of signs in (7.54) indicates that holes and electrons will rotate in opposite senses in a magnetic field.

It is interesting to consider the order of magnitude of several physical quantities relevant to the experiment. We make the estimates using $m^*/m \cong 0.1$, which is not unrepresentative. For $f_c = 24{,}000$ mc/sec, or $\omega_c = 1.5 \times 10^{11}$ radians/sec, we have $H \cong 860$ oersteds

---

[5] This equation is easily derived in an elementary way. The centrifugal force $m^*\omega_c^2 r$ is equal to the Lorentz force $\pm e\omega_c rH/c$, where r is the oribtal radius. On canceling $\omega_c r$, we have $\omega_c = \pm eH/m^*c$. The $\pm$ signs are included to describe both electrons and holes.

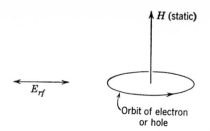

FIG. 7.13. Arrangement of fields in a cyclotron resonance experiment in a semiconductor.

at resonance. At 4°K the mean velocity for a Maxwellian distribution is 4×10^6 cm/sec, and so the radius of the orbit is $r = v/\omega_c \cong 3 \times 10^{-5}$ cm. The line width is determined, as we shall see below, by the collision relaxation time τ, and it is necessary that $\omega_c \tau \geq 1$ in order to obtain a distinctive cyclotron resonance. In other words, the mean free path must be large enough to permit the average carrier to get $1/2\pi$ of the way around a circle between successive collisions. For $\omega_c = 1.5 \times 10^{11}$ sec^{-1}, we require $\tau = 10^{-11}$ sec or longer. At room temperature the relaxation times of carriers in crystals are commonly in the range 10^{-13} to 10^{-15} sec. It is usually necessary to work with high-purity crystals in the liquid hydrogen or liquid helium range to obtain relaxation times long enough to permit the observation of cyclotron resonance with K band microwave equipment. These requirements may be relaxed significantly with the use of millimeter or infrared radiation.

We give now a brief classical discussion of cyclotron resonance absorption[6] by a carrier of isotropic effective mass, assuming an isotropic effective mass m^* and an isotropic relaxation time τ, both independent of the velocity.

The equation of motion for the drift velocity is

$$(7.55) \qquad m^* \left(\frac{d\mathbf{v}}{dt} + \frac{1}{\tau} \mathbf{v} \right) = e \left(\mathbf{E} + \frac{\mathbf{v} \times \mathbf{H}}{c} \right).$$

We take H as the static field along the z axis and neglect the r-f magnetic field. For plane-polarized radiation E_x, we have

$$m^* \left(i\omega + \frac{1}{\tau} \right) v_x = eE_x + \frac{e}{c} v_y H;$$

$$(7.56)$$

$$m^* \left(i\omega + \frac{1}{\tau} \right) v_y = - \frac{e}{c} v_x H.$$

[6] References to early papers in the field are given by Dresselhaus, Kip, and Kittel, *Phys. Rev.* **98**, 368 (1955).

We solve for v_x, finding for the complex conductivity,

$$(7.57) \qquad \sigma = \frac{j_x}{E_x} = \frac{Nev_x}{E_x} = \sigma_0 \left[\frac{1 + i\omega\tau}{1 + (\omega_c^2 - \omega^2)\tau^2 + 2i\omega\tau} \right],$$

where $\sigma_0 = Ne^2\tau/m^*$ is the static conductivity; N is the carrier concentration. This result exhibits the resonance at $\omega = \omega_c$.

The neighborhood of the conduction band edge point in both germanium and silicon consists of a set of spheroidal energy surfaces located in equivalent positions in $\mathbf{k}$ space. By band edge point we mean the point of lowest energy in the conduction band and the point of highest energy in the valence band. We discuss now the theory of cyclotron resonance for spheroidal surfaces. We choose Cartesian coordinate axes with the z axis parallel to the figure axis of the spheroid, and we measure the wave vector components from the center of the spheroid. For points in $\mathbf{k}$ space sufficiently close to a band edge point, the energy is described by the equation

$$(7.58) \qquad E(\mathbf{k}) = \hbar^2 \left(\frac{k_x^2 + k_y^2}{2m_t} + \frac{k_z^2}{2m_l} \right).$$

Here m_l is the longitudinal mass parameter and m_t is the transverse mass parameter.

Shockley has given the solution of the cyclotron frequency problem for a general ellipsoidal energy surface. For the spheroidal surface (7.58) the effective mass determining the cyclotron frequency when the static magnetic field makes an angle θ with the longitudinal axis of the energy surface is

$$(7.59) \qquad \left(\frac{1}{m^*} \right)^2 = \frac{\cos^2 \theta}{m_t^2} + \frac{\sin^2 \theta}{m_t m_l}.$$

A typical cyclotron resonance run in germanium is shown in Fig. 7.14. In Fig. 7.15 we give a plot of the experimental points obtained for electrons in germanium at 4°K as a function of the angle between the direction of the static magnetic field in a (110) plane and a [001] direction lying in the plane. The mass values derived from the theoretical fit to the experimental points are $m_l = (1.58 \pm 0.04)m$ and $m_t = (0.082 \pm 0.001)m$; we assume that there are a set of crystallographically equivalent energy spheroids oriented along the $\langle 111 \rangle$ directions in the Brillouin zone, as proposed originally by Lax et al.

In silicon the energy surfaces near the band edge of the conduction band are spheroids oriented along the equivalent $\langle 100 \rangle$ directions in the Brillouin zone, with mass parameters $m_l = (0.97 \pm 0.02)m$ and

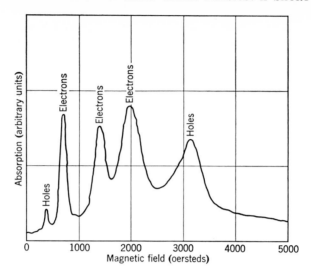

FIG. 7.14. Typical cyclotron resonance results in germanium near 24,000 mc/sec and 4°K: direct copy from a recorder trace of power absorption versus static magnetic field in an orientation in a (110) plane at 60° from a [100] axis.

$m_t = (0.19 \pm 0.01)m$. The surfaces of constant energy are drawn to scale in Fig. 7.16.

The structures of the valence band edges in germanium and silicon are complicated. The holes in these crystals are characterized by two effective masses, and we speak of light and heavy holes. There is some anisotropy, easily apparent for the heavy hole (Fig. 7.17). The energy surfaces are of the form

$$(7.60) \quad E(k) = Ak^2 \pm [B^2k^4 + C^2(k_x{}^2k_y{}^2 + k_y{}^2k_z{}^2 + k_z{}^2k_x{}^2)]^{1/2},$$

where the constants have the approximate values, in units $\hbar^2/2m$,

$$\text{Si:} \quad A = -4.2; \quad B = 0.9; \quad |C| = 3.3 \pm 0.5;$$

$$\text{Ge:} \quad A = -13.2; \quad B = -8.9; \quad |C| = 10.5.$$

The choice of sign in (7.60) distinguishes the two masses. Roughly speaking, the holes in germanium have masses $0.04m$ and $0.3m$; in silicon, $0.16m$ and $0.5m$.

The two hole masses arise in this way: at the center of the Brillouin zone ($\mathbf{k} = 0$) the bands formed from a p level of the isolated atoms have the threefold orbital degeneracy characteristic of p states, so we might expect three valence bands coincident at $\mathbf{k} = 0$ and exhibiting three effective masses. However, we recall that in the isolated atom the spin-orbit interaction energy of the form $\mathbf{L} \cdot \mathbf{S}$ splits the p level into states $p_{3/2}$ and $p_{1/2}$ with total angular momentum $J = \frac{3}{2}$ and $\frac{1}{2}$, respectively, according to the relative orientation of the orbital and spin angular momenta. In the valence band the states associated with the $p_{3/2}$ level are uppermost and form the valence band edge. Of the three bands coincident at $\mathbf{k} = 0$ without spin-orbit interaction, two bands remain with the $p_{3/2}$ level, and one band connected with the $p_{1/2}$ level is lowered in energy by the amount of the spin-orbit interaction energy. In germanium the spin-orbit splitting of the valence band

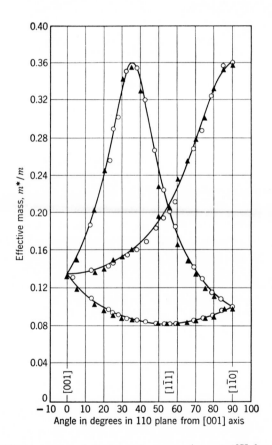

FIG. 7.15. Effective mass of electrons in germanium at 4°K for magnetic field directions in a (110) plane; the theoretical curves are calculated with $m_l = 1.58m$; $m_t = 0.082\ m$. (After Dresselhaus, Kip, and Kittel.)

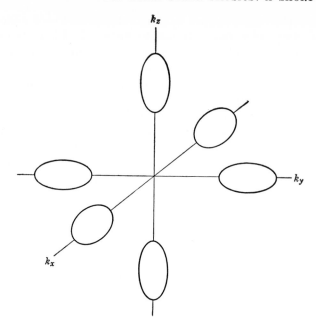

FIG. 7.16.   Constant energy ellipsoids for electrons in silicon, $m_l^*/m_t^* = 5$.

states is of the order of 0.2 ev.   The two bands connected with the $p_{3/2}$ level give rise to the two hole masses observed.

In InSb the electron effective mass is isotropic and approximately equal to $0.014m$.   The low value of the effective mass is a consequence of the low value of the energy gap, which is only 0.18 ev in InSb.

RADIATION DAMAGE IN SEMICONDUCTORS

Lattice defects are produced in crystals when they are irradiated by high energy particles.   The principal effect of irradiation often is to displace atoms of the crystal from regular lattice positions to interstitial positions, creating in this way vacancies and interstitial atoms. Semiconductor crystals may be excellent vehicles for the study of the effects of radiation damage, as shown by the pioneer work of Lark-Horovitz and co-workers using deuterons, alpha particles, fast neutrons, and electrons.   The electrical properties of semiconductors in the impurity (extrinsic) range are highly sensitive, as we have seen, to the concentration of donors and acceptors.   It has been found that the effect of irradiation in germanium is dominated by the acceptors produced, so that it is possible to convert the conductivity type of an

n-type specimen to p-type by a low concentration ($\sim 1:10^7$, depending on the specimen) of radiation-induced defects. In Fig. 7.18 we show the variation of conductivity of germanium specimens, one originally p-type and the other originally n-type, as a function of the integrated flux of deuterons to which the specimens have been exposed. The decrease of conductivity of the p-Ge is caused by the production of lattice defects which provide additional scattering. The variation of conductivity of the specimen initially n-type is attributed to the production of acceptors which gradually with increasing irradiation compensate the initial donor excess in the specimen, thereby converting the specimen to p-type. The conductivity minimum shown in the figure marks approximately the point of optimum compensation with $n \approx p$. Under further bombardment the specimen becomes more conducting as the total carrier concentration increases. Reference may be made to Problem 7.2.

Klontz and Lark-Horovitz have used electron irradiation to determine the threshold energy transfer to a germanium atom to produce an effect. They find 30 ev are required: this is compatible with estimates of the energy required to displace a germanium atom from

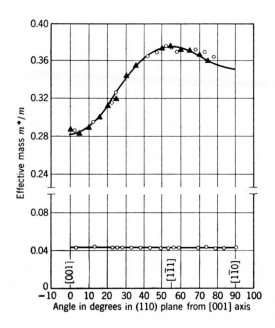

FIG. 7.17.   Effective mass of holes in germanium at 4°K for magnetic field directions in a (110) plane.

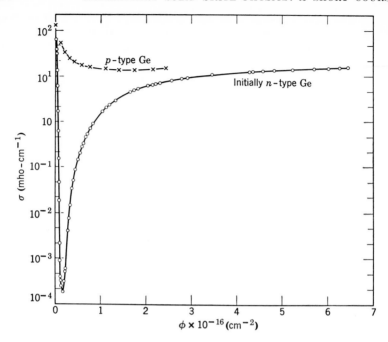

FIG. 7.18.   Conductivity of germanium specimens originally n- and p-type as a function of the integrated deuteron flux to which the specimens have been exposed. (After Purdue group.)

its normal lattice position to an interstitial position.   It is found in silicon that the majority carrier concentrations in both n- and p-type specimens decrease steadily with irradiation and become nearly intrinsic, with resistivity over 10^4 ohm-cm at room temperature.   This behavior requires both donor and acceptor states to be produced, but the effect of the states depends on the position of the Fermi level.

BARRIER RECTIFICATION

A rectifier is a device which has a current-voltage characteristic asymmetrical with respect to voltage, as shown for example in Fig. 7.19. The rectification process requires a low conductivity barrier layer at the contact between two materials of different conductivity, usually a metal and a semiconductor.   A rectifier is always of asymmetrical construction, whether by choice of materials, form of the contacts, or surface treatment.

It is easier to understand the physics of rectification by considering first an insulating barrier between two metals that differ in work function.   The contact is assembled as shown in Fig. 7.20.   The relative positions of the energy bands are determined after equilibrium has been established by the principle that *the Fermi levels must be equal for elements in contact.*

Immediately after the contact is made in (b) of Fig. 7.20 electrons will flow over the top of the insulating barrier—that is, through the vacant conduction band of the insulator—preferentially in the direction $2 \rightarrow 1$ because the electrons in the conduction band of metal 2 are closer to the top of the barrier.   The flow continues until a double layer of charge as shown in (c) is built up, bringing the Fermi levels of the two metals into coincidence.   The positive charge in metal 2 results from the electron deficiency now existing there.   When the Fermi levels are equal, there is no longer a net flow of electrons, and equilibrium obtains.

The effect of applying a voltage to the contact is shown in Fig. 7.21. In (a) the conduction band is raised on one side, favoring the emission of electrons from the metal of lower work function to the metal of higher work function.   In (b) the voltage is reversed and the cur-

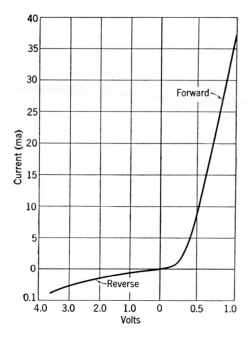

FIG. 7.19.   Current versus voltage characteristic for a copper oxide rectifier; note the change of scale of the axes about the origin.

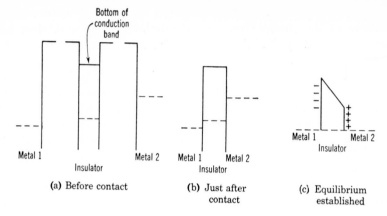

(a) Before contact

(b) Just after contact

(c) Equilibrium established

FIG. 7.20. Formation of a rectifying barrier between two metals of different work function. The broken line indicates the position of the Fermi level, which must be constant in thermal equilibrium when contact is established.

rent flow is greatly reduced. To get significant rectification, $e \times$ the applied voltage must be comparable with kT, which is 0.026 ev at room temperature. It should be noted that the height of the barrier as viewed from metal 1 is independent of the applied voltage.

Many rectifiers are based on the rectifying barrier formed between a metal and a semiconductor, as shown in Fig. 7.22. The Fermi levels here are brought into coincidence in part by electrons flowing from donor impurity levels in the semiconductor to the metal and in

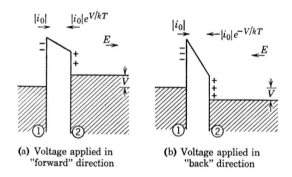

(a) Voltage applied in "forward" direction

(b) Voltage applied in "back" direction

FIG. 7.21. Effect of an applied voltage on the current flow through the contact of Fig. 7.20, exhibiting the origin of rectification. In (a) the electrons flow from 2 to 1 with low resistance; in (b) the electrons flow from 2 to 1 with high resistance; the resistance to electrons flowing from 1 to 2 is the same in both (a) and (b).

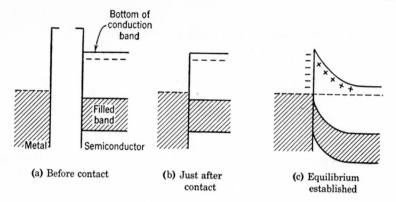

(a) Before contact   (b) Just after   (c) Equilibrium
                           contact   established

FIG. 7.22.   Rectifying barrier between a metal and an n-type semiconductor.
The Fermi level is shown as a broken line.

part by surface state effects.   The positively ionized impurity levels
form an electrical double layer by attracting electrons in the metal
toward the contact.   The region in the semiconductor, which is practically stripped of conduction electrons, is known as the *barrier layer*.
The conductivity of the barrier layer is reduced by the removal of
electrons, and it has all the properties of an insulating barrier, as
required for rectification.

Over most of the potential curve of the barrier layer $eV \gg kT$, so
that the density of conduction electrons may be supposed to be zero
in this region for the purpose of estimating the form of the potential
variation.   Now

(7.61)   (gaussian)   div $D = 4\pi\rho$,

or, for the potential ϕ, taking e as positive here,

(7.62) $$\frac{\partial^2 \phi}{\partial x^2} = \frac{4\pi N e}{\epsilon},$$

assuming N ionized donor atoms per unit volume in the barrier layer.
As the solution of (7.62) is

(7.63) $$\phi = \frac{2\pi N e}{\epsilon} x^2,$$

the thickness D of the barrier layer for a potential drop of ϕ_0 is

(7.64) $$D = \left(\frac{\epsilon\phi_0}{2\pi e N}\right)^{1/2}.$$

Taking $N = 10^{18}$ cm^{-3}, $\epsilon = 12$, $\phi_0 = 0.5$ volt, we find $D \approx 3 \times 10^{-6}$ cm. The barrier layer thus formed plays the part of the insulating layer in Fig. 7.21; the greater part of any voltage drop across the contact takes place in the barrier.

The current-voltage relationship for the rectifying contact illustrated in Figs. 7.20 and 7.21 may be derived easily. If $\bar{v}$ is the average velocity of an electron, the number striking a unit area of the barrier from the left in unit time is $\frac{1}{4}N\bar{v}$, using a result of elementary kinetic theory. Here N is the electron concentration. The electric current density incident on the barrier from the left is then $\frac{1}{4}Ne\bar{v}$. The current crossing the barrier from left to right is just this quantity times $e^{-e\phi_0/kT}$, as this factor gives the probability that an electron will have energy in excess of the barrier energy $e\phi_0$. The current density across the barrier in the opposite direction, from right to left, is given by $\frac{1}{4}Ne\bar{v}e^{-e(\phi_0-V)/kT}$ when the voltage V is applied across the contact. The situation is made plain by the currents shown in Fig. 7.21. The net current density across the barrier is given by the difference between the separate currents, or

$$(7.65) \qquad\qquad j = \tfrac{1}{4}Ne\bar{v}e^{-e\phi_0/kT}(e^{eV/kT} - 1).$$

When eV is negative and larger in magnitude than kT, the current density is small and approximately equal to $\frac{1}{4}Ne\bar{v}e^{-e\phi_0/kT}$. This current in the back or reverse direction is substantially independent of the applied voltage in the assumed range. When eV is positive, the current is given essentially by $\frac{1}{4}Ne\bar{v}e^{-e\phi_0/kT}e^{eV/kT}$. The forward current may be very large if $eV/kT \gg 1$. The expression (7.65) is of the general form of the experimental results; see, for example, Fig. 7.19.

p-n JUNCTION RECTIFICATION

It is possible to produce in several ways a germanium or silicon crystal in which there are both p-type and n-type regions with a very thin interface between them. The interface between the different regions is called a p-n junction. Such junctions have important electrical properties, including rectification and transistor action; the theory of the p-n junction is basic to a large amount of the development of transistor physics.

Suitable junctions in germanium have been prepared in several ways. They were first prepared by the crystal-pulling process in which a crystal is pulled slowly from a melt of molten germanium as the crystal is being grown. If the melt initially has an excess of donor impurities, the crystal will be n-type. At a certain stage of the process

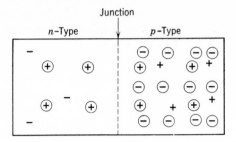

FIG. 7.23.   A p-n junction comprising a p-type region produced by overcompensation.   The circles indicate ionized impurity atoms; un-ionized impurity atoms are not shown.   (After Shockley.)

acceptor impurities are suddenly added to the melt, and the part of the crystal grown subsequently will be p-type.   The acceptors are introduced in such concentration that they overcompensate the donors, as in Fig. 7.23.   The right half of the crystal shown contains donors; the left half contains both donors and acceptors, with the acceptors present in greater abundance.   Most of the acceptors are un-ionized and are not shown in the figure.   In the alloy process for the production of junctions a small pellet of indium (for example) is placed on a crystal of n-type germanium.   On heating, the indium melts and dissolves some germanium; on subsequent cooling, most of the dissolved germanium precipitates on the main body of germanium forming a regrowth layer heavily doped with indium and consequently p-type. A third process for the production of junctions is the rate-grown method which depends on the circumstance that the solubility of antimony (particularly) in solid germanium increases with the rate of growth of the crystal.   When the crystal growth rate is large, the crystal is rich in antimony and is n-type; when the growth rate is slow, the more soluble acceptor impurities are dominant and the crystal is p-type.   Alternate regions of n- and p-type germanium may be produced by cycling the growth rate of the crystal.   A fourth method, known as the diffusion method, consists of heating a specimen in a gaseous atmosphere of donors or acceptors at high temperature so that the impurities from the atmosphere diffuse into the specimen.   The solar battery is made in silicon by this technique and is the most efficient converter of solar energy to electrical power [(electrical energy output) divided by (total incident solar energy) equals 12%] yet developed.

The actual thickness of the transition region between n- and p-type material should be small in comparison with the diffusion length, the distance that a carrier diffuses in a lifetime. We saw in (7.52) that the diffusion length L_p of holes in germanium at room temperature is 0.2 cm for a hole lifetime of 1 msec. If the lifetime were as low as 0.1 μsec, the diffusion length would drop to the order of 10^{-3} cm and the device applications would suffer. We see, therefore, that there is a lower limit to the lifetime that carriers in a semiconductor may have if the material is to be made into p-n junctions or transistors.

We shall first give a qualitative description of the operation of a p-n junction as a rectifier before going into the quantitative details. In a crystal containing a p-n junction we expect that in thermal equilibrium the conduction electrons contributed by the donors will be found chiefly in the n region where the electrons neutralize the space charge of the donor ions, whereas similarly the holes contributed by the acceptor ions will be found chiefly in the p region. It is not possible for the electrons and holes to remain entirely separated in this way unless an electric field exists in the junction region of the crystal in equilibrium—without an electric field the electrons and holes would intermix by diffusion. If we suppose that initially there is no electric field across the junction, holes will diffuse in one direction leaving behind on one side of the junction negatively charged acceptor ions, while electrons will diffuse in the opposite direction leaving behind positively charged donor ions. This initial diffusion will therefore establish an electrostatic dipole layer at the junction, with an associated electric field in a sense which opposes further diffusion across the junction.

Because of the possibility of recombination of a hole and an electron, with the simultaneous emission of phonons or photons, there will be a small flow of holes from the p region into the n region, the holes ending their lives by recombination. This flow will be balanced by holes which are generated in the n region by thermal fluctuations and which diffuse to the p region. In equilibrium the recombination I_r and thermal generation I_g hole currents are equal and opposite, as shown in Fig. 7.24a.

We are now in a position to demonstrate the rectification action of a p-n junction. For reverse voltage bias (Fig. 7.24b), negative voltage is applied to the p region and positive to the n region, so that the potential difference between the two regions is increased. Now practically no holes can climb the potential hill, and the recombination current I_r drops to a very small value; I_g is not much affected by the reverse bias, as the distance a hole diffuses in its lifetime is large compared with the width of the dipole layer at the junction. When a forward bias V is applied (Fig. 7.24c), I_r increases according to the

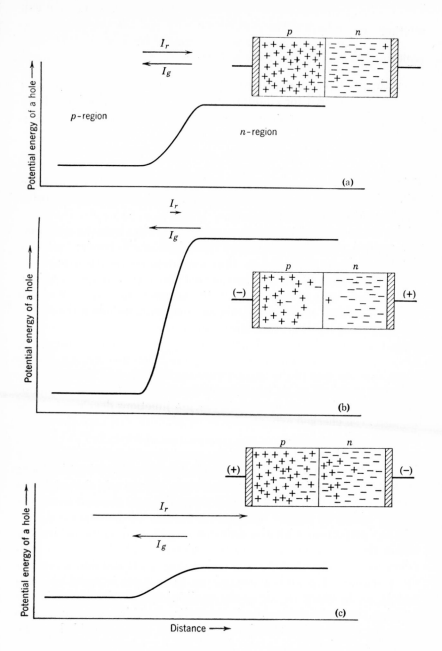

FIG. 7.24.   Dependence of recombination I_r and generation I_g hole currents across a p-n junction upon applied voltage bias.   The inserts show the distribution of current carriers.   (a) Thermal equilibrium, no bias.   (b) Reverse bias.   (c) Forward bias.   (After Shockley.)

relation

(7.66) $I_r = I_g e^{eV/kT}$

from the Boltzmann distribution law; we note that for zero bias $I_r = I_g$, as required for equilibrium. The net current of holes from the p region to the n region is given by the difference (compare Eq. 7.65)

(7.67) $I_r - I_g = I_g(e^{eV/kT} - 1)$.

This current is zero when $V = 0$, increases exponentially to large values for positive eV, and decreases when eV is negative toward a negative saturation value $-I_g$.

The electron current flowing across the junction behaves similarly. The applied voltage which lowers the height of the barrier for holes also lowers it for electrons, so that large numbers of electrons flow from the n region to the p region under the same voltage conditions that produce large hole currents in the opposite direction. We note that the electrical currents add; the total current, including the effects of both holes and electrons, is given by

(7.68) $I = I_s(e^{eV/kT} - 1)$,

where I_s is the sum of the two generation currents. As shown in Fig. 7.25, this equation is well satisfied for p-n junctions in germanium. The diffusion theory of rectification in p-n junctions developed above has also been checked experimentally by photoelectric experiments by Goucher and co-workers.

We now estimate the value of the saturation or generation current I_s. A detailed analysis of the problem has been given by Shockley; the analysis supports a quite simple picture of events in the neighborhood of the barrier. Let us consider first the hole generation current density which we denote by j_{ps}. We assume the junction region is thin in comparison with the diffusion length, and so recombination within the junction proper may be neglected. The holes under consideration are generated in the n region (Fig. 7.24) and diffuse over to the p region. The current carried by these holes is equal approximately to the charge $|e|$ times the equilibrium hole density p_n in the n region times the mean diffusion velocity v_p, which we may take to be of the order of the diffusion length $L_p = (D_p \tau_p)^{1/2}$ divided by the lifetime τ_p. Thus

(7.69) $v_p = \dfrac{(D_p \tau_p)^{1/2}}{\tau_p} = \dfrac{D_p}{L_p}$,

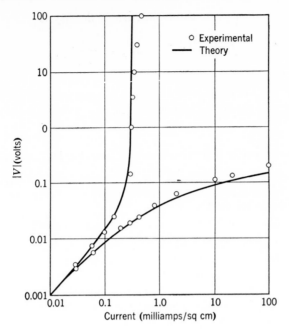

FIG. 7.25. Rectification characteristic for a p-n junction in germanium. (After Shockley.)

and may be of the order of 200 cm/sec for holes at room temperature in germanium having a lifetime of 10^{-3} sec. The hole generation current density is then

$$(7.70) \qquad j_{ps} \approx \frac{p_n |e| D_p}{L_p} = \frac{p_n \mu_p kT}{L_p},$$

using the Einstein relation $D = \mu kT/e$.

We can derive (7.70) from a slightly different viewpoint. The equilibrium value p_n of the hole density in the n region holds nearly up to the edge of the n side of the junction region. If now a potential V is applied across the barrier, the hole concentration just at the n side of the barrier becomes $p_n e^{eV/kT}$, which is an increase over the equilibrium value by the quantity

$$(7.71) \qquad p_0 = p_n(e^{eV/kT} - 1).$$

As we go farther into the n region the excess nonequilibrium hole concentration varies because of recombination as

$$(7.72) \qquad p = p_0 e^{-x/L_p},$$

according to (7.49).   The diffusion current density is

$$(7.73) \qquad j_p = -|e| D_p \text{ grad } p = \frac{|e| D_p}{L_p} p,$$

which at the junction has the value

$$(7.74) \qquad j_p = \frac{p_n |e| D_p}{L_p} (e^{eV/kT} - 1).$$

Thus the net current density across the junction is

$$(7.75) \quad j = j_n + j_p = \left(\frac{p_n |e| D_p}{L_p} + \frac{n_p |e| D_n}{L_n} \right)$$
$$(e^{eV/kT} - 1) \equiv j_s (e^{eV/kT} - 1),$$

in agreement with (7.68) and (7.70).   It is seen that the current in the reverse direction is low if both diffusion lengths L_p and L_n are long. It should be noted that the current reaches its "saturation" value j_s when V is several times $kT/e = -0.026$ volt at room temperature, and that the rectification ratio is $e \cong 2.73$ for $V = \pm kT/e$.   For somewhat smaller values of V, the junction is substantially an ohmic resistance. These characteristics, which actual p-n junctions possess quite precisely, are a consequence of the fact that the current carriers have a charge of one electron.   In fact, p-n junctions have as good rectification curves as it is possible to have for simple structures using carriers of one electron charge.

TUNNEL DIODES

The tunnel diode, discovered by Esaki,[7] is a semiconductor diode made of heavily doped silicon or germanium for use as an active circuit element.   It exhibits a negative resistance over a limited voltage range in the forward direction.   It has applications at high frequencies and low output levels as an amplifier, oscillator, and computer switch.

The doping concentration in a tunnel diode may be of the order of 10^{20} atoms per cubic centimeter.   At such concentrations almost all the donors and acceptors are ionized at all temperature—this condition is referred to as degenerate, and in a sense the semiconductors may be viewed as semimetals.   For a tunnel diode to operate, the concentration of electrons on the one side and of holes on the other side of the junction must be high enough to produce a barrier potential high enough to move the Fermi level within the valence band on the p side

[7] L. Esaki, *Phys. Rev.* **109**, 603 (1958); for a review, see L. Esaki and Y. Miyahara, *Solid State Electronics* **1**, 13 (1960).

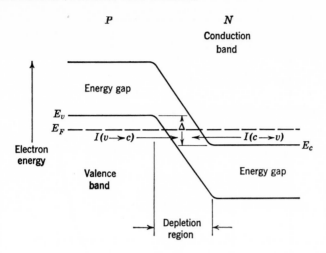

FIG. 7.26. Energy-band scheme at junction of an Esaki diode at thermal equilibrium. At $0°K$ all states below E_F are filled with electrons.

and within the conduction band on the n side, as shown in Fig. 7.26. At lower doping levels, in the usual p-n junctions, the Fermi level falls on both sides within the forbidden gap. But in the tunnel diode there is an overlap Δ of the band edges. Now electrons can penetrate through the barrier between the n and the p sides. This penetration is a specifically quantum-mechanical effect; it is known as the *tunnel effect*. It was first considered by Zener, who showed that electrons in the valence band can, without changing their energy, tunnel across the forbidden gap into empty states in the conduction band, and vice versa, under the action of an intense local electric field.

The current characteristics of such a junction can be discussed conveniently in terms of changes of one sign alone. With no external bias the net current must be zero: the barrier potential will adjust itself to ensure this. But the net tunnel current must also vanish for a forward voltage $eV = \Delta$ which just destroys the overlap. For intermediate voltages a net forward current flows. Superposed on these tunnel currents we have the usual diffusion currents (as in Fig. 7.25) of a p-n junction, so that the total current-voltage characteristic is as shown in Fig. 7.27.

We can write down a formal expression for the tunnel current. Consider the current caused by electrons tunneling from the valence to the conduction band in an energy state interval dE of the overlap region. This current will be proportional to the number of valence electrons

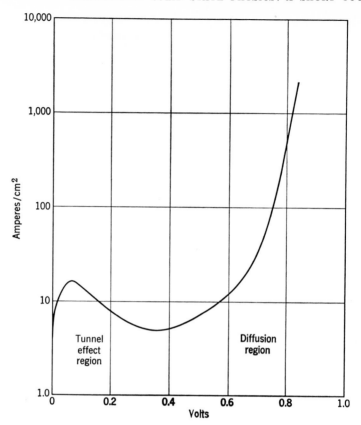

FIG. 7.27.   Current-voltage characteristics in the forward direction, after Esaki, for a silicon tunnel diode.

occupying the states in this energy interval, the number of electronic states in this same interval in the conduction band which are empty and are available for occupation, and the transition probability of tunneling from the valence to the conduction bands.   Let $\rho_c(E)$ and $\rho_v(E)$ represent the energy-state densities in the conduction and valence bands, respectively, $f_c(E)$ and $f_v(E)$ the corresponding Fermi distribution functions denoting the probability that a given energy state is occupied, and $Z_{v \to c}$ and $Z_{c \to v}$ the transition probabilities in the two directions.   Then $f_v(E)\rho_v(E)$ = density of valence-band electron states *occupied* in dE; $(1 - f_c)\rho_c(E)$ = density of conduction-band electron states *unoccupied* in dE.

Thus

$$I_{v \to c} = K \int_{E_c}^{E_v} Z_{v \to c} \rho_v(E) \rho_c(E) f_v(1 - f_c) \, dE,$$

where K is a constant. The region of integration is from the conduction-band edge of the n side E_c to the valence-band edge of the p side E_v. Similarly

$$I_{c \to v} = K \int_{E_c}^{E_v} Z_{c \to v} \rho_v(E) \rho_c(E) f_c(1 - f_v) \, dE.$$

If we take $Z_{c \to v} = Z_{v \to c}$, the net current is

$$(7.76) \qquad I = I_{c \to v} - I_{v \to c} = K \int_{E_c}^{E_v} Z(f_c - f_v) \rho_c \rho_v \, dE.$$

At thermal equilibrium, the probability that a given energy state E is occupied by electrons is the same for the valence band or the conduction band, so that $f_c(E) = f_v(E)$. Hence $I_{c \to v} = I_{v \to c}$ and $I = 0$. When a forward bias V is applied to the junction, the energy states, Fermi level, and band edges of the p side shift downwards by an amount eV with respect to those of the n side. Thus the band overlap Δ changes on application of a forward bias, and each current component also changes. When $V = \Delta/e$, the overlap is completely destroyed, tunneling stops, and both components reduce to zero. That is, K goes to zero when $eV = \Delta$.

To understand how the negative resistance arises, it is convenient to consider the tunneling process at absolute zero. On the p side the distribution function $f_v(E)$ implies that all energy states below the Fermi level F_{F_p} are occupied and all above are empty. A similar statement holds for $f_c(E)$ and E_{F_n} on the n side.

In Fig. 7.28a, the cross-hatched regions in the energy-band sketch denote the occupied states at zero bias. Here both currents are zero. With a forward bias V, the picture is changed to that of Fig. 7.28b. Tunneling originating in the valence band is not allowed for all values of forward bias, because all occupied valence states correspond to occupied conduction-band states. Thus $I_{v \to c}$ is identically zero for $V \geq 0$. Tunneling does occur, however, from the conduction band because some of the occupied conduction states correspond to empty valence states; thus $I_{c \to v} > 0$. Because $I_{c \to v}$ is again zero at $V = \Delta/e$, it must have a maximum somewhere in the interval $0 < V < \Delta/e$. For a reverse bias, the picture changes to that of Fig. 7.28c. By parallel reasoning, no tunneling from the conduction band can take place for any reverse bias because all states are empty above E_{F_n} in the conduction band. Thus $I_{c \to v}$ is identically zero. Tunneling does

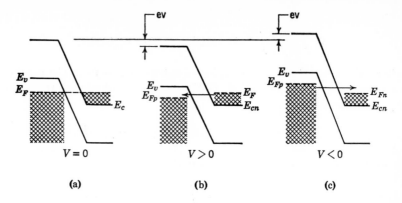

FIG. 7.28.   Electron populations and tunnel currents at 0°K for various bias voltages.   (After R. A. Pucel.)

occur in the opposite direction and increases very rapidly with bias because of the enhanced overlap.

The tunneling probability Z in Eq. (7.76) can be determined experimentally from the I-V characteristics; Esaki and Miyahara find $Z = \exp(-2 \times 10^6/F)$ in germanium, where F is the electric field in the junction in volts per centimeter. This result is in good agreement with estimates based on Zener's theory.

POINT CONTACT TRANSISTORS

The point contact transistor, discovered by Bardeen and Brattain,[8] is the first semiconductor device that performs the functions of a vacuum tube triode, such as amplification and modulation. It is now possible to build advanced types of electronic circuits entirely without vacuum tubes, using semiconductor rectifiers and triodes, with benefit from the absence of filament current, reduced size and weight, and increased life. Germanium is generally employed in transistors because the mobilities are higher in germanium than in any other common semiconductor; silicon is employed when stability over a wide range of temperature is required.

There are now a number of different types of transistors. We discuss first the original version of Bardeen and Brattain, known as type A. It consists of a small block of n-type germanium as shown in Fig. 7.29, with a large area base contact and with two closely spaced point contacts with a separation of the order of 0.01 cm. The emitter

[8] J. Bardeen and W. H. Brattain, *Phys. Rev.* **75**, 1208 (1949).

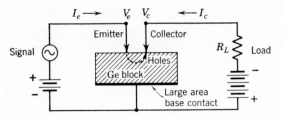

FIG. 7.29. Schematic drawing of a point-contact transistor with a circuit for amplification of an a-c signal. The convention regarding the signs of the currents is shown. The normal bias is I_e, V_e positive; I_c, V_c negative.

point is normally biased in the forward (low resistance) direction of current flow, and the collector point is biased in the back (high resistance) direction.

Transistor action depends on the fact that the current from the emitter is composed largely of positive holes. The holes are attracted to the collector point by the electric field in the germanium arising from the current flowing to the collector which has a strong negative voltage bias, as shown in Fig. 7.30. Although the holes are inside the rectifying barrier region next to the collector point, they modify the barrier

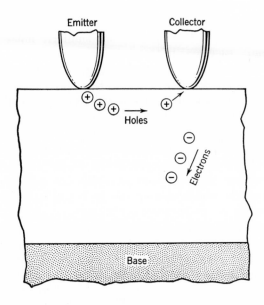

FIG. 7.30. Transistor mechanism. (After Ryder and Kircher.)

rectification properties. Only a little hole current is required before the concentration of holes near the collector becomes substantially greater than the normal concentration of conduction electrons in the germanium. The modification of the collector barrier by the holes injected by the emitter makes possible modulation of the collector current by the emitter current. The current amplification factor α is defined by

$$(7.77) \qquad \alpha = -\left(\frac{\partial I_c}{\partial I_e}\right)_{V_c = \text{const}},$$

and is found to have values of the order of 2. The power amplification may be quite large, of the order of 20 db or more, because the collector current flows in the high resistance direction. Even without current amplification, it is still possible to have power amplification.

JUNCTION TRANSISTORS

Shockley, Sparks, and Teal[9] have described an important type of transistor in which transistor action takes place within the germanium at the junctions between regions of n-type and p-type conductivity. Such a junction transistor action had been predicted by Shockley[10] earlier on the basis of the diffusion theory of p-n junctions. An n-p-n transistor is shown in Fig. 7.31. When the unit is used as an amplifier, the junction J_c is biased in the "reverse" direction as shown in the figure; therefore electrons in the collector region are not encouraged to move to the base region; similarly holes are held in the base region. Electrons in the emitter region may easily enter the base region and then may diffuse to the right p-n junction. The flow over the potential barrier may be varied by applying a variable potential to the emitter while keeping the base at a constant potential. The emitter region is made more highly conducting than the base region, so that most of the current across the left n-p junction consists of electrons moving to the right, rather than holes moving to the left. Under these conditions the behavior of the device is closely analogous to that of a vacuum tube: the emitter region corresponds to the cathode, the base to the region around the grid, and the collector to the plate.

When the collector electrode is biased positively with respect to the base electrode ("reverse" direction for collector p-n junction), only a small back current of electrons and holes will diffuse across the collector barrier. If now the emitter n-p barrier is biased negatively (in the

[9] Shockley, Sparks, and Teal, *Phys. Rev.* **83**, 151 (1951).

[10] W. Shockley, *Bell Syst. Tech. J.* **28**, 435 (1949).

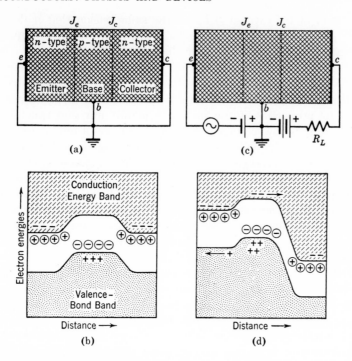

FIG. 7.31. An *n-p-n* transistor and the energy level scheme: (a) and (b) thermal equilibrium; (c) and (d) biased as an amplifier. The thickness of the base region must be much less than a diffusion length. (After Shockley, Sparks, and Teal.)

forward direction) with respect to the base, a relatively large forward current of electrons will flow across the reduced emitter barrier into the base region. If the base region is sufficiently thin so that the electrons coming from the emitter do not recombine with holes in the *p*-type base region, the electrons will diffuse to the collector barrier. From here they are collected with the help of the collector field. Because the electrons were injected through the low forward impedance and collected through the high reverse impedance of bulk *p-n* junctions, high voltage amplification will result. Power gains are as high as 50 db.

In the same sense that a *p-n* junction is nearly a perfect rectifier at room temperature, a junction transistor is nearly a perfect electronic valve. To be more specific the current in a junction transistor depends on voltage to the maximum degree possible for a device using carriers of one electronic charge. The reason for this is that the current injected across the emitter junction varies with voltage through a

Boltzmann factor exp (eV/kT) for the same reason that it does in a simple p-n junction. Consequently, for a transistor in the operating range at room temperature, the collector current increases by a factor of $e = 2.72$ for each increase of kT/e in the forward voltage across the emitter base junction, and this is the highest sensitivity possible for a structure with singly charged current carriers controlled by a potential hill. The properties of p-n junctions permit junction transistors to operate at very low voltage. In fact, a voltage of one or two tenths of a volt across the collector junction will bring the collector current into the saturation range so that the pentodelike characteristic of very high collector impedance is obtained. This high impedance contributes greatly to the high gain of the junction transistor. The modest collector voltage requirement arises from the Boltzmann factor at the collection junction, which leads to saturation at a few times kT/e or a few tenths of a volt just as it does in a simple p-n junction.

The theory of p-n-p transistors is similar to that of n-p-n transistors, the roles of electrons and holes being reversed. The existence of transistors of opposite polarities gives a flexibility of circuit design not possible for vacuum tubes, and advantage has already been taken of this fact by electrical engineers in designing push-pull amplifiers, flip-flop circuits, and the like.

Junction transistors can operate down to very low power levels, of the order of a microwatt, and are therefore well adapted for miniaturization and for battery operation. They are much less noisy than point contact transistors and in many applications are superior to vacuum tubes. Compared to point contact transistors, junction transistors enjoy freedom from short circuit instability; the input and output impedances are always positive whether the transistor is connected grounded-emitter, grounded-base, or grounded-collector. The gain is high: power gains of 40 to 50 db per stage are possible. The efficiency is high: in class A operation it is possible to obtain efficiencies of 48 or 49 percent of an ideal 50 percent. The small size of the unit (which is enclosed in a plastic bead $\frac{3}{16}$ inch in diameter) makes for ruggedness. In the audio-frequency range the junction devices are relatively free from microphonics. The power consumption is small: an audio-frequency oscillator may use microwatts of power from the supply, as contrasted with the watts required to heat the filament of an ordinary vacuum tube.

PROBLEMS

7.1. Indium antimonide has $E_g = 0.18$ ev; $\epsilon = 17$; $m_e = 0.014m$. Calculate (a) the donor ionization energy; (b) the radius of the ground state orbit. (c) At what minimum donor concentration will appreciable overlap effects between the orbits of adjacent impurity atoms occur? (d) If $N_d = 1 \times 10^{14}$ cm^{-3} for a particular specimen, calculate the concentration of conduction electrons at 4°K.

7.2. (a) Discuss the phenomenon of impurity compensation, which is the reduction of carrier concentration and conductivity in a semiconductor initially of one conductivity type (n or p) by the addition of impurities of the other type.

(b) Suppose $N_d = 10^{17}$ cm^{-3} in a germanium specimen at room temperature; estimate n before and after adding $N_a = 10^{17}$ cm^{-3}. Assume $m_e = m_h$ and equal ionization energies for donors and acceptors.

(c) Does a nearly intrinsic resistivity prove the specimen is pure? Can the resistivity be greater than intrinsic? Why?

7.3. The mobility of electrons is 3600 cm^2/volt-sec and for holes 1600 cm^2/volt-sec in a sample of germanium. This sample shows no Hall effect. What fraction of the current is carried by holes?

7.4. A semiconductor has 10^{18} acceptors per cubic centimeter. The energy level of these acceptors is 0.5 ev above the valence band of the crystal. If the mobility of holes in this band is 100 cm^2/volt-sec, calculate the conductivity of the material at room temperature (300°K) and at the temperature of liquid oxygen (90°K)

7.5. Show that, if N_a, N_d are comparable and both large in comparison with n_+^0, n_-^0, then

$$\frac{n}{p} \cong \left(\frac{m_e}{m_h}\right)^{3/2} \frac{N_d\, e^{-E_d/kT}}{N_a\, e^{-E_a/kT}},$$

where E_d, E_a are the donor and acceptor ionization energies, respectively.

7.6. Why do silicon and germanium look silvery and rather like metals to the eye, whereas diamond does not?

7.7. The work function of two metals differs by 2 ev. If these metals are brought into contact, some electrons will flow from one into the other. This phenomenon is entirely limited to the surface of the metal, and it may be assumed that the electrons are displaced over a distance of 3×10^{-8} cm. How many electrons per square centimeter will be transferred?

7.8. Explain in detail the mechanism whereby a p-n junction when illuminated delivers electrical energy to a circuit. This is the principle of the silicon solar battery. [See W. G. Pfann and W. van Roosbroeck, *J. Appl. Phys.* **25**, 1422 (1954).]

7.9. Describe briefly the design and function of the following devices:

(a) Phototransistor.

(b) A p-n-i-p junction transistor [see J. M. Early, *Bell System Tech. J.* **33**, 517 (1954)].

7.10. The rectification ratio is defined as the ratio of forward current to inverse current at voltages $+|V|$ and $-|V|$, respectively. Find an expression for this ratio for a p-n junction, and plot on semilog paper as a function of $|V|$. The Wagner relationship neglects the bulk resistance of the rectifier.

7.11. Suppose that the excess charge in the dipole layer of a p-n junction varies linearly from plus to minus on passing through the junction. Calculate the excess charge on one side of the junction as a function of the inverse potential V and of the barrier thickness L; show that the capacitance of the junction varies as $V^{-1/3}$.

7.12. Design a simple one-stage transistor amplifier for use in a hearing aid, using the characteristics of a commercial transistor.

REFERENCES

A. Coblenz and H. L. Owens, *Transistors: theory and applications*, McGraw-Hill Book Co., New York, 1955.

W. Crawford Dunlap, Jr., *Introduction to semiconductors*, John Wiley and Sons, New York, 1957.

H. Y. Fan, "Valence semiconductors," *Solid State Physics* **1**, 284 (1955).

H. K. Henisch, editor, *Semiconducting materials*, Butterworths Scientific Publications, London, 1951.

L. P. Hunter, *Handbook of semiconductor electronics*, McGraw-Hill Book Co., New York, 1956.

I. Joffe, *Semiconductors*, Infosearch, London, 1960.

D. H. Menzel, editor, *Fundamental formulas of physics*, Prentice-Hall, Englewood Cliffs, New Jersey, 1955: Chapter 25, "Solid State," C. Herring.

N. F. Mott and R. W. Gurney, *Electronic processes in ionic crystals*, Clarendon Press, Oxford, 2nd ed., 1950.

Present status of physics, American Association for the Advancement of Science, 1954: K. Lark-Horovitz, pp. 57–127; J. Bardeen, pp. 128–149. The paper by Lark-Horovitz contains an exceptionally full bibliography.

M. G. Say, editor, *Crystal rectifiers and transistors*, Newnes, London, 1954.

R. F. Shea, *Transistor circuits*, John Wiley and Sons, New York, 1953.

W. Shockley, *Electrons and holes in semiconductors*, Van Nostrand, Princeton, New Jersey, 1950.

R. A. Smith, *Semiconductors*, Cambridge University Press, Cambridge, 1959.

E. Spenke, *Elektronische Halbleiter*, Springer, Wiesbaden, 1955.

M. J. O. Strutt, *Transistoren*, Hirzel, Zürich, 1954.

Transistor technology, 2 vols., Bell Telephone Laboratories and Western Electric Co., 1952.

A. H. Wilson, *Semiconductors and metals; an introduction to the electron theory of metals*, Cambridge University Press, Cambridge, 1939.

8 Magnetism and magnetic resonance

The chapter begins with the classical Langevin theory of the diamagnetic and paramagnetic susceptibilities of gases, followed by a quantum-mechanical treatment. The properties of paramagnetic ions in solids are discussed, and an account is given of the attainment of very low temperatures by the adiabatic demagnetization of paramagnetic salts. A discussion is given of the elements of the theory of magnetic resonance in nuclear and electronic systems at radio and microwave frequencies. The essential aspects of ferromagnets and antiferromagnets are treated.

DIAMAGNETISM

Substances with a negative magnetic susceptibility are called *diamagnetic*. Substances with a positive susceptibility are called *paramagnetic*. The magnetic susceptibility per unit volume is defined as

$$\chi = \frac{M}{H},$$

where M is the magnetic moment per unit volume, or the *magnetization*, and H is the magnetic field intensity. Quite frequently the susceptibility may also be defined referred to unit mass or to a mole of the substance. The molar susceptibility is written χ_M.

Almost all magnetics research in the world is published in gaussian units, and there is little motivation to express the principal equations of this chapter in both gaussian and MKS units, as we did in the chapter on dielectrics. In gaussian units H is expressed in oersteds; to obtain a result in oersteds, we multiply the number of ampere-turns/meter by $4\pi/10^3$. In gaussian units, B is expressed in gauss: to obtain a result in gauss we multiply the number of webers/meter^2

by 10^4.   Where in MKS

$$B = \mu_0\mu H = \mu_0(H + M),$$

we have

$$B = \mu H = H + 4\pi M$$

in gaussian units, so that

$$\mu = \frac{B}{H} = 1 + 4\pi \left(\frac{M}{H}\right) = 1 + 4\pi\chi$$

in gaussian units.

Diamagnetism is associated with the tendency of electrical charges partially to shield the interior of a body from an applied magnetic field.   In electromagnetism we are familiar with *Lenz's law*, which states that when the flux through an electrical circuit is changed an induced current is set up in such a direction as to oppose the flux change.   In a resistanceless circuit, in a superconductor, or in an electron orbit within an atom, the induced current persists as long as the field is present, and the magnetic moment associated with the current is a diamagnetic moment.

DERIVATION OF THE LANGEVIN DIAMAGNETISM EQUATION

The usual classical derivation employs the Larmor theorem,[1] which states that for an atom in a magnetic field the motion of the electrons is, to the first order in H, the same as a possible motion in the absence of H except for the superposition of a common precession of angular frequency

(8.1) $$\omega_L = -\frac{eH}{2mc},$$

or $f_L = 1.40$ mc/oersted.   Furthermore, if the field is applied slowly, the motion in the rotating reference system will be the same as the original motion in the rest system before the application of the field. The precession of the electron distribution is equivalent to diamagnetic current

(8.2) $$I = -\frac{Ze(eH/2mc)}{2\pi c}$$

in electromagnetic units.   As the magnetic moment μ of a current loop

---

[1] For a discussion of the Larmor theorem, see H. Goldstein, *Classical mechanics*, Addison-Wesley, Cambridge, 1953, pp. 176–178.

is given by the product of the current by the area of the loop, we have

(8.3)
$$\frac{\mu}{H} = - \frac{Ze^2}{4mc^2} \overline{\rho^2}$$

for Z electrons, where $\overline{\rho^2} = \overline{x^2} + \overline{y^2}$ is the average of the square of the perpendicular distance of the electron from the field axis. In terms of the mean square distance $\overline{r^2} = \overline{x^2} + \overline{y^2} + \overline{z^2}$ from the nucleus, we have

(8.4)
$$\overline{r^2} = \tfrac{3}{2}\overline{\rho^2}$$

for a distribution of charge which on the average is spherically symmetrical, so that $\overline{x^2} = \overline{y^2} = \overline{z^2}$. Then the diamagnetic susceptibility per unit volume is, if N is the number of atoms per unit volume,

(8.5)
$$\chi = - \frac{Ze^2N}{6mc^2} \overline{r^2},$$

which is the Langevin expression as corrected by Pauli.

Typical experimental values of the molar diamagnetic susceptibilities of rare gas atoms are the following:

$$\times 10^{-6} \text{ cm}^3/\text{mole}$$

He	$- 1.9$
Ne	$- 7.2$
A	-19.4
Kr	-28.0
Xe	-43.0

Derivation of Larmor Theorem for a Special Case. We consider an electron moving in a circular orbit of radius r about a fixed nucleus. The balance of forces requires that

$$m\omega_0{}^2 r = \frac{e^2}{r^2},$$

so that

(8.6)
$$\omega_0 = \left(\frac{e^2}{mr^3}\right)^{\frac{1}{2}}.$$

In a magnetic field H normal to the plane of the orbit we have the additional Lorentz force $\mathbf{F} = (e/c)\mathbf{v} \times \mathbf{H}$; therefore

$$m\omega^2 r = \frac{e^2}{r^2} - \frac{e}{c} r\omega H,$$

and

$$(8.7) \qquad \omega = \pm \left[\left(\frac{eH}{2mc} \right)^2 + \left(\frac{e^2}{mr^3} \right) \right]^{1/2} - \frac{eH}{2mc}.$$

Now, if $\omega_0 \gg eH/2mc$, we have approximately

$$(8.8) \qquad \omega = \pm \omega_0 - \frac{eH}{2mc},$$

in agreement with (9.1). We may note that for a free electron $\omega = eH/mc$; this is known as the magnetron or cyclotron frequency, and it is twice the Larmor frequency for a bound electron.

In solids the diamagnetic contribution of the ion cores is described roughly by the Langevin result (8.5). The contribution of conduction electrons may be considerably more complicated; in particular, carriers of very light effective mass give a diamagnetic susceptibility which may be considerably enhanced (for $m^*/m \gg 1$) over the free electron value referred to in Chapter 5.

The usual methods of measuring diamagnetic and paramagnetic susceptibilities depend in one way or another on the force exerted on a specimen by a nonuniform magnetic field. The force $\mathbf{F}$ is given by the gradient of the magnetic energy

$$(8.9) \qquad \mathbf{F} = \tfrac{1}{2} \,\mathrm{grad} \int \chi H^2 \, dV,$$

where now χ is the volume susceptibility.

PARAMAGNETISM

Electronic paramagnetism (positive contribution to χ) is found in:

1. All atoms and molecules possessing an odd number of electrons, as here the total spin of the system cannot be zero. Examples: free sodium atoms; gaseous nitric oxide (NO); organic free radicals such as triphenylmethyl, $C(C_6H_5)_3$.

2. All free atoms and ions with a partly filled inner shell: transition elements; ions isoelectronic with transition elements; rare earth and actinide elements. Examples: Mn^{2+}, Gd^{3+}, U^{4+}. Paramagnetic properties are exhibited by many of these ions when incorporated into solids, and as ions in solution, but not invariably.

3. A few miscellaneous compounds with an even number of electrons, including molecular oxygen and organic biradicals.

4. Metals: the paramagnetism of conduction electrons is treated in Chapters 5 and 6.

LANGEVIN THEORY OF PARAMAGNETISM

We treat a medium containing N atoms per unit volume, each bearing a magnetic moment μ. Magnetization results from the orientation of the magnetic moments in an applied magnetic field; thermal disorder resists the tendency of the field to orient the moments. The energy of interaction with an applied magnetic field H is

$$(8.10) \qquad V = -\mathbf{\mu} \cdot \mathbf{H}.$$

The magnetization in thermal equilibrium is calculated by following exactly the steps in the derivation of the Debye orientational polarizability in Chapter 4, with μ written for p and H for E. The magnetization is then given by

$$(8.11) \qquad M = N\mu L(a),$$

where $a = \mu H/kT$, and the Langevin function $L(a)$ is

$$L(a) = \operatorname{ctnh} a - \frac{1}{a}.$$

For $a \ll 1$, $L(a) = a/3$, and

$$(8.12) \qquad M \cong \frac{N\mu^2 H}{3kT}.$$

For an electron $\mu \approx 10^{-20}$; at room temperature in a field of 10^4 oersteds we have $\mu H/kT \approx \frac{1}{400}$, so that here we may safely approximate the Langevin function by $\mu H/3kT$. At low temperatures saturation effects are observed, as shown in Fig. 8.1.

The magnetic susceptibility in the limit $\mu H/kT \ll 1$ is

$$(8.13) \qquad \chi = \frac{M}{H} = \frac{N\mu^2}{3kT} = \frac{C}{T},$$

where the Curie constant C is equal to $N\mu^2/3k$. The $1/T$ temperature dependence is known as the Curie law, and the whole expression is known as the Langevin equation.

Quantum Theory of Paramagnetism. We treat first the paramagnetism caused by electron spins with angular momentum $\frac{1}{2}$ as measured in units of $\hbar$. In a magnetic field H the energy levels are separated, as in the elementary theory of the Zeeman effect, by

$$(8.14) \qquad \Delta W = 2|\mu_z|H = g\frac{e\hbar}{2mc}H = g\mu_B H,$$

where for an electron spin the g factor or *spectroscopic splitting factor* is

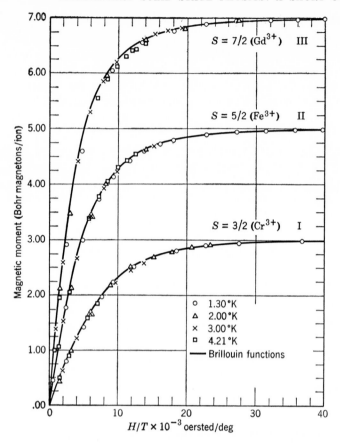

FIG. 8.1. Plot of magnetic moment versus H/T for spherical samples of (I) potassium chromium alum, (II) ferric ammonium alum, and (III) gadolinium sulfate octahydrate. Over 99.5% magnetic saturation is achieved for 1.3°K and about 50,000 gauss. [After W. E. Henry, *Phys. Rev.* **88**, 559 (1952).]

equal to 2.00; $\mu_B = e\hbar/2mc = -0.927 \times 10^{-20}$ erg/oersted is the Bohr magneton. The splitting for an electron spin is shown in Fig. 8.2. For free atoms where orbital angular momentum may also be present, the g factor is given by the Landé equation

$$(8.15) \qquad g = 1 + \frac{J(J+1) + S(S+1) - L(L+1)}{2J(J+1)},$$

where J, S, L refer, respectively, to the total, spin, and orbital angular momentum quantum numbers.

Where there are only two levels in the magnetic field the populations in thermal equilibrium are

(8.16)
$$\frac{N_1}{N} = \frac{e^{\mu H/kT}}{e^{\mu H/kT} + e^{-\mu H/kT}};$$

$$\frac{N_2}{N} = \frac{e^{-\mu H/kT}}{e^{\mu H/kT} + e^{-\mu H/kT}};$$

here N_1, N_2 are the populations of the lower and upper levels, and $N = N_1 + N_2$ is the total number of atoms. The projection of the magnetic moment of the upper state along the field direction is $g\mu_B/2$, and of the lower state is $-g\mu_B/2$, so that the resultant magnetization for N atoms per unit volume is

(8.17)
$$M = \frac{Ng\mu_B}{2} \cdot \frac{e^x - e^{-x}}{e^x + e^{-x}} = \frac{Ng\mu_B}{2} \tanh x,$$

where $x = g\mu_B H/2kT$. For $x \ll 1$, $\tanh x \cong x$, and

$$M \cong \frac{Ng\mu_B}{2} \cdot \frac{g\mu_B H}{2kT}.$$

An atom with angular momentum quantum number J has $2J + 1$ equally spaced energy levels in a magnetic field. The magnetization is given by

(8.18)
$$M = NgJ\mu_B B_J(x),$$

where $x = gJ\mu_B H/kT$, and the Brillouin function B_J is given by

(8.19)
$$B_J = \frac{2J + 1}{2J} \operatorname{ctnh}\left(\frac{(2J + 1)x}{2J}\right) - \frac{1}{2J} \operatorname{ctnh}\frac{x}{2J}.$$

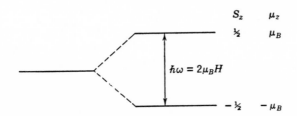

FIG. 8.2. Energy levels splitting scheme for one electron, with only spin angular momentum, in a magnetic field H directed along the positive z axis. Note that the Bohr magneton $\mu_B = e\hbar/2mc$ is a negative number as used here.

For $x \ll 1$, the susceptibility is

$$(8.20) \qquad \chi = \frac{NJ(J+1)g^2\mu_B{}^2}{3kT} = \frac{Np^2\mu_B{}^2}{3kT},$$

where the effective number of Bohr magnetons is defined as

$$(8.21) \qquad p = g[J(J+1)]^{\frac{1}{2}}.$$

The order of magnitude of the volume susceptibility for $N \approx 10^{22}$ atoms per cubic centimeter as in a solid and $\mu \approx 10^{-20}$ cgs is $\sim 1/400T$. For $T = 300°$K, $\chi \sim 10^{-5}$; for $T = 0.3°$K, $\chi \sim 10^{-2}$.

Rare Earth Ions. The discussion just given applies principally to atoms which in the absence of a magnetic field have a $(2J + 1)$-fold degenerate ground state, the degeneracy being lifted upon application of a magnetic field; the influence of all higher energy states of the system is neglected. These conditions appear from Table 8.1 to be satisfied by a number of the rare earth ions, except Sm^{3+} and Eu^{3+}. The calculated magneton numbers are obtained by using g values from the Landé formula (8.15) for the ground state level assignment predicted by the Hund theory of spectral terms, which tells us that for equivalent electrons the ground state has the maximum multiplicity $2S + 1$ allowed by the Pauli principle and the maximum L consistent

TABLE 8.1
EFFECTIVE MAGNETON NUMBERS FOR TRIVALENT RARE EARTH IONS
(Near room temperature)

Ion	Configuration	Basic Level	$p(\text{calc}) =$ $g[J(J+1)]^{\frac{1}{2}}$	$p(\exp)$ Approx.
Ce^{3+}	$4f^1 5s^2 p^6$	$^2F_{5/2}$	2.54	2.4
Pr^{3+}	$4f^2 5s^2 p^6$	$^3H_4$	3.58	3.5
Nd^{3+}	$4f^3 5s^2 p^6$	$^4I_{9/2}$	3.62	3.5
Pm^{3+}	$4f^4 5s^2 p^6$	$^5I_4$	2.68	....
Sm^{3+}	$4f^5 5s^2 p^6$	$^6H_{5/2}$	0.84	1.5
Eu^{3+}	$4f^6 5s^2 p^6$	$^7F_0$	0	3.4
Gd^{3+}	$4f^7 5s^2 p^6$	$^8S_{7/2}$	7.94	8.0
Tb^{3+}	$4f^8 5s^2 p^6$	$^7F_6$	9.72	9.5
Dy^{3+}	$4f^9 5s^2 p^6$	$^6H_{15/2}$	10.63	10.6
Ho^{3+}	$4f^{10} 5s^2 p^6$	$^5I_8$	10.60	10.4
Er^{3+}	$4f^{11} 5s^2 p^6$	$^4I_{15/2}$	9.59	9.5
Tm^{3+}	$4f^{12} 5s^2 p^6$	$^3H_6$	7.57	7.3
Yb^{3+}	$4f^{13} 5s^2 p^6$	$^2F_{7/2}$	4.54	4.5

TABLE 8.2
EFFECTIVE MAGNETON NUMBERS FOR IRON GROUP IONS

Ion	Config-uration	Basic Level	$p(\text{calc}) =$ $g[J(J+1)]^{1/2}$	$p(\text{calc}) =$ $2[S(S+1)]^{1/2}$	$p(\text{exp})$†	$g(\text{exp})$‡
Ti^{3+}, V^{4+}	$3d^1$	$^2D_{3/2}$	1.55	1.73	1.8	......
V^{3+}	$3d^2$	$^3F_2$	1.63	2.83	2.8	(1.98)
Cr^{3+}, V^{2+}	$3d^3$	$^4F_{3/2}$	0.77	3.87	3.8	(1.97)
Mn^{3+}, Cr^{2+}	$3d^4$	$^5D_0$	0	4.90	4.9	2.0
Fe^{3+}, Mn^{2+}	$3d^5$	$^6S_{5/2}$	5.92	5.92	5.9	2.0
Fe^{2+}	$3d^6$	$^5D_4$	6.70	4.90	5.4	2.2
Co^{2+}	$3d^7$	$^4F_{9/2}$	6.63	3.87	4.8	2.5
Ni^{2+}	$3d^8$	$^3F_4$	5.59	2.83	3.2	2.3
Cu^{2+}	$3d^9$	$^2D_{5/2}$	3.55	1.73	1.9	2.2

† Representative values.
‡ In this column $g = p(\text{exp})/[S(S+1)]^{1/2}$.

with this multiplicity; furthermore, the J value is equal to $|L - S|$ when the shell is less than half full and $L + S$ when the shell is more than half full.

Iron Group Ions. Table 8.2 shows that, for salts of the iron transition group of the periodic table, the experimental magneton numbers are in poor agreement with (8.21), but instead, as noted by Sommerfeld, Bose, and Stoner, agree quite well with magneton numbers

$$(8.22) \qquad\qquad p = 2[S(S+1)]^{1/2}$$

calculated as if the orbital moment were not there at all. One expresses this situation by saying that the orbital moments are "quenched."

The basic reason for the difference in behavior of the rare earth and iron group salts is that the $4f$ shell responsible for paramagnetism in the rare earth ions lies deep inside the ions, being partly shielded from the environment by the outer $5s$ and $5p$ shells, whereas in the iron group the $3d$ shell responsible for paramagnetism is the outermost shell in the ionic state. The $3d$ shell is thus exposed to the intense local electric fields produced by neighboring ions and the dipole moments of water of hydration in the crystal. The interaction of the paramagnetic ions with the crystalline electric fields has two major effects: the coupling of **L** and **S** vectors is largely broken up, so that the states are no longer specified by their J values; furthermore, the $2L + 1$ sublevels belonging to a given L which are degenerate in the free ion may now be split up, in some cases with important effects on the contribution of the orbital motion to the magnetic moment.

Quenching of the Orbital Angular Momentum. In an electric field directed toward a fixed center such as a nucleus, the plane of a classical orbit remains fixed in space, and so the orbital angular momentum components L_x, L_y, L_z are constant. In quantum theory only one angular momentum component (usually taken as L_z) and the square of the total orbital angular momentum L^2 are constant in a central field. If an inhomogeneous electric field is superposed on the central field, the plane of the orbit will move about; the angular momentum components are no longer constant and may average to zero. That is, L_z will no longer be a constant of the motion, although to a good approximation L^2 may continue to be constant. If L_z averages to zero, it is said to be quenched.

The magnetic moment of a state is given by the average value of the magnetic moment operator $\mu_B(\mathbf{L} + 2\mathbf{S})$ over the state. For a magnetic field in the z direction the orbital contribution to the magnetic moment is proportional to the expectation value of L_z, and so the orbital magnetic moment is quenched if the mechanical moment L_z is quenched.

When the spin-orbit interaction energy is introduced as an additional perturbation on the system, the quenching may be partially lifted as the spin may carry some orbital moment along with it. If the sign of the spin-orbit interaction favors parallel orientation of the spin and orbital magnetic moments, the total magnetic moment will be larger than for the spin alone, and the g value as defined in Table 8.2 will be greater than 2. The experimental results in the table suggest, in good agreement with the known variation of sign of the spin-orbit interaction, that $g > 2$ when the $3d$ shell is more than half full, $g = 2$ when the shell is half full, and $g < 2$ when the shell is less than half full.

Nuclear Paramagnetism. The magnetic moments of nuclei are smaller than the magnetic moment of the electron by a factor $\sim 10^{-3}$; therefore according to (8.12) the susceptibility of a nuclear paramagnetic system for the same number of particles will be smaller by a factor $\sim 10^{-6}$ than that of an electronic paramagnetic system.

Values of the magnetic moments of several nuclei are given in Table 8.3.

COOLING BY ADIABATIC DEMAGNETIZATION OF A PARAMAGNETIC SALT

The universal method for attaining temperatures below 1°K is that of adiabatic demagnetization. By its use temperatures near 10^{-3}°K have been reached. The method rests on the fact that at a

TABLE 8.3
NUCLEAR MAGNETIC MOMENTS
(Magnetic moments in units of the nuclear magneton
$\mu_p = e\hbar/2M_pc = 5.05 \times 10^{-24}$ erg/oersted)

Nucleus	Spin (units $\hbar$)	Magnetic Moment
Neutron	$\frac{1}{2}$	-1.913
H^1	$\frac{1}{2}$	2.793
D^2	1	0.857
Li^7	$\frac{3}{2}$	3.256
Na^{23}	$\frac{3}{2}$	2.217
Mn^{55}	$\frac{5}{2}$	3.468
Co^{59}	$\frac{7}{2}$	4.648
Ta^{181}	$\frac{7}{2}$	2.1

fixed temperature the entropy of a system of magnetic moments is lowered by a magnetic field. The entropy is always a measure of the order of a system; the greater the disorder, the higher the entropy. In the field the moments will be partly lined up, or partly ordered, so that the entropy is lowered by the field. The entropy is also lowered by lowering the temperature as more of the moments line up. If the field can be removed without the entropy of the spin system changing, the disorder of the spin system will look as it should at a lower temperature. When the specimen is demagnetized adiabatically, heat can flow into the spin system only from the system of lattice vibrations. At the temperatures of interest the entropy of the lattice system is quite negligible, so that the entropy of the spin system alone is essentially constant during adiabatic demagnetization of the specimen.

We first find an expression for the spin or magnetic entropy of a system of N ions each of spin J at a temperature sufficiently high for the spin system to be entirely disordered. That is, T is supposed to be much higher than some temperature θ_0, which characterizes the energy of interactions tending to orient the spins preferentially. The result for the entropy S is

$$(8.23) \qquad S = Nk \log (2J + 1).$$

We establish this directly from the Boltzmann definition of the entropy as

$$(8.24) \qquad S = k \log W,$$

where W is the number of independent arrangements of the elements of the system. At a temperature so high that all sublevels are nearly equally populated, the number of arrangements W is the number of ways of arranging N spins on $2J + 1$ sublevels, as nearly all arrangements will be possible energetically. Thus

$$(8.25) \qquad W = (2J + 1)^N,$$

and

$$(8.26) \qquad S = k \log (2J + 1)^N = Nk \log (2J + 1).$$

It is this entropy which may be reduced by the application of a magnetic field, for the magnetic field splits the levels in energy. The tendency of the population to favor the lower energy levels puts the system in an arrangement which (purely combinatorially) is less probable than the arrangement with all levels equally populated; a less probable arrangement corresponds to a lower entropy.

Example. Derive an expression for the field dependence of the entropy, in the Curie law region.

As the entropy is a function of H and T, we have

$$(8.27) \qquad dS = \left(\frac{\partial S}{\partial H}\right)_T dH + \left(\frac{\partial S}{\partial T}\right)_H dT.$$

In an isothermal process the second term may be set equal to zero, and so

$$(8.28) \qquad dS = \left(\frac{\partial S}{\partial H}\right)_T dH.$$

We note that, by a modified Maxwell thermodynamic relation, $(\partial S/\partial H)_T = (\partial M/\partial T)_H$, and so

$$dS = \left(\frac{\partial M}{\partial T}\right)_H dH.$$

Therefore in isothermal magnetization,

$$(8.29) \qquad S(H, T) - S(0, T) = \int_0^H \left(\frac{\partial M}{\partial T}\right)_H dH.$$

In the Curie law region, using (8.20),

$$(8.30) \qquad S = S_0 - \tfrac{1}{6}Nk \left(\frac{p\mu_B H}{kT}\right)^2.$$

The steps carried out in the cooling process are shown in Fig. 8.3. The field is applied at temperature T_1 with the specimen in good ther-

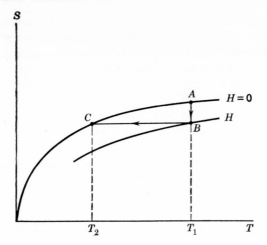

FIG. 8.3. Entropy-temperature plot for adiabatic demagnetization.

mal contact ($\Delta T = 0$) with the surroundings, giving the isothermal path AB. The specimen is then insulated ($\Delta S = 0$) and the field removed, so that the specimen follows the isoentropic path BC, ending up at temperature T_2. The lowest temperature reached in adiabatic demagnetization is largely limited by the natural splitting of the spin energy levels occurring even in the absence of external magnetic fields. The zero field splitting may be caused by electrostatic interaction with the other ions in the crystal, by the interaction of the magnetic moments with each other, or by nuclear interactions. The zero field splitting causes the entropy at T_2 for $H = 0$ to be less than it would be for a smaller splitting; thus the final temperature is not as low as it might otherwise be.

MAGNETIC RESONANCE

Studies of electronic and nuclear magnetism by high-frequency techniques have made many important contributions to our understanding of the structure of solids and liquids. It is convenient to refer to the entire field as *magnetic resonance*, even though the investigations are not always carried out close to the resonance condition derived in the following discussion. There is a basic distinction between magnetic resonance and cyclotron (or plasma) resonance: in magnetic resonance the system is driven by the magnetic component of an electromagnetic field acting on the magnetic moment of the system; in cyclotron resonance the electric component of the electromagnetic field drives the electric charge.

To get an idea of what happens in a magnetic resonance experiment, consider a free particle of spin S in a uniform static magnetic field H. We know from the theory of the spectroscopic Zeeman effect that the $2S + 1$ energy levels coincident in energy in $H = 0$ will split into equally spaced levels in the presence of the field. The $2S + 1$ magnetic states are labeled by the magnetic quantum number $m_s = S$, $S - 1$, $S - 2$, $\cdots$, $-S + 1$, $-S$; here m_s denotes the value in units of $\hbar$ of the component S_z of the spin S for a field H parallel to the z axis.

The energy differences between successive states in the magnetic field are

$$(8.31) \qquad \left| E(m_s) - E(m_s - 1) \right| = \left| g\mu_0 H \right|.$$

Here μ_0 is usually taken for electrons as the Bohr magneton $\mu_B = e\hbar/2m_e c$ and for nuclei as the nuclear magneton $\mu_n = e\hbar/2M_p c$. We then define g as the factor which makes the energy difference come out correctly; g is called the g *factor* or the *spectroscopic splitting factor*. An alternate form of (8.31) is

$$(8.32) \qquad \left| E(m_s) - E(m_s - 1) \right| = \left| \hbar\gamma H \right|,$$

where, as we shall see later, γ is the ratio of the magnetic moment to the angular momentum of the system.

The spectroscopic selection rule for the magnetic (dipole) transitions with which we are concerned is that $\Delta m_s = \pm 1$; that is, the transitions occur between adjacent levels. Thus, from (8.31) and (8.32), energy will be absorbed from a radiation field of circular frequency ω when

$$(8.33) \qquad \hbar\omega = g\mu_0 H = \hbar\gamma H.$$

This is a *resonance condition*. A schematic experimental setup for the observation of magnetic resonance is shown in Fig. 8.4. The specimen

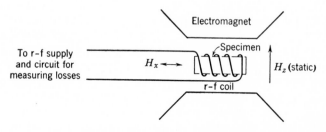

FIG. 8.4. Schematic arrangement for spin resonance absorption experiments.

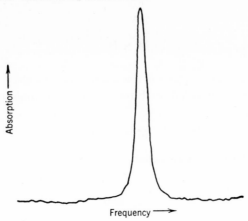

FIG. 8.5.   Proton spin resonance absorption in ferric nitrate solution; fixed magnetic field, varying frequency.   For a frequency of 30 mc/sec the resonance occurs
at 7050 oersteds.   [After Bloembergen, Purcell, and Pound, *Phys. Rev.* **73**, 679
(1948).]

is placed in the static magnetic field H_z of an electromagnet.   An r-f
magnetic field H_x of fixed angular frequency ω is applied perpendicular
to the static field.   The r-f power absorbed in the specimen is determined by electrical measurements, as by measuring the Q of the coil.

Experimental results for proton spin resonance in water (with some
dissolved ferric nitrate) are shown in Fig. 8.5.   The electron spin
resonance relation for $g = 2.00$ is

$$(8.34) \qquad f(mc) \cong 2.80H \text{ (oersteds)},$$

and the proton resonance relation is

$$(8.35) \qquad f(kc) \cong 4.26H \text{ (oersteds)}.$$

For $H \sim 5000$ oersteds, the electron resonance frequency falls in the
microwave range and the proton resonance frequency in the short
wave communications range.   Magnetic resonance furnishes an accurate method for the determination of magnetic field intensity.

Macroscopic Equations.   It is useful to consider the resonance
process in terms of the magnetic moment of the entire specimen rather
than in terms of the levels of an individual ion.   Writing **M** for the
magnetization (magnetic moment/volume) and **J** for the angular
momentum density, the classical equation of motion

$$\frac{d\mathbf{J}}{dt} = \text{torque/volume}$$

becomes

$$(8.36) \qquad \frac{d\mathbf{J}}{dt} = \mathbf{M} \times \mathbf{H},$$

using the elementary result for the torque on a magnet.

If the spin system is free with respect to anisotropic lattice interactions, we may write

$$(8.37) \qquad \mathbf{M} = \gamma \mathbf{J},$$

where for electrons we know that

$$(8.38) \qquad \gamma = \frac{ge}{2mc}.$$

The equation of motion for the magnetization becomes

$$(8.39) \qquad \frac{d\mathbf{M}}{dt} = \gamma \mathbf{M} \times \mathbf{H}.$$

We obtain very simply an approximate solution of this equation. We take the static field as H_z and the r-f field as H_x. The component equations may be written, for time dependence $e^{i\omega t}$,

$$(8.40) \qquad \begin{aligned} i\omega M_x &= \gamma M_y H_z; \\ i\omega M_y &= \gamma(M_z H_x - M_x H_z); \\ \dot{M}_z &= -\gamma M_y H_x \cong 0. \end{aligned}$$

The third equation may be neglected as long as $M_y \ll M_z$. There is always a static time-independent term in M_z caused by the static magnetic field H_z. We may then solve for M_x, finding

$$-\omega^2 M_x = \gamma^2(M_z H_z H_x - M_x H_z^2),$$

or, for the r-f susceptibility χ_x,

$$(8.41) \qquad \chi_x = \frac{M_x}{H_x} = \frac{\gamma^2 M_z H_z}{(\gamma H_z)^2 - \omega^2}.$$

The condition for resonance is obviously that $\omega = \gamma H_z$, in exact agreement with (8.33). The macroscopic approach to the resonance problem allows us to picture the vector $\mathbf{M}$ as precessing about the static field $\mathbf{H}$. The macroscopic equations permit the introduction in an approximate way of damping and line-width terms in the equations of motion.

Relaxation of the Longitudinal and Transverse Components of Magnetization. The magnetic energy density is given by $-M_z H_z$; thus the energy of a paramagnetic specimen is lowered when a magnetic field is applied to a specimen originally in an unmagnetized condition. The decrease in magnetic energy is balanced by an increase in lattice energy, but the specimen cannot become magnetized faster than the lattice can acquire the excess energy. The interaction between the spin system and the lattice determines the rate of energy transfer; we define the *spin-lattice relaxation time* T_1 by the equation

$$(8.42) \qquad \left(\frac{dM_z}{dt}\right)_{\text{relax}} = -\frac{M_z - M_0}{T_1},$$

where M_0 is the value of M_z in thermal equilibrium under the conditions of the experiment. From this equation we see that the time variation of M_z after application of a steady magnetic field at time $t = 0$ is given by

$$(8.43) \qquad M_z = M_0(1 - e^{-t/T_1}).$$

The transverse components M_x, M_y of the magnetization are not involved directly in the magnetic energy, and their relaxation may proceed somewhat independently of the longitudinal magnetization M_z. We define the transverse relaxation time T_2 by the equations

$$(8.44) \qquad \left(\frac{dM_x}{dt}\right)_{\text{relax}} = -\frac{M_x}{T_2}; \qquad \left(\frac{dM_y}{dt}\right)_{\text{relax}} = -\frac{M_y}{T_2}.$$

We shall see that T_2 determines the width of the resonance line; T_2 is essentially a measure of the phase coherence time of the precessing system of spins. As such, T_2 is decreased by any inhomogeneity in the system or in the applied magnetic field. The magnetic field seen by any particular spin varies because the magnetic moment of the adjacent spins, randomly oriented, gives rise to a random magnetic field $|\Delta H| \approx \mu/r^3$, where μ is the magnetic moment and r the distance between the spins. In some circumstances this effect alone gives a contribution to $1/T_2$ of magnitude

$$(8.45) \qquad \frac{1}{T_2} \approx \gamma|\Delta H| \approx \frac{\gamma\mu}{r^3}.$$

The magnetic dipole interaction is called a spin-spin interaction.

Interaction mechanisms which contribute to T_1 will usually contribute to T_2, but the inverse statement is not necessarily true. Thus a static nonuniform applied magnetic field broadens the resonance line and simulates a contribution to T_2; the field does not involve the lattice and cannot contribute to T_1.

Including the relaxation terms, the complete equations of motion become

$$(8.46) \qquad \frac{dM_x}{dt} = \gamma(M_yH_z - M_zH_y) - \frac{M_x}{T_2};$$

$$(8.47) \qquad \frac{dM_y}{dt} = \gamma(M_zH_x - M_xH_z) - \frac{M_y}{T_2};$$

$$(8.48) \qquad \frac{dM_z}{dt} = \gamma(M_xH_y - M_yH_x) - \frac{M_z - M_0}{T_1}.$$

We are interested first in establishing the connection between T_2 and the line width. For weak r-f fields we neglect dM_z/dt, as before. Then

$$(8.49) \qquad i\left(\omega - \frac{i}{T_2}\right)M_x = \omega_0 M_y - \omega_s H_y;$$

$$(8.50) \qquad i\left(\omega - \frac{i}{T_2}\right)M_y = \omega_s H_x - \omega_0 M_x.$$

Here $\omega_0 = \gamma H_z$ and $\omega_s = \gamma M_z$. It is convenient to form $M^+ = M_x + iM_y$; $H^+ = H_x + iH_y$. Then (8.49) and i times (8.50) may be combined as

$$i\left(\omega - \frac{i}{T_2}\right)M^+ = -i\omega_0 M^+ + i\omega_s H^+,$$

or

$$(8.51) \qquad \chi^+ = \frac{M^+}{H^+} = \frac{\omega_s}{\omega + \omega_0 - (i/T_2)}.$$

The power absorption is proportional always to the imaginary part of the susceptibility:

$$(8.52) \qquad \operatorname{Im} \chi^+ = \frac{\omega_s/T_2}{(\omega + \omega_0)^2 + (1/T_2)^2}.$$

The resonance occurs at $\omega = -\omega_0 = -\gamma H_z$; the negative sign is a question of the sense of the circular polarization of the r-f field involved in H^+. We note that at resonance ($\omega = -\omega_0$) there is a maximum in $\operatorname{Im} \chi^+$ equal to $\omega_s T_2$. For $\omega + \omega_0 = 1/T_2$ the value of $\operatorname{Im} \chi^+$ is one-half that at resonance; thus $1/T_2$ is the half-width in frequency at one-half the maximum power absorption. We may define $(\Delta H)_{\frac{1}{2}}$ as the width (in terms of magnetic field) associated with this frequency width by the relation

$$(8.53) \qquad\qquad (\Delta H)_{\frac{1}{2}} = \frac{1}{\gamma T_2}.$$

The experimental determination of the spin-lattice relaxation time T_1 may be accomplished from the response of the system (see Problem 8.7) at high power levels, sufficiently high that M_z no longer has its static value. Another method utilizes the phenomenon of spin echoes —a phenomenon in the response of the spin systems to strong pulses of r-f energy. By the method of spin echoes we may also distinguish those contributions to T_2 caused by inhomogeneous static magnetic fields from those contributions caused by dynamic interactions (motional effects). The analysis of the observations of T_1 and T_2 provides an important source of information about the physics of the particular system.

In the method of nuclear *induction* one observes the magnetization component out-of-phase with the driving field; one observes essentially the real part of χ^+, whereas in a resonance absorption one observes Im χ^+. We have

$$(8.54) \qquad\qquad \mathrm{Re}\ \chi^+ = \frac{\omega_s(\omega + \omega_0)}{(\omega + \omega_0)^2 + (1/T_2)^2}.$$

This expression changes sign when ω passes through the resonance value $-\omega_0$. At high frequencies far above resonance $(|\omega| \gg |\omega_0|)$, we have Re $\chi^+ \approx \omega_s/\omega$ and Im $\chi^+ \approx (\omega_s/\omega)(1/\omega T_2)$, provided $\omega T_2 \gg 1$. We see that the real part of the r-f susceptibility is dominant when we are far from resonance. This observation provides the basis for low-loss microwave devices, such as the *gyrator*, which rotate the plane of polarization of an electromagnetic wave.

Zero Field Electronic Splitting. In many solids, as we have previously mentioned, the ground state of the paramagnetic ion is split by the crystalline electric field, and it is possible to observe r-f transitions between the sublevels without necessarily applying a static magnetic field. This was first done by Bleaney and co-workers. Usually, however, a static field is applied, and the zero field separation of the levels is deduced from a theoretical interpretation of the several absorption lines observed under these conditions of combined crystalline and Zeeman splittings.

In paramagnetic salts which have been diluted with a nonmagnetic isomorphous salt it is often possible to resolve a line structure caused by the interaction of electrons with nuclear spins. This is a very important tool in the determination of the electronic structure of defects in solids. The hyperfine structure of Mn^{2+} ions in aqueous solution is shown in Fig. 8.6.

FERROMAGNETIC RESONANCE ABSORPTION

Spin resonance absorption experiments at microwave frequencies in ferromagnetic substances are similar in principle to the nuclear and electronic spin resonance experiments just described. The total magnetic moment of the specimen precesses about the direction of the static magnetic field, and energy is absorbed strongly from the r-f transverse field when its frequency is equal to the precessional frequency. We may equally well think of the macroscopic vector representing the total spin of the entire saturated ferromagnet as quantized in the large static field, with energy levels separated by the order of the usual Zeeman frequencies; the selection rule $\Delta m_s = \pm 1$ allows transitions only between adjacent levels.

Ferromagnetic resonance was discovered first in experiments by Griffiths. The intensity of ferromagnetic resonance absorption is usually tremendous in comparison with paramagnetic resonance because of the large macroscopic magnetic moment of ferromagnets, usually at least 10^3 times larger than in electronic paramagnets at room tem-

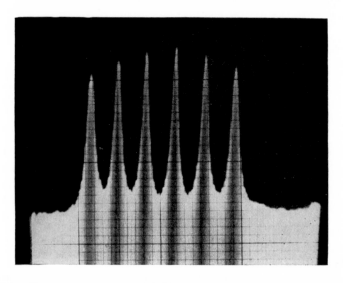

FIG. 8.6.   Hyperfine structure of Mn^{2+} ions in water. [After Tinkham, Weinstein, and Kip, *Phys. Rev.* **84**, 848 (1951).]   The nuclear spin is $I = \frac{5}{2}$, and the electronic spin is $S = \frac{5}{2}$.

perature. In the experiments it is found that the apparent g values are often very much higher than the free electron g value 2.00 when the results are interpreted in terms of the usual resonance relation (8.33):

$$(8.55) \qquad \omega = \frac{ge}{2mc} H.$$

When all demagnetizing effects are included, with the usual experimental arrangement with metals—a thin disk specimen with the static field H parallel to the disk—the resonance relation becomes

$$(8.56) \qquad \omega = \frac{ge}{2mc} (BH)^{1/2},$$

where $B = H + 4\pi M_s$. The g values obtained in this way are not far from the free spin value.

The derivation of (8.56) is straightforward. We start with

$$\frac{d\mathbf{M}}{dt} = \gamma \mathbf{M} \times \mathbf{H},$$

with $\gamma = ge/2mc$. If the sample is thin in the y direction, the demagnetizing factors are $N_x = 0$, $N_y = 4\pi$, $N_z = 0$. The components of $\mathbf{H}$ for free precession are $(0, -4\pi M_y, H)$, where $H_y = -4\pi M_y$ is the demagnetizing field which arises when in the course of the precession the magnetization vector acquires a component M_y in the y direction; and H is the static field in the z direction. Then, for time dependence $e^{i\omega t}$ and neglecting squares and products of small quantities on the assumption $M_x, M_y \ll H_z$, we have

$$(8.57) \qquad \begin{aligned} i\omega M_x &= \gamma(M_y H + 4\pi M_y M_z); \\ i\omega M_y &= -\gamma M_x H. \end{aligned}$$

These equations have a nontrivial solution only when the determinant of the coefficients of M_x, M_y vanishes:

$$(8.58) \qquad \begin{vmatrix} i\omega & -\gamma B \\ \gamma H & i\omega \end{vmatrix} = 0;$$

thus the resonance frequency is given by

$$(8.59) \qquad \omega = \gamma(BH)^{1/2}.$$

FERROMAGNETISM

We call a substance ferromagnetic if it possesses a spontaneous magnetic moment, that is, a magnetic moment even in the absence of an applied magnetic field. The saturation magnetization M_s is defined as the spontaneous magnetic moment per unit volume. In technical literature the saturation flux density $B_s = 4\pi M_s$ is often used. The Curie point T_c is the temperature above which the spontaneous moment vanishes.

If we could add to a paramagnetic substance an interaction tending to make the ionic and atomic magnetic moments line up the same way, we would have a ferromagnetic substance. Let us postulate such an interaction and call it the Weiss field. It is also called the molecular field or the exchange field; Weiss was the first to imagine such a field. The orienting effect of the Weiss field is opposed by the motion of thermal agitation of the elementary moments. We consider the Weiss field the equivalent of an effective magnetic field H_E acting on the electron spins. The interaction energy of a spin with the Weiss field must be of the order of magnitude of the thermal energy of a spin at the Curie point. Hence

$$(8.60) \qquad gS\mu_B H_E \approx kT_c,$$

or

$$(8.61) \qquad H_E \approx \frac{kT_c}{gS\mu_B}.$$

For iron we have $T_c \approx 1000°K$, $g \approx 2$, $S \approx 1$; therefore $H_E \approx 10^{-13}/2 \times 10^{-20} = 5 \times 10^6$ oersteds. This field is much stronger than that produced by the magnetic moments of the other ions in the crystal, as the magnetic interaction is only $\sim \mu_B/a^3 \sim 10^3$ oersteds, where a is the lattice constant.

Pierre Weiss (1907), inventor of this concept, showed that it will account for several important attributes of ferromagnetism provided that one assumes that the Weiss field H_E is proportional to the magnetization:

$$(8.62) \qquad H_E = \lambda M,$$

where λ stands for a constant called the Weiss field constant. The susceptibility above the Curie point is deduced by postulating that the Curie law (8.13) holds if we take as the magnetic field the sum of the applied field H and the Weiss field H_E. Then

$$(8.63) \qquad \frac{M}{H + \lambda M} = \frac{C}{T},$$

or

$$(8.64) \qquad \chi = \frac{M}{H} = \frac{C}{T - C\lambda}.$$

This gives a nonzero magnetization for zero applied field at the Curie point expressed by

$$(8.65) \qquad\qquad T_c = C\lambda,$$

and so

$$(8.66) \qquad\qquad \chi = \frac{C}{T - T_c}.$$

This expression, known as the Curie-Weiss law, describes quite well the observed susceptibility variation in the paramagnetic region above the Curie point.[5] From (8.65) and the definition (8.13) and (8.20) of the Curie constant C we may determine the value of the Weiss field constant:

$$(8.67) \qquad\qquad \lambda^{-1} = \frac{C}{T_c} = \frac{Ng^2 S(S + 1)}{3kT_c} \mu_B{}^2,$$

and so for iron, $\lambda \approx (4 \times 10^{-13})/(8 \times 10^{-17}) \approx 5000$, in agreement with the earlier estimate of H_E.

The physical origin of the Weiss field is in the quantum-mechanical exchange integral, as pointed out by Frenkel and Heisenberg. On certain assumptions it can be shown[6] that the energy of interaction of atoms i, j bearing spins S_i, S_j contains a term

$$(8.68) \qquad\qquad E_{ex} = -2J\mathbf{S}_i \cdot \mathbf{S}_j,$$

where J is the exchange integral and is related to the overlap of the charge distributions i, j. The exchange energy has no classical analogue, although it is of electrostatic origin. It expresses the difference in Coulomb interaction energy of the systems when the spins are parallel or antiparallel. It is a consequence of the Pauli exclusion principle that in quantum mechanics one cannot usually change the relative direction of two spins without making changes in the spatial charge distribution in the overlap region. The resulting changes in the Coulomb energy of the system may conveniently be written in the form[7]

---

[5] Experimentally the susceptibility well above the Curie point is given quite accurately by $C/(T - \theta)$, where θ, called the paramagnetic Curie point, may be slightly greater than the actual transition temperature (ferromagnetic Curie point) T_c.

[6] This is shown in most texts on quantum theory; see also J. H. Van Vleck, *Revs. Modern Phys.* **17**, 27 (1945).

[7] Equation (8.68) is really an operator equation in the spin operators $\mathbf{S}_i, \mathbf{S}_j$, but for many purposes in ferromagnetism it is a good approximation to treat the spins as classical vectors.

(8.68), so that it appears *as if* there were a direct coupling between the spins S_i, S_j.

We establish an approximate connection between the exchange integral J and the Weiss field constant λ. Suppose that the atom under consideration has z nearest neighbors, each connected with the central atom by the interaction J; for more distant neighbors we take J as zero. Then the interaction energy may be written, neglecting components of S perpendicular to the average magnetization,

$$E_{ex} \cong -2Jz\bar{S}^2 = -g\bar{S}\mu_B H_E = -g\bar{S}\mu_B\lambda(g\bar{S}\mu_B\Omega^{-1}),$$

where the term in parentheses is equal to M_s; here Ω is the atomic volume. Then

$$(8.69) \qquad J = \frac{\lambda g^2\mu_B{}^2}{2z\Omega},$$

and, using (8.67) and recalling that $N = 1/\Omega$,

$$(8.70) \qquad J = \frac{3kT_c}{2zS(S+1)}.$$

This is the connection, as given by the Weiss field theory, between the exchange integral and the Curie point. More exact theories give somewhat different results.

TEMPERATURE DEPENDENCE OF THE SPONTANEOUS MAGNETIZATION

On the Weiss theory we must use the complete expression (8.18) for the magnetization in calculating the spontaneous magnetization as a function of temperature. We have

$$(8.71) \qquad M_s = NSg\mu_B B_s(x),$$

where now in the absence of an applied magnetic field

$$(8.72) \qquad x = \frac{Sg\mu_B\lambda M_s}{kT}.$$

At a temperature $T < T_c$ we obtain M_s by plotting M_s versus x as given by both (8.71) and (8.72) and looking for the intercept of the two curves, as shown in Fig. 8.7. The Curie point is the highest temperature for which the curves have an intercept; as defined in this way it is consistent with the earlier result (8.65).

The curves of M_s versus T obtained in this way reproduce the general features of the experimental results, as shown in Fig. 8.8 for nickel. At low temperatures the method of spin waves gives a better approximation.

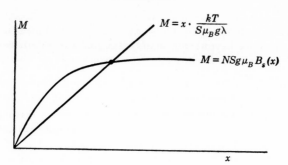

FIG. 8.7. Method for finding the spontaneous magnetization at a temperature T, according to the Weiss theory. The value of M_s is given by the intersection of the two curves.

SPONTANEOUS MAGNETIZATION AT ABSOLUTE ZERO

In Table 8.4 are representative values of the spontaneous magnetization, effective magneton number, and Curie point. The effective magneton number n_{eff} relates to the saturation magnetization, and must not be confused with the paramagnetic effective magneton num-

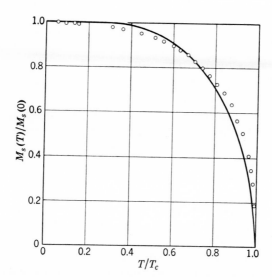

FIG. 8.8. Saturation magnetization of nickel as a function of temperature, together with the theoretical curve for $S = \frac{1}{2}$ on the Weiss theory. [Experimental values by P. Weiss and R. Forrer, *Ann. Phys.* **5**, 153 (1926).]

TABLE 8.4

EFFECTIVE NUMBER n_{eff} OF BOHR MAGNETONS PER MAGNETIC ATOM,
AND DATA ON SATURATION MAGNETIZATION AND CURIE POINTS
(General reference: R. M. Bozorth, *Ferromagnetism*, Van Nostrand, Princeton, New Jersey, 1951.)

Substance	Saturation Magnetization M_s Room Temperature	$0°K$	n_{eff} $(0°K)$	Ferromagnetic Curie Temperature $(°K)$
Fe	1707	1752	2.221	1043
Co	1400	1446	1.716	1400
Ni	485	510	0.606	631
Gd	1090	1980	7.10	289
Dy	1830(80°K)	....	.....	105
MnBi	600	675	3.52	630
Cu$_2$MnAl	430	(580)	(4.0)	603
MnSb	710	....	3.53	587
CrO$_2$	(500)	....	2.07	390
MnOFe$_2$O$_3$	358	....	5.0†	783
FeOFe$_2$O$_3$	485	....	4.2†	848
UH$_3$	....	230	0.90	180

† Calculated per molecule $MOFe_2O_3$, where M is the bivalent cation.

ber p defined by (8.21). Observed magneton numbers are usually considerably smaller than the theoretical values calculated from the free ions and also are frequently nonintegral.

It is possible to modify ionic models to account for the results by allowing mixtures of various ionicity. The most natural way of accounting for the nonintegral magneton numbers is to use a band model on which the $3d$ electrons are visualized as being in two energy bands, as in Fig. 8.9, one for electrons with spin up and the other for electrons with spin down. The bands are separated in energy by the exchange interaction.

FERROMAGNETIC DOMAINS

At temperatures well below the Curie point the electronic magnetic moments of a ferromagnetic specimen are essentially all lined up when regarded on a microscopic scale. Yet, looking at a specimen as a whole, the over-all moment may be very much less than that corresponding to saturation, and the application of an external magnetic field may

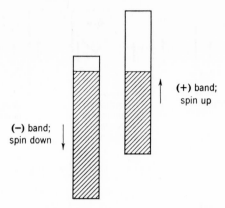

FIG. 8.9. Schematic explanation (for $3d$ electrons) of non-integral magneton numbers, on the band model. The $+$ and $-$ bands contain 5 states per atom each. The case of 7 electrons, 4.25 in one band and 2.75 in the other, is shown; the effective magneton number is 1.5.

be required to saturate the specimen. The behavior observed in single crystals is similar to that in polycrystalline specimens.

Weiss explained this phenomenon, the existence of the technical magnetization curve, by assuming that actual specimens are composed of a number of small regions called domains, within each of which the local magnetization is saturated; the directions of magnetization of different domains, however, need not necessarily be parallel. A schematic arrangement of domains with zero resultant magnetic moment is shown in Fig. 8.10 for a single crystal and in a polycrystal.

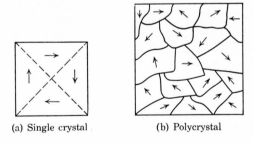

(a) Single crystal   (b) Polycrystal

FIG. 8.10. Schematic domain arrangements for zero resultant magnetic moment in a single crystal (a) and in a polycrystalline specimen (b). The domain structure of the polycrystalline specimen has been drawn for simplicity as if each crystallite contained only a single domain; this is not usually the case. Domains can be larger than or smaller than a crystal grain, depending on the circumstances.

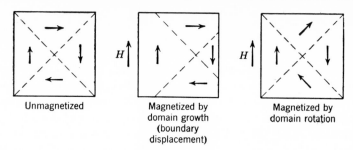

| Unmagnetized | Magnetized by domain growth (boundary displacement) | Magnetized by domain rotation |

FIG. 8.11.   Fundamental magnetization processes.

The increase in the value of the resultant magnetic moment of the specimen under the action of an applied magnetic field may be imagined to take place, according to the domain theory, by two independent processes, as suggested by R. Becker: by an increase in the volume of domains which are favorably oriented with respect to the field at the expense of unfavorably oriented domains; or by rotation of the directions of magnetization toward the direction of the field. These two methods by which the resultant magnetization may change are shown in Fig. 8.11.

Closer examination reveals that in weak fields the magnetization changes usually proceed by means of domain boundary displacements, and so the domains change in size.   In strong fields the magnetization usually changes by means of rotation of the direction of magnetization. Technical terms are defined by Fig. 8.12.

The domain structure of ferromagnetic materials affects closely the technically important properties, which in a transformer core include high permeability, and in a permanent magnet include high coercive force.[8]   By suppressing the possibility of boundary displacement we may achieve a high coercivity; the suppression may be accomplished by using very fine powders or, as in Alnico V, by precipitating a second metallurgical phase so that the specimen is heterogeneous on a very fine scale.   By making the material pure, homogeneous, and well oriented we facilitate boundary displacement and thereby attain high permeability; values of the permeability up to 3.8×10^6 have been reported.

[8] The *coercive force* is defined as the reverse field needed to reduce the induction B or the magnetization M to zero, starting in a saturated condition.   Usually the definition is understood to refer to B, except in theoretical work.   When referred to M, one writes $_IH_c$ or $_MH_c$.

ORIGIN OF DOMAINS

Now we shall show, following Landau and Lifshitz, that domain structure is a natural consequence of the various contributions to the energy—exchange, anisotropy, and magnetic—of a ferromagnetic body. The existence of domains may be inferred from the character of the magnetization curve itself. But the most direct evidence of domain structure is furnished by photomicrographs of domain boundaries obtained by the technique of magnetic powder patterns. This method, applied originally by Bitter (1931), has provided convincing proof that domains exist and behave as expected theoretically. The powder pattern method consists in placing a drop of a colloidal suspension of finely divided ferromagnetic material, such as magnetite, on the carefully prepared surface of the ferromagnetic crystal under study. It is found on observation through a microscope that the colloid particles in the suspension become strongly concentrated about certain well-defined lines which represent the boundaries between domains magnetized in different directions. The reason the colloid particles concentrate near these boundaries is that in their vicinity very strong local magnetic fields exist which attract the magnetic particles. A photograph of a relatively simple domain structure in iron is shown in Fig. 8.13. Domain structures may also be observed with polarized light, following Fowler and Fryer.

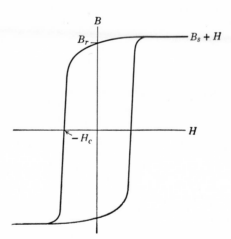

FIG. 8.12. The technical magnetization curve. The *coercive force* H_c is the reverse field necessary to bring the induction B to zero; the *remanence* B_r is the value of B at $H = 0$; the *saturation induction* B_s is defined as the limiting value of $(B - H)$ for large H.

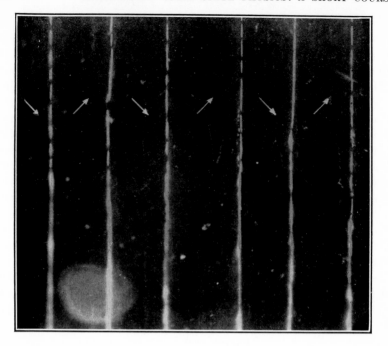

FIG. 8.13. Simple domain structure in Si-Fe single crystal. [After Williams, Bozorth, and Shockley, *Phys. Rev.* **75**, 155 (1949).]

We may understand the origin of domains by considering the structures shown in Fig. 8.14, each representing a cross section through a ferromagnetic single crystal. In (a) we have a saturated configuration consisting of a single domain; as a consequence of the magnetic "poles" formed on the surfaces of the crystal this configuration will have a high value of the magnetic energy $(1/8\pi) \int H^2 \, dV$. The magnetic energy for a square cross section will be of the order of $M_s{}^2 \approx 10^6$ ergs/cm^3; here M_s denotes the saturation magnetization.

In (b) the magnetic energy has been reduced by a factor of roughly one-half as a result of dividing the crystal into two domains magnetized in opposite directions. The subdivision process may be carried further as in (c): with N domains the magnetic energy is reduced (because of the reduced spatial extension of the field) to approximately $1/N$ of the magnetic energy of the saturated configuration (a).

The subdivision process continues until the energy required to establish an additional boundary layer or interface, separating two domains magnetized oppositely, is greater than the reduction in magnetic field energy consequent on the finer subdivision. A boundary layer does have a certain amount of energy associated with it: on opposite sides of the boundary the magnetization is directed in antiparallel directions; as the exchange forces favor parallel and oppose antiparallel orientations of the magnetization, energy will be required to establish a boundary layer. Later we shall calculate this energy and we shall find that it is of the order of 1 erg/cm². If then we suppose tentatively that there are $N = 10^3$ domains/cm, the total boundary energy in a crystal cube 1 cm on each edge will be of the order of 10^3 ergs and the magnetic energy will also be of the order of 10^3 ergs. This situation represents approximately the equilibrium number of domains for the particular geometrical arrangement shown.

It is possible to devise domain arrangements such as (d) and (e) for which the magnetic energy is zero. Here the boundaries of the triangular prism domains (termed "domains of closure") near the end faces of the crystal make equal angles—45°—with the magnetization in the rectangular domains and with the magnetization in the domains of closure: therefore the component of magnetization normal to the boundary is continuous across the boundary, and no poles are

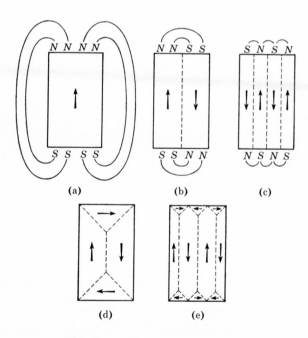

(a)   (b)   (c)

(d)   (e)

FIG. 8.14.   The origin of domains.

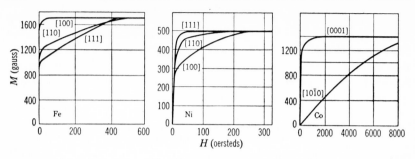

FIG. 8.15.   Magnetization curves for single crystals of iron, nickel, and cobalt.

formed anywhere in the crystal.   As there are no poles there is no magnetic field associated with the magnetization, and we may speak of the flux circuit being completed within the crystal—thus giving rise to the phrase "domains of closure" for the domains near the surfaces of the crystal which act to complete the flux circuit.

The energy required to form a domain of closure in a uniaxial crystal such as cobalt comes principally from what is called the *crystalline anisotropy energy*.   The anisotropy energy tends to make the magnetization of a domain line up along certain crystallographic axes. The axes thus favored are known as preferred axes, or axes of easy magnetization.   A considerably larger amount of energy may be required to saturate a specimen along an arbitrary axis than along one of the preferred axes.   In cobalt the hexagonal axis of the crystal is the only preferred axis, and cobalt is accordingly referred to as uniaxial.   In iron, which is cubic, the preferred axes are the cube edges; in nickel, which is also cubic, the preferred axes are the body diagonals. Figure 8.15 shows magnetization curves for iron, nickel, and cobalt in directions of easy and hard magnetization.

The termination structures revealed by powder patterns are often more complicated than the simple cases we have discussed, but *domain structure always has its origin in the possibility of lowering the energy of a system by going from a saturated configuration with high magnetic energy to a domain configuration with a lower energy.*

A particularly simple type of domain structure is shown in Fig. 8.16.   This structure has been obtained by Williams and Shockley[9] with a single crystal of silicon iron which was cut to the form of a hollow rectangle with legs accurately parallel to [001] and [010] crystal axes.   When the crystal is saturated entirely in one sense the domain

[9] H. J. Williams and W. Shockley, *Phys. Rev.* **75**, 178 (1949).

boundaries are the 45° lines shown in (a); when part of the crystal is magnetized clockwise and part counterclockwise, the square-shaped boundary in (b) is formed in addition. Magnetization changes are then found to take place by the movement of the square-shaped boundary, the flux changes corresponding quantitatively to the displacements of the domain wall.

COERCIVE FORCE AND HYSTERESIS

The coercive force is perhaps the most sensitive property of ferromagnetic materials which is subject to our control, and it is one of the most important criteria in the selection of ferromagnetic materials for practical application. The essential difference between material for permanent magnets and material for transformer cores lies in the coercive force, which may range from the value of 600 oersteds in a loudspeaker magnet (Alnico V) and 20,000 in a special high stability magnet (Fe-Pt) to the value of 0.5 in a commercial power transformer (Si-Fe) or 0.004 in a pulse transformer (Supermalloy). Thus the coercive force may be varied over a range of 5×10^6.

The problem is to interpret the observed values of the coercivity in terms of the physical state of the material. A certain amount of progress has been made, although the problem is beset with the usual difficulty in determining quantitatively the relevant physical factors such as impurities, lattice imperfections, and internal strains. The saturation hysteresis loss at low frequencies is closely related to the coercive force, because the area enclosed by the hysteresis loop is approximately given by the product of the saturation induction B_s and the coercive force. The coercive force diminishes as the precipitate or impurity

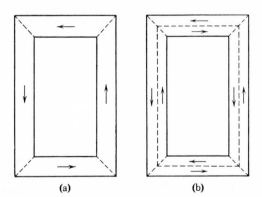

(a)   (b)

FIG. 8.16.   Simple domain structures in single crystal of iron in form of rectangular loop, with legs parallel to [001] and [010] axes.

content decreases and also as internal strains are removed through annealing (slow cooling); alloys containing a precipitated phase may be magnetically hard.

The coercive force of one type of magnetically hard material is well understood; we refer to materials composed of very small grains or fine powders where each particle is always magnetized to saturation as a single domain. The fact that a sufficiently small particle, with diameter less than 10^{-4} or 10^{-5} cm, is composed of a single domain is a result of domain theory, which has been confirmed by experiment. It can be shown[10] that with such very small particles the formation of a domain boundary is energetically unfavorable, because frequently too large a proportion of the volume of a small particle would be contained within the wall, the wall thickness being independent of the particle size.

If a small particle is constrained to remain as a single domain, it will not be possible for magnetization reversal to take place by means of the process of boundary displacement which usually requires relatively weak fields; instead the magnetization of the particle must rotate as a whole, a process which may require large fields depending on the anisotropy energy of the material or the shape of the particle: the reason is that we must rotate the magnetization over the energy hump corresponding to a direction of hard magnetization.

The coercive force of fine iron particles is expected theoretically to be about 250 oersteds on the basis of rotation opposed by the crystalline anisotropy energy, and this is of the order of the value reported by several observers. Higher coercivities have been reported for elongated iron particles, the rotation here being opposed by the shape anisotropy of the demagnetization energy. The high coercivity of powders of MnBi ($_M H_c > 12,000$), according to Guillaud, is in line with the rotation concept, with anisotropy energy as the factor opposing rotation.

REVERSIBLE PERMEABILITY

The extent of the range of field strength over which the permeability is reversible is determined by the distance through which a domain boundary may move without passing over a peak in the curve of wall energy versus distance.

The reversible permeability is determined by the irregularities of the curve of boundary energy versus displacement, and is thus determined by essentially the same physical conditions as the coercive force. A comparison of the initial permeability μ_0 and the coercive force H_c for

[10] C. Kittel, *Phys. Rev.* **70**, 965 (1946), L. Néel, *Compt. rend.* **224**, 1488 (1947).

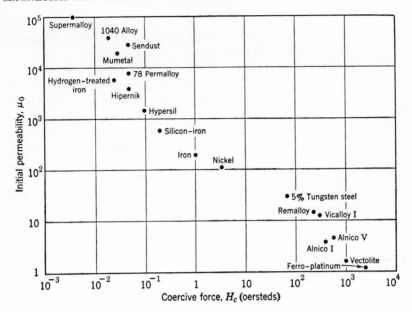

FIG. 8.17.   Correlation between the initial permeability and coercive force of a wide range of magnetic materials.

a wide range of magnetic materials is shown in Fig. 8.17.   There is a very close correlation, materials with high coercivities having low permeabilities, and vice versa.

The range of properties is a striking illustration of the sensitivity of domain processes to the state of stress and subdivision and to the values of the anisotropy and magnetostriction of the ferromagnetic material. In developing a high-permeability material we wish to make the domain boundaries move as freely as possible, free from trapping by strain centers, crystal boundaries, impurities, inclusions, and cavities; we look accordingly for highly purified, oriented, annealed materials of low anisotropy and low magnetostriction (low coupling with internal stresses).   In developing a permanent-magnet alloy we wish to suppress completely the existence or motion of domain boundaries, leaving only the domain rotation processes, and these we wish to make as difficult as possible.

ANISOTROPY ENERGY

The anisotropy energy or, as it is sometimes called, the magneto-crystalline energy of a ferromagnetic crystal acts in such a way that the magnetization tends to be directed along certain definite crystallo-

graphic axes which, accordingly, are called directions of easy magnetization; the directions along which it is most difficult to magnetize
the crystal are called hard directions.

As an example of anisotropy energy we may consider cobalt, which
is a hexagonal crystal. The direction of the hexagonal axis is the
direction of easy magnetization (at room temperature), whereas all
directions in the basal plane, normal to the axis, are hard directions.
The magnetization curves of a single crystal of cobalt are shown in
Fig. 8.15. The energy represented by the magnetization curve in the
hard direction is given by $\int H\, dM$ per unit volume and amounts to an
excess energy of about 5×10^6 ergs/cm^3 for the curve shown.

In cobalt it is found that a very good representation of the experimental observations is given by the two terms

$$(8.73) \qquad f_K = K_1' \sin^2 \theta + K_2' \sin^4 \theta,$$

where θ is the angle the magnetization makes with the hexagonal axis.
At room temperature

$$K_1' = 4.1 \times 10^6 \text{ ergs/cm}^3; \qquad K_2' = 1.0 \times 10^6 \text{ ergs/cm}^3.$$

MAGNETOSTRICTION

It is observed in ferromagnetic single crystals that the length of the
crystal in a given direction relative to the crystal axes depends in
general on the direction of the magnetization relative to the crystal
axes. In cubic crystals the dimensional changes may be expressed
approximately by the relation

$$(8.74) \qquad \frac{\delta l}{l} = \tfrac{3}{2}\lambda_{100}(\alpha_1^2\beta_1^2 + \alpha_2^2\beta_2^2 + \alpha_3^2\beta_3^2 - \tfrac{1}{3})$$

$$+ 3\lambda_{111}(\alpha_1\alpha_2\beta_1\beta_2 + \alpha_2\alpha_3\beta_2\beta_3 + \alpha_3\alpha_1\beta_3\beta_1),$$

where α_1, α_2, α_3 are the direction cosines of the magnetization direction
referred to the cubic axes, and β_1, β_2, β_3 are the direction cosines of the
direction in which δl is measured; λ_{100} and λ_{111} are the saturation
values of the longitudinal magnetostriction in the directions [100] and
[111], respectively. Experimental values are

	$\lambda_{100} \times 10^6$	$\lambda_{111} \times 10^6$
Fe	19.5	−18.8
Ni	−46	−25

For nickel, expression (8.74) does not give a very good fit to the observations, and an expression involving four parameters instead of two is
often used.

Physically it is useful to think of magnetostriction as arising from the dependence of the crystalline anisotropy energy on the state of strain of the lattice; thus it may be energetically favorable for the crystal to deform slightly from the exactly cubic condition if doing so will lower the anisotropy energy by more than the elastic energy is raised.

In devising high-permeability materials an effort is often made to find an alloy composition with low magnetostriction so that internal strains will not induce a local anisotropy energy. In Permalloy, for example, both the anisotropy energy and the magnetostriction are very low.

THE BLOCH WALL

The term "Bloch wall" denotes the transition layer which separates adjacent domains magnetized in different directions.

The essential idea of the Bloch wall is that the entire change in spin direction between domains magnetized in different directions does not occur in one discontinuous jump across a single atomic plane. Rather, the change of direction will take place in a gradual way over many atomic planes (Fig. 8.18). The reason for the gradual nature of the change is that for a given total change of spin direction the exchange

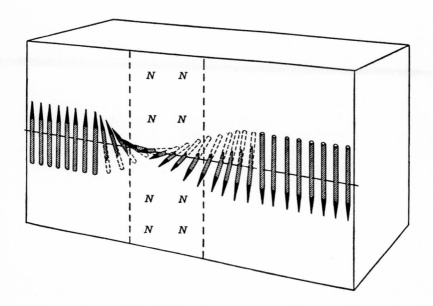

FIG. 8.18. The structure of the transition layer separating domains. In iron the thickness of the transition region is about 300 lattice constants.

energy is lower when the change is distributed over many spins than when the change occurs abruptly.

This behavior may be understood from the expression

$$(8.75) \qquad w_{ex} = JS^2\phi^2$$

for the exchange energy between two spins making a small angle ϕ with each other; here J is the exchange integral and S is the spin quantum number. We obtain this equation by interpreting (8.68) classically, and replacing cos ϕ by $1 - \frac{1}{2}\phi^2$. Let the total desired change of angle be ϕ_0; if the change occurs in N equal steps, the angle change between neighboring spins is ϕ_0/N, and the exchange energy between each pair of neighboring atoms is

$$(8.76) \qquad w_{ex} = JS^2\left(\frac{\phi_0}{N}\right)^2.$$

The total exchange energy of the line of $N + 1$ atoms is thus

$$(8.77) \qquad E_{ex} = \frac{JS^2\phi_0{}^2}{N}.$$

If the total change of angle between domains is $\phi_0 = \pi$, corresponding to a reversal of magnetization direction on passing through the wall, the exchange energy of a line of atoms through a wall 100 atoms in thickness is of the order of $kT_c/100$, as compared with kT_c for a wall only one atom layer in thickness.

Because the exchange energy of a wall is inversely proportional to the thickness (8.77), the wall might spread out until it filled a sizable proportion of the crystal were it not for the restraining effect of the anisotropy energy, which acts to limit the width of the transition layer. As the spins contained within the wall are largely directed away from the axes of easy magnetization, there is a certain amount of anisotropy energy associated with the wall, roughly proportional to the thickness.

The actual thickness and energy of the transition layer is the result of a balance between the competing claims of exchange energy and anisotropy energy, the former tending to increase the thickness and the latter tending to decrease the thickness.

We proceed to make a rough order-of-magnitude estimate of the thickness and energy of a Bloch wall. Let us consider a wall parallel to the cube face of a simple cubic lattice and separating domains magnetized in opposite directions. We wish to determine the thickness of the wall in terms of the number N of atomic planes contained within the wall, and also to determine the energy per unit surface area, σ_w.

The energy may be represented to a good approximation as the sum of contributions from exchange and anisotropy energies:

$$(8.78) \qquad \sigma_w = \sigma_{\text{ex}} + \sigma_{\text{anis}}.$$

The exchange energy is given approximately by (8.77) for each line of atoms through the wall and normal to the plane of the wall. There are $1/a^2$ such lines per unit area, where a is the lattice constant; whence

$$(8.79) \qquad \sigma_{\text{ex}} = \frac{\pi^2 J S^2}{N a^2}.$$

The anisotropy energy is of the order of the anisotropy constant times the volume, or

$$(8.80) \qquad \sigma_{\text{anis}} \approx K N a;$$

therefore

$$(8.81) \qquad \sigma_w \approx \frac{\pi^2 J S^2}{N a^2} + K N a,$$

which is a minimum with respect to N when

$$(8.82) \qquad \frac{\partial \sigma_w}{\partial N} = 0 = -\frac{\pi^2 J S^2}{N^2 a^2} + K a,$$

or

$$(8.83) \qquad N = \left(\frac{\pi^2 J S^2}{K a^3} \right)^{\frac{1}{2}}.$$

For order of magnitude, in iron,

$$N \approx \left(\frac{k T_c}{K a^3} \right)^{\frac{1}{2}} \approx \left(\frac{10^{-13}}{10^5 10^{-23}} \right)^{\frac{1}{2}} \approx 300 \text{ lattice constants}$$

$$\approx 1000 \text{ A.}$$

The total wall energy per unit area is

$$(8.84) \qquad \sigma_w = 2\pi \left(\frac{J K S^2}{a} \right)^{\frac{1}{2}},$$

which in iron is of the order of magnitude

$$\sigma_w = \left(\frac{k T_c K}{a} \right)^{\frac{1}{2}} \approx 1 \text{ erg/cm}^2.$$

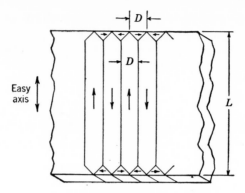

FIG. 8.19.   Flux-closure domain configuration in a uniaxial crystal.

In the above estimate we have rather arbitrarily supposed that the total change in spin direction is shared equally by each of the N atoms on a line through the wall; we have also used a very rough estimate of the anisotropy energy of the spin system within the wall.   More accurate calculation for a $180°$ wall in a (100) plane gives

$$(8.85) \qquad\qquad \sigma_w = 2 \left(\frac{2K_1 J S^2}{a} \right)^{\!\frac{1}{2}},$$

which gives for iron 1.8 ergs/cm^2.

DOMAIN DIMENSIONS

We carry through, following the original treatment by Landau and Lifshitz, the calculation of the domain width for a flux-closure arrangement of domains (Fig. 8.19) in a uniaxial crystal.   The wall energy per unit area of the crystal surface is approximately

$$w_{\text{wall}} = \frac{\sigma_w L}{D}.$$

The volume contained within the domains of closure is oriented in a direction of hard magnetization and involves an energy K per unit volume, where K is the anisotropy constant.   Per unit area of crystal surface on one side, the volume in the domains of closure on both sides is $D/2$, and so

$$(8.86) \qquad\qquad w_{\text{anis}} = \frac{KD}{2}.$$

The wall energy tends to increase the domain width, whereas the anisotropy energy tends to decrease the width.

The total energy is

$$w = \frac{\sigma_w L}{D} + \frac{KD}{2}$$

per unit area, and this is a minimum with respect to the domain width D when

$$\frac{\partial w}{\partial D} = -\frac{\sigma_w L}{D^2} + \frac{K}{2} = 0.$$

The condition for the minimum is then

$$(8.87) \qquad D = \left(\frac{2\sigma_w L}{K}\right)^{\frac{1}{2}}.$$

If we arbitrarily substitute the approximate values of the constants for iron, and take the length L as 1 cm, we have

$$D = \left[\frac{(2)(2)(1)}{4 \times 10^5}\right]^{\frac{1}{2}} \approx 3 \times 10^{-3} \text{ cm.}$$

ANTIFERROMAGNETISM

The antiferromagnetic state is characterized by an ordered antiparallel arrangement of electron spins. When the exchange integral J in (8.68) is positive, we have ferromagnetism; when J is negative, we have antiferromagnetism. On passing below the Curie point of an antiferromagnetic the spins lock in (Fig. 8.20) with antiparallel orientations, and at the Curie point the susceptibility attains its maximum value, as shown in Fig. 8.21. We recognize antiferromagnetism by a well-defined kink in the susceptibility versus temperature curve. The transition is also marked by anomalies in the heat capacity and thermal expansion coefficient. Neutron diffraction experiments are of great importance in determining the spin order in antiferromagnetics.

FIG. 8.20. Comparison of spin ordering in the ferromagnetic and antiferromagnetic states.

Table 8.5 summarizes important data regarding antiferromagnetics. The effective magneton numbers, as deduced from the Curie constant C in the high temperature susceptibility, are not tabulated as the values are generally in close agreement with the values obtaining in ordinary paramagnetic salts. However, the moments for metallic manganese and chromium are much smaller than the free ion values; Shull finds by neutron diffraction that chromium has $0.4\ \mu_B$ and α-manganese 0.5 μ_B. The results for chromium appear to vary considerably according to the preparation of the specimen.

TWO-SUBLATTICE MODEL

The simplest situation in antiferromagnetism arises when the lattice of paramagnetic ions can be divided into two interpenetrating sublattices A, B such that all nearest neighbors of an ion on sublattice A lie on sublattice B. This condition is, for example, satisfied by the sc and bcc lattices, but not by the fcc lattice. If the only interactions are antiferromagnetic interactions between nearest neighbors, we may write for the magnetization above the Curie point on the Weiss field theory

$$(8.88) \qquad \begin{aligned} TM_A &= C'(H - \lambda M_B); \\ TM_B &= C'(H - \lambda M_A). \end{aligned}$$

Here C' is the Curie constant for one sublattice, and the effective field on sublattice A is written as $H - \lambda M_B$, which for positive λ corre-

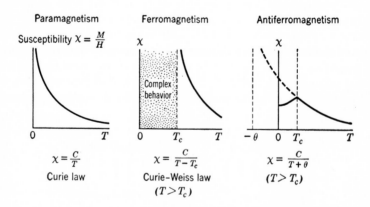

FIG. 8.21. Distinguishing features of the temperature dependence of the magnetic susceptibility in paramagnetism, ferromagnetism, and antiferromagnetism.

TABLE 8.5

SUMMARY OF ANTIFERROMAGNETIC DATA

For a bibliography relating to experimental data on antiferromagnetic substances, see T. Nagamiya, K. Yosida, and R. Kubo, *Advances in Physics* **4,** 1–112 (1955). The value of θ is obtained by fitting an expression of the form $\chi = C/(T + \theta)$ to the susceptibility above the actual transition temperature T_N. The transition temperature is referred to as the Néel temperature.

Substance	Paramagnetic Ion Lattice	Néel Temperature $T_N(°K)$	Curie-Weiss $\theta(°K)$	θ/T_N	$\dfrac{\chi(0)}{\chi(T_N)}$
MnO	Fcc	122	610	5.0	$\frac{2}{3}$
MnS	Fcc	165	528	3.2	0.82
MnSe	Fcc	~150(?)	~ 435(?)	~3	
MnTe	Hex. layer	307			
MnF$_2$	Bc rect.	72	113	1.57	0.76
FeF$_2$	Bc rect.	79	117	1.48	0.72
FeCl$_2$	Hex. layer	23.5	48	2.0	<0.2
FeO	Fcc	198	570	2.9	0.8
CoCl$_2$	Hex. layer	24.9	38.1	1.53	
CoO	Fcc	291			
NiCl$_2$	Hex. layer	49.6	68.2	1.37	
NiO	Fcc	523			
α-Mn	Complex	~100			
Cr	Bcc	475			
CrSb	Hex. layer	725	~1000	1.4	$\sim\frac{1}{4}$
Cr$_2$O$_3$	Complex	310			
TiCl$_3$	Complex	~100			
FeCO$_3$	Complex	57			$\sim\frac{1}{4}$

sponds to antiferromagnetic interactions between A and B. Adding,

$$TM = T(M_A + M_B) = 2C'H - C'\lambda M,$$

and so

$$\chi = \frac{2C'}{T + C'\lambda},$$

or

(8.89)
$$\chi = \frac{C}{T + \theta},$$

with

(8.90)
$$C = 2C'; \qquad \theta = C'\lambda.$$

The transition temperature is that below which each sublattice A and B possesses a magnetic moment even without a field.   Below the Curie point it is not legitimate to treat the moment as a linear function of the effective field, but, as saturation is not important close to the Curie point, linearity may be assumed in the equations for the Curie point.

The transition temperature T_N is then the temperature at which equations (8.88) have a nontrivial solution for the magnetization when $H = 0$.   The condition for this is that the determinant of the coefficients of the unknowns M_A, M_B should be zero:

$$\begin{vmatrix} T & \theta \\ \theta & T \end{vmatrix} = 0,$$

or

(8.91) $$T_N = \theta.$$

On this model the Néel temperature T_N should be equal to the constant θ in the Curie-Weiss law (8.89).   The experimental values in Table 8.5 indicate that values of θ/T_N are usually of the order 1.5 to 5. Values of θ/T_N of the observed magnitude may be obtained when next nearest neighbor interactions are provided for, and when more general kinds of sublattice arrangements are considered.   It is a simple exercise to show that, if a molecular field constant $-\varepsilon$ is introduced to describe interactions within a sublattice, then (Problem 8.10)

$$\frac{\theta}{T_N} = \frac{\lambda + \varepsilon}{\lambda - \varepsilon}.$$

ANTIFERROMAGNETIC RESONANCE

Spin resonance absorption in antiferromagnetic crystals at temperatures above the Curie point is similar to that observed in paramagnetic crystals, but below the Curie point there is a strong effective field leading to a zero field splitting of the resonance line.   In the simplest situation at 0°K the effective field, apart from the applied magnetic field, is given by

(8.92) $$H_{\text{eff}} = [H_A(2H_E + H_A)]^{1/2},$$

where H_A is the effective anisotropy field of one sublattice and H_E is the exchange field.   For manganese fluoride the effective field amounts to 1.0×10^5 oersteds, corresponding to a zero field splitting of 1 mm wavelength.   This has been observed by Johnson and Nethercot.

DETERMINATION OF SPIN LATTICES BY NEUTRON DIFFRACTION

Shull originated with remarkable success the determination of the arrangement of spins into lattices in ferromagnetic and antiferromagnetic substances by neutron diffraction experiments. The experimental spin structure of manganese oxide in the antiferromagnetic state is shown in Fig. 8.22. The most surprising feature about the observed spin lattice structure is that it suggests a strong next nearest neighbor interaction. The strength of the next nearest neighbor interaction may be interpreted on the Kramers picture of superexchange, according to which the possibility of excited paramagnetic states of the intervening anion (oxygen in this case) serves to carry the exchange interaction diametrically across the anion, thereby linking the spin systems of two manganese ions situated too far apart for direct exchange to be important.

FERRITES

The simplest ferrites of magnetic interest belong to the group of compounds of composition represented by the chemical formula $MOFe_2O_3$,

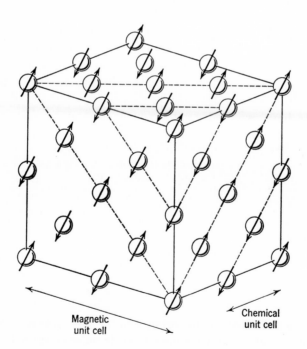

Magnetic unit cell

Chemical unit cell

FIG. 8.22. Arrangement of spins of the Mn^{2+} ions in manganese oxide, MnO, as determined by neutron diffraction methods.

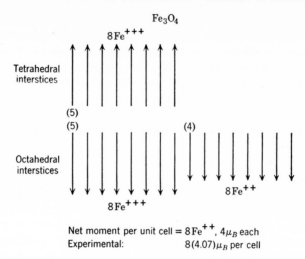

Net moment per unit cell $= 8\,Fe^{++}$, $4\mu_B$ each
Experimental: $8(4.07)\mu_B$ per cell

FIG. 8.23. Schematic spin arrangements in magnetite, $FeO \cdot Fe_2O_3$, showing how the moments of the Fe^{+3} ions cancel out, leaving only the moments of the Fe^{+2} ions.

where M is a divalent metal ion such as Mn, Co, Ni, Cu, Mg, Zn, Cd, Fe^{2+}, or a mixture of these ions. These ferrites are cubic and have the spinel structure, after the mineral spinel ($MgAl_2O_4$). Ferrites may be imagined as derived from magnetite, Fe_3O_4, by replacing the ferrous ions by the divalent ions just listed.

Ferrites have acquired great practical interest because their high electrical resistivities are useful in magnetic applications at high frequencies. The resistivities of commercial ferrites are in the range 10^2 to 10^6 ohm-cm, as compared with 10^{-5} ohm-cm for iron. The original commercial development is due to Snoek, Verwey, and others at the Philips Laboratories. Ferroxcube 3 (Zn-Mn ferrite) and Ferroxcube 4 (Zn-Ni ferrite) are representative of the materials of interest.

We mention here several aspects of the Néel theory of the saturation magnetization of ferrites. We note first from Table 8.4 that the value 485 for the saturation magnetization of Fe_3O_4 corresponds only to 4.2 Bohr magnetons per molecule Fe_3O_4, whereas the value expected if the one Fe^{2+} and two Fe^{3+} ions per molecule are lined up parallel to one another is about $14\mu_B$ per molecule. Néel accounts for the experimental facts by supposing that the Fe^{3+} ions are antiparallel to each other, and so the resultant moment arises only from the Fe^{2+} ion, as in Fig. 8.23. This has a moment of $4\mu_B$ corresponding to a spin of 2: the agreement with the observed moment of magnetite is

quite satisfactory.   Néel terms a situation of this type *ferrimagnetism;*
the idea was used also in the work of Guillaud on manganese compounds such as MnBi.   Néel suggests that all the interactions in
ferrites are antiferromagnetic, but the condition of minimum free
energy may often require, when two types of ions are involved, that
the total magnetization be different from zero.   Ferrimagnetics over
their Curie point are characterized by a plot of $1/\chi$ versus T which is
concave downwards, as shown in Fig. 8.24 for magnetite.   Here χ is
the susceptibility.

The Néel theory accounts in a natural way for the variation with
zinc content of the saturation magnetization curves shown in Fig.
8.25.   The moments for zero zinc content agree quite well with the
idea that the Fe^{3+} ions do not contribute, and the trend of the moments
toward zero for $ZnO \cdot Fe_2O_3$ is also plausible, as shown in Fig. 8.26.
In the intermediate region the zinc ions cause an unbalance in the
system, increasing the total moment.   The situation is discussed by
Went and Gorter.

The spinel structure (Fig. 8.27) may be visualized as a cubic close
packing of oxygen ions with the Fe^{3+} and M^{2+} ions distributed among
the various interstices between the O^{2-} ions.   The unit cell is about
8.4 A on a side and contains 64 tetrahedral interstices (A) each with
four O^{2-} nearest neighbors and 32 octahedral interstices (B) each
with six O^{2-} nearest neighbors.   Eight of the tetrahedral and sixteen
of the octahedral sites are occupied, thus accommodating 24 metal
ions in the unit cell.   The exchange interactions $A - A$, $B - B$, and

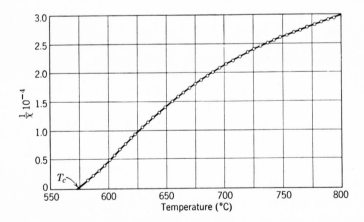

FIG. 8.24.   Reciprocal susceptibility of magnetite, $FeO \cdot Fe_2O_3$, above the Curie
temperature.

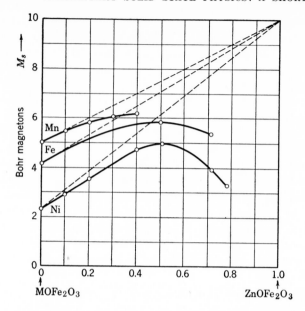

FIG. 8.25. Saturation magnetization of mixed Mn-Zn, Fe-Zn, and Ni-Zn ferrites, as a function of the zinc content. [After J. J. Went and E. W. Gorter, *Philips Tech. Rev.* **13**, 181 (1952).]

$A - B$ are all antiferromagnetic. The $A - B$ interaction is usually considerably the strongest, so the A and B lattices are individually ferromagnetic but with the magnetizations M_A, M_B oppositely directed. If, however, $M_A = 0$ as in zinc ferrite, the only effective exchange interaction is $B - B$; so the B ions will be antiferromagnetically ordered and $M_B = 0$.

The circumstance that three antiferromagnetic interactions can

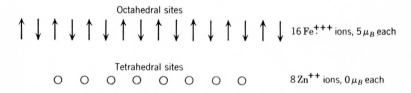

FIG. 8.26. Explanation of zero saturation magnetization in zinc ferrite; the zinc ions are diamagnetic and occupy the tetrahedral sites (Fig. 8.27). The antiferromagnetic interaction of the ferric ions on the octahedral sites controls the magnetic structure.

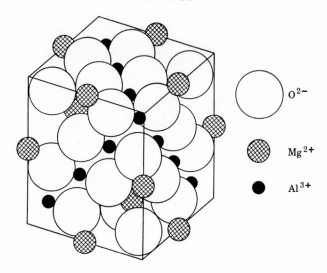

FIG. 8.27. Crystal structure of the mineral spinel ($MgAl_2O_4$); the Mg^{+2} ions occupy tetrahedral sites, each surrounded by four oxygen ions; the Al^{+3} ions occupy octahedral sites, each surrounded by six oxygen ions. This is a *normal* spinel arrangement.

result in ferromagnetism is worth looking into more closely. The molecular fields acting on the A and B spin lattices may be written

(8.93)
$$\mathbf{H}_A = -\lambda\mathbf{M}_A - \mu\mathbf{M}_B;$$
$$\mathbf{H}_B = -\mu\mathbf{M}_A - \nu\mathbf{M}_B;$$

taking λ, μ, ν to be positive if the interactions are all antiferromagnetic. The interaction energy is then

(8.94)
$$E = -\tfrac{1}{2}(\mathbf{H}_A \cdot \mathbf{M}_A + \mathbf{H}_B \cdot \mathbf{M}_B)$$
$$= \tfrac{1}{2}\lambda M_A{}^2 + \mu\mathbf{M}_A \cdot \mathbf{M}_B + \tfrac{1}{2}\nu M_B{}^2,$$

which is lower when M_A is antiparallel than when it is parallel to M_B. The energy when antiparallel must be compared with zero; the energy for $M_A = M_B = 0$. Thus when

(8.95)
$$\mu M_A M_B > \tfrac{1}{2}(\lambda M_A{}^2 + \nu M_B{}^2),$$

the ground state will have M_A directed oppositely to M_B. The saturation magnetization is $M_s = |\mathbf{M}_A + \mathbf{M}_B|$.

Yttrium iron garnet $3Y_2O_3 \cdot 5Fe_2O_3$ is a ferrimagnetic dielectric crystal which is very important to research concerned with dynamic

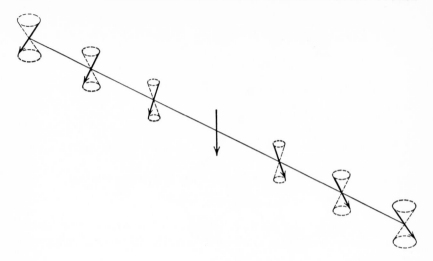

FIG. 8.28.   Standing spin wave on a line of atoms.

ferromagnetic processes, such as resonance, relaxation, and spin waves. It was discovered by Bertaut and Forrat.   YIG, as it is called, does not have the spinel structure, but has the more complicated garnet structure, which is also cubic.   The yttrium ions Y^{3+} are diamagnetic; the iron is all present as Fe^{3+}, each having $5\mu_B$ magnetic moment, but for each 3 Fe^{3+} ions magnetized one way there are 2 Fe^{3+} ions magnetized in the opposite sense.   All the magnetic ions are identical, and there is no ambiguity about the valency of the magnetic ion occupying a given site—thus the magnetic structure is much more perfect than that of the spinels, where ferric and ferrous ions are often interchanged.   Aided by its chemical and structural perfection, YIG in the form of highly polished single crystal spheres has the sharpest known ferromagnetic resonance line—of the order of 0.1 oersted.

SPIN WAVES

We are often concerned in solid state physics with the low-energy and long-wavelength collective excitations of complex systems.   The low-lying excited vibrational states of a crystal lattice are elastic waves (phonons), whereas the detachment of a single atom from the crystal involves a greater energy.   The low lying excited states of a system of spins with exchange interactions are spin waves (magnons), in which the individual spin directions are tilted in a wavelike pattern, as shown in Fig. 8.28.   States in which a single spin is turned around have a higher energy in general.

We can represent a spin wave quite simply. We consider a ferro-magnet magnetized on the average along the z direction. Let

$$\mathbf{S} = \mathbf{S}_0 + \boldsymbol{\varepsilon},$$

where $\mathbf{S}_0$ is the unperturbed spin vector, and $\boldsymbol{\varepsilon}$ represents a spin wave of small amplitude. We look for states of the form

(8.96)
$$\varepsilon_x = \varepsilon_0 \sin \omega t \sin k_x x \sin k_y y \sin k_z z;$$
$$\varepsilon_y = \varepsilon_0 \cos \omega t \sin k_x x \sin k_y y \sin k_z z.$$

It may be shown that (8.68) leads to the dispersion relation

(8.97) $$\hbar \omega = 2 S_0 J a^2 k^2,$$

where a is the lattice constant for spins on a simple cubic lattice. These waves have been observed directly in several microwave experiments.

PROBLEMS

8.1. The wave function of the hydrogen atom in its ground state $(1s)$ is

$$\psi = (\pi a_0{}^3)^{-\frac{1}{2}} e^{-r/a_0},$$

where $a_0 = \hbar^2/me^2 = 0.529 \times 10^{-8}$ cm. The charge density is $\rho(x,y,z) = e|\psi|^2$, according to the statistical interpretation of the wave function. Show that for this state

$$\overline{r^2} = 3 a_0{}^2,$$

and calculate the molar diamagnetic susceptibility of atomic hydrogen $(-2.36 \times 10^{-6}$ cm^3/mole$)$.

8.2. Show that on the Langevin theory the first two terms in a series expansion of the differential susceptibility are

$$\chi = \frac{dM}{dH} = \frac{N\mu^2}{3kT} \left[1 - \frac{(\mu H/kT)^2}{5} + \cdots \right].$$

8.3. Some organic molecules have a triplet $(S = 1)$ excited state not far above a singlet $(S = 0)$ ground state. Plot the susceptibility as a function of temperature for a zero field splitting $\Delta/k = 100°$K, where k is the Boltzmann constant. Show that the susceptibility for $kT \gg \Delta$ is approximately independent of Δ.

8.4. Making *rough* calculations, compare the electronic spin entropy (for $H = 0$) at $2°$K of 1 cm^3 of the salt iron ammonium alum, $FeNH_4(SO_4)_2 \cdot 12H_2O$, with the lattice phonon entropy of 1 cm^3 of lead at the same temperature. This result shows that we may use the salt to cool other substances. At $2°$K, $T/\theta_0 > 10$ for iron ammonium alum, where $k\theta_0$ is the zero field splitting. Neglect nuclear spin effects.

8.5. A paramagnetic salt contains 10^{22} ions/cm^3 with magnetic moment 1 Bohr magneton. (a) Calculate the surplus fraction, that is, the percentage indicating how many more spins are parallel rather than antiparallel to a magnetic field of 10,000 oersteds at 300°K.   (b) Calculate the magnetization in this field.

8.6. Express Im χ^+ from (8.52) in terms of the static parallel susceptibility $\chi_0 = M_z/H_z$; show that at resonance

$$\frac{\text{Im } \chi^+}{\chi_0} = \gamma H_z T_2 = \omega_0 T_2 = \frac{H}{\Delta H},$$

which is a measure of the amplification or Q factor of the susceptibility at resonance.

8.7. (a) The rate of energy absorption at resonance by a system of spins having $S = \frac{1}{2}$ is proportional to $H_{rf}{}^2$ Im χ^+, and thus to $H_{rf}{}^2 T_2 \Delta n$, where Δn is the excess of population in the ground state over the upper state. We have used the fact that $M_z \propto \Delta n$. Show that because in the steady state the relaxation losses balance the energy input

$$\frac{-(\Delta n - \overline{\Delta n})}{T_1} = C H_{rf}{}^2 T_2 \Delta n,$$

from (8.42), where C is a constant and $\overline{\Delta n}$ is the value of Δn at thermal equilibrium. Solve for the value of $H_{rf}{}^2$ for which $\Delta n = \frac{1}{2}\overline{\Delta n}$. This result is sometimes used to determine T_1, but it is applicable principally when $T_1 \approx T_2$. (b) One form of paramagnetic amplifier (maser) depends on the establishment at time zero of an inverted thermal population $\Delta n(0) = \overline{\Delta n}$. After $t = 0$ the system is free. Derive expressions for $\Delta n(t)$ with and without an r-f field H_{rf}, and observe that the r-f field stimulates the emission of energy.

8.8. Show that the condition for ferromagnetic resonance in a general ellipsoid with demagnetizing factors N_x, N_y, N_z is

$$\omega = \gamma\{[H + (N_x - N_z)M][H + (N_y - N_z)M]\}^{\frac{1}{2}},$$

where the static field H is in the z direction. It is assumed that the ellipsoid is small in comparison with the wavelength and is made of an insulating ferromagnetic substance, such as a ferrite, so that eddy current effects may be neglected.

8.9. Consider a small spherical single domain particle. Show that the effective permeability for a weak field applied perpendicular to the easy axis is

$$\mu = 1 + 2\pi \left(\frac{M_s{}^2}{k}\right),$$

and show that $2K/M_s$ may be regarded as an effective anisotropy field. Show also that the reverse field along the axis required to reverse the magnetization is

$$H = \frac{2K}{M_s}.$$

The coercive force for a single domain particle is of this magnitude.

8.10. Taking the effective fields on the two sublattice model of an antiferromagnetic as

$$H_A = H - \lambda M_B - \epsilon M_A,$$

$$H_B = H - \lambda M_A - \epsilon M_B,$$

show that

$$\frac{\theta}{T_N} = \frac{\lambda + \epsilon}{\lambda - \epsilon}.$$

8.11.* The theory of the microwave *gyrator* is discussed by C. L. Hogan, *Bell System Tech. J.* **31**, 1 (1952); applications are reviewed by J. H. Rowen, *Bell System Tech. J.* **32**, 1333 (1953). A plane-polarized electromagnetic wave is incident normally on a ferrite slab of thickness l. A static magnetic field H_0 is applied parallel to the propagation direction. Neglecting attenuation, show that the rotation θ of the plane of polarization in the ferrite is $\theta \cong \frac{1}{2}\epsilon^{1/2}\omega_1 l$, where ϵ is the dielectric constant of the ferrite, $\omega_1 = 4\pi M\gamma \cong \gamma H_0$, where γ is defined by Eq. (8.38). The derivation proceeds most easily by substituting $\dot{\mathbf{M}} = \gamma \mathbf{M} \times \mathbf{H}$ in the Maxwell equation for curl **E**, giving

$$c \text{ curl } \mathbf{E} = -(\dot{\mathbf{H}} + \omega_1 \times \mathbf{H}).$$

Proceeding in the usual way, find a wave equation for **H**. Let $h^{\pm} = H_x \pm iH_y$, and look for solutions of the form $e^{i(\omega t - kz)}$. Assume $\omega_1 \ll \omega$, and $H_0 < 4\pi M_s$, so that an elementary consideration of the demagnetization conditions gives $4\pi M \cong H_0$ for the average (nonsaturation) magnetization; the z component of the static field within the slab is $H_0 - 4\pi M \cong 0$ and may be neglected.

REFERENCES

A. Abragam, *Nuclear magnetism*, Oxford, 1961.

L. F. Bates, *Modern magnetism*, Cambridge University Press, Cambridge, 3rd ed., 1951.

R. Becker and W. Döring, *Ferromagnetismus*, J. Springer, Berlin, 1939.

B. Bleaney and K. W. H. Stevens, "Paramagnetic resonance," *Repts. Prog. Phys.* **16**, 108 (1953).

K. D. Bowers and J. Owen, "Paramagnetic resonance II," *Repts. Prog. Phys.* **18**, 304 (1955).

R. M. Bozorth, *Ferromagnetism*, Van Nostrand, Princeton, New Jersey, 1951.

H. B. G. Casimir, *Magnetism and very low temperatures*, Cambridge University Press, Cambridge, 1940.

K. K. Darrow, "Magnetic resonance," *Bell System Tech. J.* **32**, 74–99, 384–405 (1953).

C. G. B. Garrett, *Magnetic cooling*, Harvard University Press, Cambridge, 1954.

C. J. Gorter, editor, *Progress in low temperature physics*, Interscience, New York, 1955.

C. J. Gorter, *Paramagnetic relaxation*, Elsevier, Amsterdam, 1947.

C. Kikuchi and R. D. Spence, "Microwave methods in physics: II. Microwave absorption in paramagnetic substances," *Am. J. Phys.* **18**, 167 (1950).

C. Kittel, Physical theory of ferromagnetic domains, *Revs. Modern Phys.* **21**, 541 (1949); C. Kittel and J. K. Galt, *Solid State Physics*, **3** (1956).

A. Lidiard, "Antiferromagnetism," *Repts. Prog. Phys.* **17**, 201–244 (1954).

W. Low, "Paramagnetic resonance in solids." *Solid state physics*, Vol. 2 supplement, edited by F. Seitz and D. Turnbull, Academic Press, New York, 1960.

K. Mendelssohn, *Cryophysics*, Interscience, New York, 1960.

U. M. Martius, "Ferromagnetism," *Progress in Metal Physics* **3**, 140–175 (1952).

T. Nagamiya, K. Yosida, and R. Kubo, "Antiferromagnetism," *Advances in Physics* **4**, 1–122 (1955).

ONR Maryland Magnetism Conference, *Revs. Modern Phys.* (January, 1953).

G. E. Pake, "Nuclear magnetic resonance." *Solid state physics*, Vol. 2, edited by F. Seitz and D. Turnbull, Academic Press, New York, 1956.

H. Reich, "Die Theorie des ferromagnetischen Resonanz und die Ergebnisse ihrer experimentellen Untersuchung," *Z. angew. Physik* **6**, 326–338 (1954).

M. G. Say, editor, *Magnetic alloys and ferrites*, Newnes, London, 1954.

P. W. Selwood, *Magnetochemistry*, Interscience Publishers, New York, 1943.

J. Smit and H. P. J. Wijn, *Ferrites*, John Wiley and Sons, New York, 1959.

K. H. Stewart, Ferromagnetic domains, Cambridge University Press, Cambridge, 1954.

E. C. Stoner, "Ferromagnetism," *Rept. Prog. Phys.* **11**, 43 (1948); **13**, 83 (1950).

E. C. Stoner, *Magnetism and matter*, Methuen and Co., Ltd., London, 1934.

J. H. Van Vleck, "A survey of the theory of ferromagnetism," *Revs. Modern Phys.* **17**, 27 (1945).

J. H. Van Vleck, "Recent developments in the theory of antiferromagnetism," *J. phys. radium* **12**, 262 (1951).

J. H. Van Vleck, "Quelques aspects de la théorie du magnétisme," *Ann. inst. Henri Poincaré* **10**, 57 (1947).

J. H. Van Vleck, *The theory of electric and magnetic susceptibilities*, Clarendon Press, Oxford, 1932.

Note: The detailed proceedings of a large magnetics conference held annually in the United States appear as supplements to the *Journal of Applied Physics*, starting in 1958.

9 Dislocations: strength of solids

This chapter is concerned principally with the interpretation of the mechanical properties of crystalline solids in terms of the theory of dislocations. The plasticity of pure single crystals of many solids is a striking feature of their mechanical behavior. This fundamental weakness of crystals is exhibited in various ways depending on the crystal, but there appear to be few exceptions to the rule that pure crystals are plastic and are not strong. Pure silver chloride melts at 455°C, yet at room temperature it has a cheeselike consistency and can be rolled into sheets. Pure aluminum crystals are elastic only to a strain of about 10^{-5}, after which they deform plastically, small crystals of pure tellurium deform under their own weight at room temperature. Theoretical estimates of the elastic limit of perfect crystals give values as much as 10^3 or 10^4 higher than the observed values, although it is more usual to find a factor of the order of 10^2. A few pure crystals are inherently strong: highly purified germanium and silicon are not plastic at room temperature and fail only by fracture. Glass also fails only by fracture at room temperature, but it is not crystalline. The fracture of glass is believed to be caused by stress concentration at minute cracks.

SHEAR STRENGTH OF SINGLE CRYSTALS

Frenkel gave a simple method of estimating the theoretical shear strength of a perfect crystal. Referring to Fig. 9.1, we consider the force needed to shear two planes of atoms past each other. In the region of small elastic strains the stress σ is related to the displacement x by

(9.1)
$$\sigma = \frac{Gx}{d},$$

305

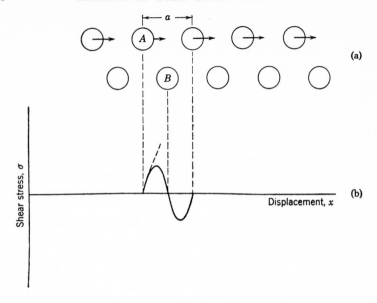

FIG. 9.1.   (a) Relative shear of two planes of atoms (shown in cross section) in a uniformly strained crystal; (b) shear stress as a function of the relative displacement of the planes from their equilibrium position.   The heavy broken line is drawn at the initial slope corresponding to the shear modulus G.

where d is the interplanar spacing and G is the shear modulus, given by c_{44} for shear in a $\langle 100 \rangle$ direction on a $\{100\}$ plane in a cubic crystal. When the displacement has proceeded to the point that atom A is directly over atom B in the figure, the planes of atoms are in a configuration of unstable equilibrium and the stress is zero.   As a first approximation we may represent the stress-displacement relation by a sine function:

$$(9.2) \qquad \sigma = \frac{Ga}{2\pi d} \sin \frac{2\pi x}{a},$$

where a is the interatomic spacing in the direction of shear.   For small x this relation reduces to (9.1).   The critical shear stress σ_c at which the lattice becomes unstable is given by the maximum value of σ, or

$$(9.3) \qquad \sigma_c = \frac{Ga}{2\pi d}.$$

If $a \approx d$, $\sigma_c \approx G/2\pi$; the critical shear stress should be of the order of $\frac{1}{6}$ of the shear modulus.

Reference to the observations in Table 9.1 shows that the observed values of the elastic limit are much smaller than (9.3) would suggest. We note for comparison with values tabulated in handbooks that a value given in kilograms per square millimeter is to be multiplied by approximately 0.98×10^8 to obtain dynes per square centimeter, and a value given in (long) tons per square inch is to be multiplied by 1.54×10^8 to obtain dynes per square centimeter. The theoretical estimate may be improved by taking into account the actual form of the intermolecular forces and by consideration of other configurations of mechanical stability that the lattice may develop as it is sheared. Mackenzie has shown that these two effects may reduce the theoretical shear strength to about $G/30$, corresponding to a critical shear strain of about two degrees.

It is clear that the shear strength cannot be discussed simply by extending the theory of elasticity to large strains, but we must instead look for imperfections that can act as sources of mechanical weakness in real crystals. It is now known that special crystal imperfections called dislocations exist in almost all crystals, and their presence is responsible for slip at very low applied stresses.

In many crystals plastic deformation occurs by translational *slip*, as shown in Fig. 9.2. Here one part of the crystal slides as a unit across an adjacent part. The surface on which slip takes place is often a plane, which is known as the slip plane. The direction of motion is known as the slip direction. The visible intersection of a slip plane with the outer surface of the crystal is known as a slip band.

The great importance of lattice properties for plastic strain is indi-

TABLE 9.1

COMPARISON OF SHEAR MODULUS AND ELASTIC LIMIT

(After Mott)

	Shear Modulus G (dynes/cm^2)	Elastic Limit B (dynes/cm^2)	G/B
Sn, single crystal	1.9×10^{11}	1.3×10^7	15,000
Ag, single crystal	2.8×10^{11}	6×10^6	45,000
Al, single crystal	2.5×10^{11}	4×10^6	60,000
Al, pure, polycrystal	2.5×10^{11}	2.6×10^8	900
Al, commercial drawn	$\sim2.5 \times 10^{11}$	9.9×10^8	250
Duralumin	$\sim2.5 \times 10^{11}$	3.6×10^9	70
Fe, soft, polycrystal	7.7×10^{11}	1.5×10^9	500
Heat-treated carbon steel	$\sim8 \times 10^{11}$	6.5×10^9	120
Nickel-chrome steel	$\sim8 \times 10^{11}$	1.2×10^{10}	65

cated by the highly anisotropic nature of slip. Even in the cubic metals displacement takes place along well-defined crystallographic planes with a small set of Miller indices, such as the {111} planes in fcc metals and the {110}, {112}, and {123} planes in bcc metals. Under most conditions the slip direction lies in the line of closest atomic packing, ⟨110⟩ in fcc metals, ⟨111⟩ in bcc metals, and ⟨2 $\bar{1}$ $\bar{1}$ 0⟩ in hcp metals.

Deformation by slip is inhomogeneous: large shear displacements occur on a few widely separated slip planes while parts of the crystal lying between slip planes remain essentially undeformed. A further property of slip is the Schmid law of the critical shear stress, which states that slip takes place along a given slip plane and direction when the corresponding component of shear stress reaches a critical value.

A second mode of plastic deformation, called *twinning*, is observed in some crystals, particularly in hcp and bcc crystals. We saw that a considerable amount of displacement occurs on a few widely separated slip planes during the slip process. During twinning, on the other hand, a small amount of displacement (less than one lattice parameter)

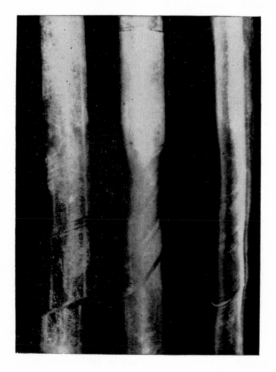

FIG. 9.2.   Translational slip in zinc single crystals.   (Courtesy E. R. Parker.)

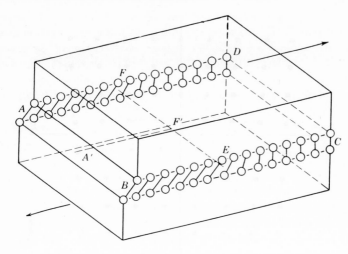

FIG. 9.3. An edge dislocation, showing the glide plane $ABCD$, the slipped region $ABEF$ in which the atoms have been displaced by more than half a lattice constant, and the unslipped region $FECD$ with displacement less than half a lattice constant. The dislocation line is EF and the slip direction is $A'F'$. (After Cottrell, *Progress in metal physics*, No. 1, Butterworths Scientific Publications, London, 1949.)

occurs successively on each of many neighboring crystallographic planes. After deformation, the deformed part of the crystal is converted to a mirror image of the undeformed part, accounting for the name of the process. Although both slip and twinning are caused by the motion of dislocations, we shall be concerned primarily with slip.

DISLOCATIONS

The low observed values of the critical shear stress can be explained in terms of the motion through the lattice of a particular type of imperfection known as a dislocation.

We first describe an edge dislocation. Figure 9.3 shows a simple cubic crystal in which slip of one atom distance has occurred over the left half of the slip plane but not over the right half. The boundary between the slipped and unslipped regions is the dislocation. It is a line imperfection, whose position is marked by the termination of an extra vertical half-plane of atoms crowded into the upper half of the crystal as shown in Fig. 9.4. Near the dislocation the crystal is highly strained. The simple edge dislocation extends indefinitely in the slip plane in a direction normal to the slip direction. In Fig. 9.5 we show a photograph of a dislocation in a two-dimensional soap bubble raft obtained by the method of Bragg and Nye.

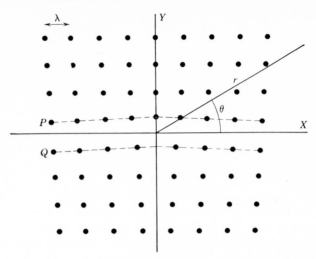

FIG. 9.4.   Structure of an edge dislocation.   The deformation may be thought of as caused by inserting an extra plane of atoms on the upper half of the y axis. Atoms in the upper half-crystal P are compressed and those in the lower half Q are extended.   This is defined as a positive dislocation; if the extra plane is put in from below, the dislocation is negative.   (After Cottrell.)

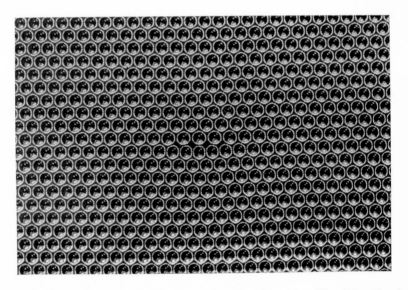

FIG. 9.5.   A dislocation in a two-dimensional bubble raft.   The dislocation is most easily seen by turning the page by 30° in its plane and sighting at a low angle. (Photograph courtesy of W. M. Lomer, after Bragg and Nye.)

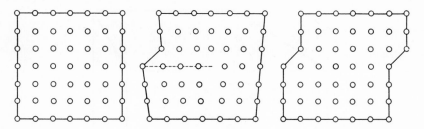

FIG. 9.6.   Motion of a dislocation under a shear tending to move the upper surface
of the specimen to the right.

The mechanism responsible for the mobility of a dislocation and the attendant ease of slip is shown in Fig. 9.6. When atoms on one side of the slip plane are moved with respect to those on the other side, part of the atoms at the slip plane will experience repulsive forces and part will experience attractive forces from their neighbors across the slip plane. To a first approximation these forces cancel, and so the external stress required to move a dislocation will be quite small. If the dislocation line is not straight, the cancellation will be even more complete. Calculations show that a dislocation in an otherwise perfect crystal can be made to move by very low stresses, probably below 10^5 dynes/cm^2. Thus dislocations may make a crystal very plastic. Passage of a dislocation through a crystal is equivalent to slip of usually one fundamental translation vector of the lattice. The motion of an edge dislocation through a crystal is analogous to the passage of a ruck (wrinkle) across a rug: the ruck moves more easily than the whole rug, but passage of the ruck across the rug does amount to sliding the rug on the floor.

The second simple type of dislocation is the screw dislocation, sketched in Fig. 9.7. It marks a boundary between slipped and unslipped crystal. The boundary parallels the slip direction, instead of lying perpendicular to it as with the edge dislocation. The screw dislocation may be thought of as being produced by cutting the crystal part way through with a knife

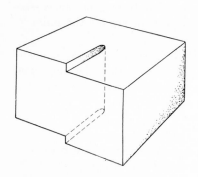

FIG. 9.7.   View of a screw dislocation. The broken vertical line
which marks the dislocation is surrounded by strained material.

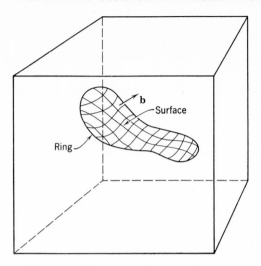

FIG. 9.8. General method of forming a dislocation ring in a medium. The medium is represented by the rectangular block. The ring is represented by the closed curve in the interior in the block. A cut is made along the surface bounded by the curve and indicated by the contoured area. The material on one side of the cut is displaced relative to that on the other by vector distance **b**, which may be arbitrarily oriented relative to the surface. Forces will be required to effect the displacement. The medium is filled in or cut away so as to be continuous after the displacement. It is then joined in the displaced state and the applied forces are relaxed. **b** is the Burgers vector of the dislocation. (After Seitz.)

and shearing it one atom spacing parallel to the edge of the cut. We note that the presence of a screw dislocation transforms successive atom planes into the surface of a helix, accounting for the name of the dislocation.

Compound and ring dislocations may be formed from segments of edge and screw dislocations. Burgers has shown that the most general form of linear dislocation pattern in a crystal can be described as shown in Fig. 9.8. We consider any closed curve not necessarily planar within a crystal, or an open curve terminating on the surface at both ends. Make a cut along any simple surface bounded by the line. Displace the material on one side of this surface by **b** relative to the other side; **b** is a fixed vector called the *Burgers vector*. In regions where **b** is not parallel to the cut surface this relative displacement will either produce a gap or cause the two halves to overlap. In these cases material is either added to fill the gap or is subtracted to prevent overlap. Then rejoin the material on both sides, leaving the strain displacement intact at the time of rewelding, but afterwards allowing the medium to come to internal equilibrium. The resulting strain pattern is that of the dislocation characterized jointly by the boundary curve and the Burgers vector. It is clear that the Burgers vector must be one of a discrete set of lattice vectors that will allow the rewelding process to maintain the crystallinity of the material.

The Burgers vector of a screw dislocation is parallel to the dislocation line, whereas that of an edge dislocation is perpendicular to the dislocation line and lies in the slip plane.

STRESS FIELDS OF EDGE DISLOCATIONS

We can see, as in Fig. 9.4, that the atoms above the dislocation line are compressed and that the atoms below are extended. If two similar edge dislocations are present, one above the other, the strain fields will tend to cancel, thereby lowering the energy of the system. Thus two dislocations, one above the other, tend to attract each other. If the edge dislocations are side by side the strain fields add, the energy is increased, and the dislocations tend to repel each other. Thus dislocation arrays will have a lower energy when the dislocations are lined up as in Fig. 9.9 than when they are lined up alongside each other.

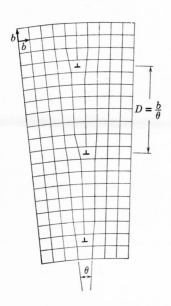

FIG. 9.9. Low-angle grain boundary. (After Burgers.) The inverted T denotes an edge dislocation, the vertical member of the T denoting an extra plane of atoms.

LOW-ANGLE GRAIN BOUNDARIES

Burgers suggested that low-angle grain boundaries in crystals consist of arrays of dislocations. A simple example of the Burgers model is shown in Fig. 9.9, in which the boundary occupies a (010) plane in a simple cubic lattice and divides two parts of the crystal that have a [001] axis in common. This is referred to as a pure tilt boundary, because the existing misorientation can be described by a small rotation (θ) of one part of the crystal relative to the other about the common [001] axis. The boundary is represented in Fig. 9.9 as an array of edge dislocations of the same sign having a spacing $D = b/\theta$, where b is the magnitude of the Burgers vector of

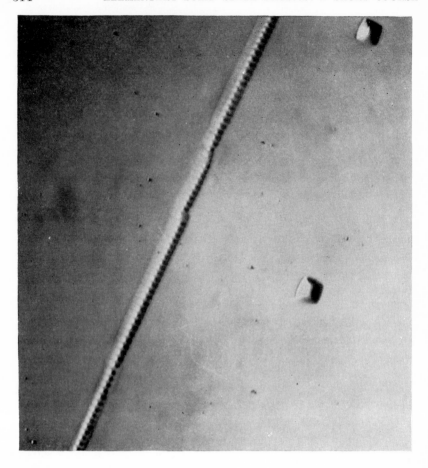

FIG. 9.10.   Dislocation etch pits in low-angle boundary on (100) face of germanium; the angle of the boundary is 27.5 sec.   The boundary lies in a $(0\,\bar{1}\,1)$ plane; the line of the dislocations is [100].   The Burgers vector is the shortest lattice translation vector, or $|\mathbf{b}| = \sqrt{2}\,a/2 = 4.0$ A.   [After F. L. Vogel, Jr., *Acta Metallurgica* **3**, 245 (1955).]

the dislocations.   It is clear from our discussion of the forces between edge dislocations that this configuration, with dislocations of like sign stacked up one above the other, is stable.

A direct verification of the Burgers model is provided by the quantitative x-ray and optical studies of low-angle boundaries in germanium crystals by Vogel and co-workers.   By counting etch pits along the intersection of a low-angle grain boundary with an etched germanium surface, Fig. 9.10, they determined the dislocation spacing D on the assumption that each etch pit marked the end of a dislocation. They then calculated the angle of tilt from the relation $\theta = b/D$, and compared it with the angle measured directly by means of x-rays. The results are in excellent agreement, as shown in Fig. 9.11.

The interpretation of low-angle boundaries as arrays of dislocations is further supported by the fact that pure tilt boundaries can be made to move normal to themselves by the application of a stress. The motion has been demonstrated in a beautiful experiment by Washburn and Parker. The nature of their results is exhibited in Fig. 9.12. The specimen consisted of a bicrystal of zinc containing a 2° tilt boundary. The dislocations are about thirty atomic planes apart. One side of the crystal was clamped, and a force was applied at a point on the opposite side of the boundary. Motion of the boundary took place by cooperative motion of the dislocations in the array, each dislocation moving an equal distance in its own slip plane. Opposite top and bottom intersections at the boundary with the surface moved approximately the same amount. The motion was produced by stresses of the order of magnitude of the yield stress for zinc crystals, a fact that

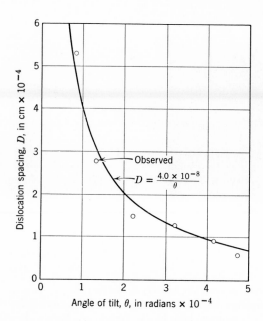

FIG. 9.11. Plot of dislocation spacing calculated from angle of tilt versus observed pit spacings. Angles range from 17.5 to 85 sec. (After Vogel.)

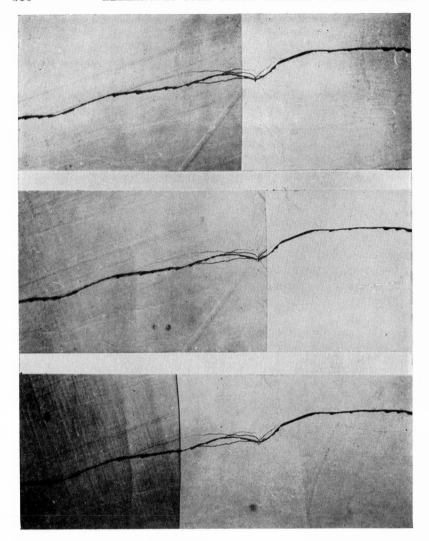

FIG. 9.12. Motion of a small-angle grain boundary under stress. The boundary is the straight vertical line, and it is photographed under vertical illumination, thereby making evident the 2° angular change in the cleavage surface of the zinc crystal at the boundary. The irregular horizontal line is a small step in the cleavage surface which serves as a reference mark. The crystal is clamped at the left; at the right it is subject to a force normal to the plane of the page. *Top*, original position of boundary; *center*, moved 0.1 mm to the right; *bottom*, moved back 0.4 mm. [After J. Washburn and E. R. Parker, *J. Metals*, **4**, 1076 (1952).] A motion picture showing these and related experiments has been prepared by Professor E. R. Parker, University of California, Berkeley, California.

gives strong evidence that ordinary deformation results from the motion of dislocations.

It has been pointed out by a number of workers that grain boundaries and dislocations offer relatively little resistance to diffusion in comparison with perfect crystalline material. It is found that the enhanced diffusion parallel to the dislocations in a low-angle grain boundary is of the same order of magnitude as that produced by a large-angle incoherent grain boundary. Diffusion at right angles to the dislocations in a low-angle boundary has been observed in one experiment to be 10 to 100 times slower at 450°C, as compared with diffusion parallel to the dislocations. Turnbull has shown that grain-boundary diffusion controls the rates of some precipitation reactions in solids: the precipitation of tin from lead-tin solutions at room temperature proceeds about 10^8 times faster than one would expect from lattice diffusion alone.

DISLOCATION DENSITIES

The density of dislocations is specified by giving the number of dislocation lines that intersect a unit area in the crystal. The density ranges from 10^2 to 10^3 dislocations/cm^2 in the best germanium and silicon crystals to as many as 10^{11} or 10^{12} dislocations/cm^2 in heavily deformed metal crystals.

The most precise dislocation density measurements have been made by counting the etch pits at the surfaces of polished and etched germanium and silicon crystals. Values of 10^2 to 10^3 etch pits/cm^2 are obtained with the best crystals, and a one-to-one correspondence between etch pits and dislocations was established by the grain-boundary studies of Vogel and co-workers. Cast metal crystals, and metal crystals that have been plastically deformed and then annealed, generally show about 10^5 to 10^9 dislocations/cm^2 by the etch pit technique. A similar density is deduced from the extinction and breadth of x-ray lines, which suggests that an annealed single crystal is usually composed of mosaic blocks perhaps 10^4 A on a side that are tilted with respect to one another by angles of the order of 10 min. This tilt corresponds to dislocations a few hundred atom distances apart in the boundaries of the blocks, giving about 10^9 dislocations/cm^2.

The actual dislocation configuration in cast or annealed crystals appears to correspond either to a group of low-angle grain boundaries or to a three-dimensional network of dislocations. Figure 9.13 shows an example of a three-dimensional network, photographed by Mitchell in a crystal of AgBr. The dislocations were made visible by proper

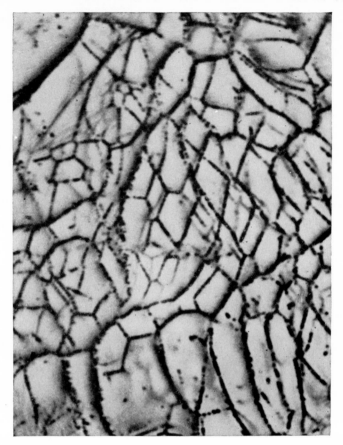

FIG. 9.13.   A three-dimensional network of dislocations below the surface of a
single crystal of AgBr.   (After J. M. Hedges and J. W. Mitchell.)

photographic development of the crystal.   Dislocations have also
been seen, and very beautifully, in x-ray transmission photographs and,
using this film, in transmission electron micrographs.

The etch pit technique is not reliable for estimating the dislocation
density in highly deformed crystals, as individual dislocations cannot
be resolved when their spacing is less than about 10^{-4} cm.   However,
we may estimate the dislocation density in deformed crystals from the
increased internal energy that results from plastic deformation.   It is
consistent with the cohesive energy to take the energy of a dislocation
as 5 to 10 ev per atom plan through which the dislocation passes,
say 5×10^{-4} erg/cm.

TABLE 9.2

MAXIMUM ENERGY STORED BY PLASTIC DEFORMATION (cal/g)

Aluminum	1.1
Copper	0.5
Iron	1.2
Nickel	0 8
Brass	0.5

The maximum energy stored in lattice distortions as a consequence of severe plastic deformation, as by twisting, filing, or compressing, has been measured thermally for several metals, with results given in Table 9.2. If the deformation is not too great, about 10 percent of the energy expended in plastic flow is stored in the lattice. Upon continued plastic flow, however, the stored energy approaches a saturation value. The observed values of the stored energy in Table 9.2 correspond to about 2×10^8 ergs/cm^3. If the energy per unit length of dislocation is 5×10^{-4} erg/cm, there must be about 4×10^{11} cm of dislocation line per cubic centimeter of crystal, or about 10^{11} dislocations per cubic centimeter passing through the average unit area. This is about one dislocation per square 100 atoms on a side, which is also believed on other grounds to be the concentration of dislocations characteristic of severely deformed metals. Analyses by Warren and Averbach of the breadth of x-ray diffraction lines from plastically deformed brass yield a stored energy of 1.4 cal/gram of the same order as the calorimetric value.

DISLOCATION MULTIPLICATION AND SLIP

A second problem is posed by the very great increase in dislocation density that is caused by plastic deformation. Dislocation density measurements show an increase from about 10^8 to about 10^{11} dislocations per cubic centimeter during deformation, a 1000-fold increase. Equally striking is the fact that, if a dislocation were to move completely across its slip plane, an offset of only one atom spacing would be produced, whereas offsets of as much as 100 to 1000 atom spacings are actually observed. Frank and Read showed how the required dislocation multiplication could occur, which is discussed in the following paragraphs.

Consider a closed circular dislocation loop of radius r surrounding a slipped area of the same radius. The loop will be partly edge, partly screw, and mostly intermediate in character. Because the strain energy of the dislocation of loop increases in proportion to its circumference, the loop will tend to shrink. However, if a shear stress σ that favors slip is acting, the sloop will tend to expand. We seek the relationship between stress and loop radius for which the loop is in (metastable) equilibrium. To simplify the calculation, the strain energy per unit length of dislocation may be taken roughly as $\frac{1}{2}Gb^2$, where G is the shear modulus and b is the Burgers vector.

The elastic energy of a dislocation loop of radius r is $2\pi r$ times its energy per unit length, or $\pi r G b^2$. If the loop is formed in the presence of a shear stress σ, the energy of the crystal will decrease by the product of σb and the area of the loop, $\pi r^2 \sigma b$. The net energy change on introducing the loop is

$$(9.4) \qquad \Delta E = \pi r G b^2 - \pi r^2 \sigma b.$$

The value of ΔE passes through a maximum when $d\,\Delta E/dr = 0$, or when

$$(9.5) \qquad \frac{2r}{b} = \frac{G}{\sigma},$$

showing that the ratio of the diameter of the critical loop to the magnitude of the Burgers vector equals the ratio of the shear modulus to the shear stress. This latter ratio is of the order 10^3 or 10^4 for the yielding of most crystals.

Loops smaller than the critical loop will contract spontaneously, and those larger than critical will expand spontaneously. The energy of the critical loop is $\Delta E_c = \pi G^2 b^3/4\sigma$, which is so large in comparison with kT (for $G/\sigma = 10^3$ and $T = 300°K$ the ratio is $\Delta E_c/kT = 3 \times 10^5$) that thermal activation cannot be responsible for their creation, and we are led again to the necessity of pre-existing dislocations for initiating slip, and to purely mechanical processes for generating new lengths of dislocation.

Frank and Read pointed out that dislocations rarely lie entirely in one slip plane, and that instead they jog from one slip plane to another until they meet the surface of the crystal or join others at a dislocation node. A segment of dislocation lying in a slip plane may be considered as pinned at its ends where it leaves the plane. When an external stress is applied, the segment cannot glide as a whole because its ends are fixed, and the only possible motion is to bend into an arc of a circle. We already have calculated the equilibrium radius of this arc (9.5) to be $2r/b = G/\sigma$. As long as $2r > L$, where L is the initial length of the segment, the configuration is stable, because further motion of the dislocation then decreases its radius. Whenever the stress rises beyond the point where $L/b = G/\sigma$, however, there is

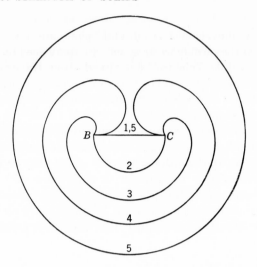

FIG. 9.14. Frank-Read mechanism for multiplication of dislocations, showing successive stages in the generation of a dislocation loop by the segment BC of a dislocation line.

no stable equilibrium, and the dislocation arc expands indefinitely as a growing partial loop. This process not only multiplies an original segment of length L into a large partial loop but also allows the partial loop to complete itself while regenerating a new segment that can repeat the whole process, as sketched in Fig. 9.14. A dislocation segment pinned at each end is called a *Frank-Read source*, and we have seen how it can lead to the generation of a large number of concentric dislocation loops on a single slip plane. This type of dislocation multiplication gives rise to slip and to the increased density of dislocations during plastic deformation.

Gilman and Johnston[1] have found another mechanism of dislocation multiplication from their etch pit studies of LiF. They find that during plastic deformation new dislocation loops arise in the wake of a moving dislocation. The new loops arise at many different points near the glide plane of the original dislocation, and have the same Burgers vector as that dislocation. As each new loop expands, small new loops are formed in its wake. Thus an entire wide glide band forms from one initial mobile dislocation. Their picture has important consequences for various mechanical processes.

[1] J. J. Gilman and W. G. Johnston, *J. Appl. Phys.* **31**, 632 (1960).

(a) *Strain-Hardening.* The drag forces resulting from trails on a dislocation that moves on a virgin glide plane are not negligible. It can be expected that still more drag will be experienced by a dislocation that moves in a glide plane that has already been traversed and hence is strewn with trails. This type of strain-hardening would be expected to be proportional to both plastic strain and dislocation density, in agreement with experiments.

(b) *Creep.* Transient creep is determined by the viscosities of dislocations plus strain-hardening. Steady-state creep, on the other hand, depends on the additional process of recovery. They suggest that recovery is simply the process of dissolution of trails through vacancy diffusion, and is thus the inverse of strain-hardening.

(c) *Fatigue.* Since some trails are incipient rows of vacancies, if their concentration becomes sufficiently large in a crystal, a fatigue crack may form.

STRENGTH OF ALLOYS

Pure crystals tend to be very plastic, and to yield at very low stresses. There appear to be four important ways of increasing the yield strength of an alloy so that it will withstand shear stresses as high as $10^{-2}G$: mechanical blocking of dislocation motion, pinning of dislocations by solute atoms, impeding dislocation motion by short-range order, and increasing the dislocation density so that tangling of dislocations results. All four of these strengthening mechanisms depend for their success upon impeding dislocation motion. A fifth mechanism, that of removing all dislocations from the crystal, may operate for certain fine hairlike crystals that are discussed in the section on crystal growth.

Mechanical blocking of dislocation motion can be produced most directly by introducing tiny particles of a second phase into a crystal. This process is followed in the hardening of steel, where particles of iron carbide are precipitated into iron, and in hardening aluminum, where particles of Al_2Cu are precipitated. If L is the mean spacing of particles on a slip plane, the stress necessary to force a dislocation between particles should be approximately

$$(9.6) \qquad \frac{\sigma}{G} = \frac{b}{L},$$

which is (9.5) rewritten. The smaller the spacing L, the higher is the yield stress σ. Orowan has discussed this mechanism of precipitation hardening. He points out that, before particles precipitate, L is large and the strength is low. Immediately after precipitation is complete and many small particles are present, L is a minimum and the strength is a maximum.   If the alloy is held at a high temperature where some particles grow at the expense of others, L increases and the strength drops.   Mechanical blocking also can be caused by the grain boundaries in polycrystalline materials, and by the microscopic stress fields that sometimes surround precipitated particles.

The strength of dilute solid solutions appears to result from the pinning of dislocations by solute atoms.   Cottrell has pointed out that the solubility of a foreign atom will be greater in the neighborhood of a dislocation than elsewhere in a crystal.   For example, an atom that tends to expand the crystal will dissolve preferentially in the expanded region near an edge dislocation.   As a result of the affinity of solute atoms for dislocations, each dislocation will collect a cloud of associated solute atoms during solidification or annealing when the mobility of solute atoms is high.   On cooling to lower temperatures, where diffusion of solute atoms effectively ceases, the solute atom cloud becomes fixed in the crystal.   When a dislocation moves, leaving its solute cloud behind, the energy of the crystal must increase.   The increase in energy can come only from an increased stress acting on the dislocation as it pulls away from the solute atom cloud, and so the presence of the cloud strengthens the crystal.

In pure crystals, the passage of a dislocation across a slip plane does not alter the binding energy across the plane after the dislocation is gone.   The internal energy of the crystal remains unaffected.   The same is true for random solid solutions, because the solution is equally random across a slip plane after slip.   Most solid solutions, however, contain short-range order.   Atoms of different species are not arranged at random on the lattice sites, but tend to have an excess or a deficiency of pairs of unlike atoms.   Fisher has pointed out that, whatever its nature, short-range order is partially destroyed by the motion of a dislocation: the internal energy across the slip plane is increased.

It is well known that the strength of a crystalline material increases with plastic deformation.   The phenomenon is called *work-hardening*. The strength is believed to increase because of the increased density of dislocations and the greater difficulty of moving a given dislocation across a slip plane that is threaded by many others.   Work-hardening frequently is employed in the strengthening of materials, but its usefulness is limited to low enough temperatures for annealing not to occur.

Each of the four mechanisms of strengthening crystals can raise the yield strength to the order of $10^{-3}G$ to $10^{-2}G$.   In combination they can give about $10^{-2}G$.   Unfortunately, all four mechanisms begin to break down at temperatures where diffusion can occur at an appre-

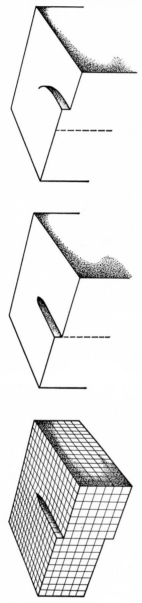

Fig. 9.15. (a) SCREW DISLOCATION, illustrated at left, produces its spiral growth steps in the manner indicated by the succeeding diagrams. A screw dislocation is the type of imperfection that would result if a cut were made part way through a crystal and the two sides slipped over one another. The result is a permanent step extending across a portion of the crystal face and anchored at the boundary of the cut.

Molecules depositing on the surface from a vapor would lodge against the step, causing it to advance. Since one end is fixed, the step would pivot around that point, with the outer points falling behind the inner, producing a never-ending spiral layer on the surface.

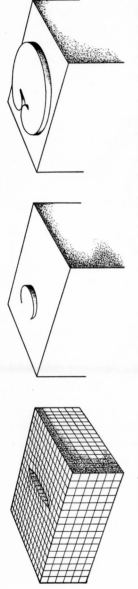

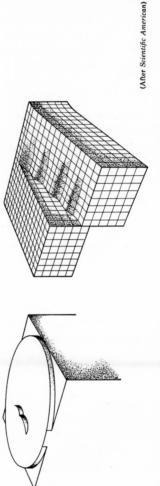

grow only by bulging. The second drawing shows the bulging step just beginning to turn back on itself. In the next figure its parts have met behind its original position. Finally the inner section detaches from

(After Scientific American)

(b) CLOSED GROWTH LOOPS can arise from a step which begins and ends within the surface (*left*) connecting a right–handed screw dislocation with a left–handed one. This step is anchored at both ends and can

FOUR–LAYERED STEP is formed by four closely spaced dislocations of the same kind. Larger groups give many-layered steps.

the completed layer and shrinks inward until it becomes a new straight step located on top of the growth loop first formed.

ciable rate. Precipitated particles begin to dissolve; solute clouds begin, by diffusion, to drift along with dislocations as they glide; short-range order repairs itself behind slowly moving dislocations; and dislocation climb and annealing tend to decrease the dislocation density. The resulting time-dependent deformation is called *creep*. The search for superalloys for use at very high temperatures is therefore a search for alloys with reduced diffusion rates, where the four strengthening mechanisms will survive to higher temperatures.

DISLOCATIONS AND CRYSTAL GROWTH

It has been shown by Frank[2] and his collaborators that in some cases dislocations may be the controlling factor in crystal growth. When crystals are grown in conditions of low supersaturation, of the order of 1 percent, it has been observed that the growth rate is very much faster than that calculated for an ideal crystal. The actual growth rate is explained by Frank in terms of the effect of dislocations on growth.

The theory of growth of ideal crystals, due to Gibbs, Volmer, Becker, and others, predicts that in crystal growth from vapor a supersaturation (pressure/equilibrium vapor pressure) of the order of 10 is required to nucleate new crystals, of the order of 5 to form liquid drops, and of 1.5 to form a two-dimensional monolayer of molecules on the face of a perfect crystal. Actually Volmer and Schultze observed growth of iodine crystals at vapor supersaturations down to less than 1 percent, where the growth rate should have been down by e^{-3000} from the rate defined as the minimum observable growth. This has been referred to as an all-time record for disagreement between observation and theory.

Frank pointed out that the large factor just mentioned expresses the difficulty of nucleating a new monolayer on a completed surface of the crystal, and that if there is a screw dislocation present as in Fig. 9.15 it is never necessary to nucleate a new layer, as the crystal will grow in helical fashion at the edge of the discontinuity shown. The calculated growth rates for this mechanism are in good agreement with observation. We therefore expect that nearly all crystals in nature grown at low supersaturation will contain dislocations, as otherwise they could not have grown.

[2] For a full review of this field see F. C. Frank, *Advances in Physics* **1**, 91 (1952); detailed calculations are given by Burton, Cabrera, and Frank, *Trans. Roy. Soc.* (*London*) **A243**, 299 (1951). A motion picture in color on the growth of crystals has been prepared by J. B. Newkirk of the General Electric Research Laboratory, Schenectady, New York.

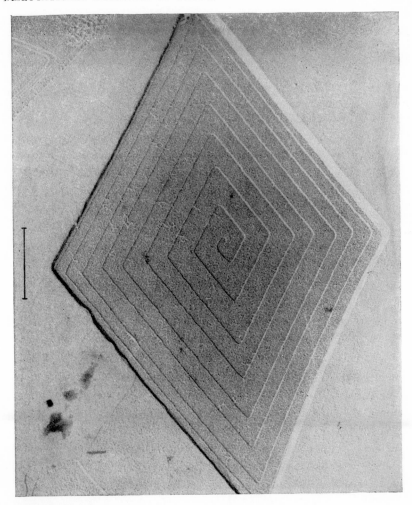

FIG. 9.16. Growth pattern from single dislocation on single crystal of paraffin n-$C_{36}H_{74}$. [Electron micrograph courtesy of H. F. Kay and B. J. Appelbe, after Dawson and Vand, *Proc. Roy. Soc.* (*London*) **A206**, 555 (1951).]

Griffin and others, using optical and electron microscopes, have observed spiral growth patterns[3] on a large number of crystals. Their photographs are convincing evidence of the reality of dislocations. A beautiful example of the growth pattern from a single screw dislocation is given in Fig. 9.16. If the growth rate were independent of direc-

[3] A beautiful collection of photographs of spiral growth is given in the book by Ajit Ram Verma cited at the end of the chapter.

tion in the plane of the surface, the growth pattern would be an Archimedes spiral,

$$(9.7) \qquad\qquad r = a\theta,$$

where a is a constant, with a limiting minimum radius of curvature near the dislocation determined by the supersaturation. If the radius of curvature is too small, atoms on the curved edge evaporate until the equilibrium curvature is attained. Away from the origin each part of the step acquires new atoms at a constant rate, so that $dr/dt =$ constant. The spiral appears to rotate with uniform angular velocity during growth, for, if $d\theta/dt$ is constant, dr/dt will appear to be constant.

Fine hairlike crystals have been observed to grow under conditions of high supersaturation without the necessity for more than perhaps one dislocation. It may be that these crystals contain a single axial screw dislocation that aids their essentially one-dimensional growth. From the absence of dislocations we would expect these crystal whiskers to have high yield strengths, of the order of the calculated value $G/30$ discussed earlier in this chapter. A single axial screw dislocation, if present, could not cause yielding because it is not subjected to a shear stress parallel to its Burgers vector. Herring and Galt have observed

FIG. 9.17. Iron whiskers grown from the vapor by hydrogen reduction of ferrous bromide at 710°C in an iron boat. (Courtesy of S. Brenner and Miss D. Kontoleon.)

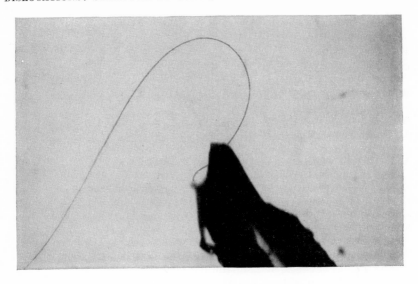

FIG. 9.18.   Copper whisker strained 1.5 percent.   (Courtesy S. S. Brenner.)

in this connection that whiskers of tin (radius $\sim 10^{-4}$ cm) have elastic properties near those expected from theoretically perfect crystals. They observed yield strains of the order of 10^{-2}, which correspond to shear stresses of order $10^{-2}G$, about 1000 times greater than in bulk tin, confirming the early estimates of perfect crystal strength.

Iron whiskers grown from the vapor are shown in Fig. 9.17. They are of the order of 15 μ in thickness, and are bcc iron bounded by four {100} planes parallel to the long axis. The largest elastic strain observed for iron was 1.4 percent, which is close to the thoeretical limit. Theoretical perfect crystal elastic properties have been observed for a number of materials, including Cu, CdS, p-toluidine, and the potassium halides. A strained Cu whisker is shown in Fig. 9.18.

PROBLEMS

9.1. Show that the lines of closest atomic packing are $\langle 110 \rangle$ in fcc structures, $\langle 111 \rangle$ in bcc structures, and $\langle 2\,\bar{1}\,\bar{1}\,0 \rangle$ in hcp structures.

9.2. A cylindrical crystal of cross section A is under a tension T. Find the expression of the Schmid law of the critical shear stress in terms of the angle λ between the slip direction and the axis of tension and the angle θ between the normal to the slip plane and the axis of tension.

9.3. (a) Find a pair of dislocations equivalent to a row of lattice vacancies; (b) find a pair of dislocations equivalent to a row of interstitial atoms.

9.4. Consider a crystal in the form of a cube of side L containing an edge dislocation of Burgers vector **b**. If the crystal is subjected to a shear stress σ on the upper and lower faces in the direction of slip, show by considering energy balance that the force acting on the dislocation is $F = b\sigma$ per unit length.

REFERENCES

C. S. Barrett, *Structure of metals: crystallographic methods, principles, data*, McGraw-Hill Book Company, New York, 3rd ed., 1952.

W. Boas, *An introduction to the physics of metals and alloys*, John Wiley and Sons, New York, 1948.

B. Chalmers, *Physical metallurgy*, John Wiley and Sons, New York, 1959.

M. Cohen, editor, *Dislocations in metals*, American Institute of Mining and Metallurgical Engineers, New York, 1954.

A. H. Cottrell, *Dislocations and plastic flow in crystals*, Clarendon Press, Oxford, 1953.

Defects in crystalline solids, Physical Society (London) 1955.

F. Frank, "Crystal growth and dislocations," *Advances in Physics* **1**, 91 (1952).

J. Friedel, *Les dislocations*, Gauthier-Villar, Paris, 1956.

N. F. Mott, "Mechanical properties of metals," *Proc. Phys. Soc. (London)* **B64**, 729 (1951).

W. T. Read, *Dislocations in crystals*, McGraw-Hill Book Co., New York, 1953.

F. Seitz, *Physics of metals*, McGraw-Hill Book Co., New York, 1943.

Shockley, Hollomon, Maurer, and Seitz, editors, *Imperfections in nearly perfect crystals*, John Wiley and Sons, New York, 1952.

Ajit Ram Verma, *Crystal growth and dislocations*, Academic Press, New York, 1953.

C. Zener, *Elasticity and anelasticity of metals*, University of Chicago Press, Chicago, 1948.

Appendix

A. PERTURBATION OF NEARLY FREE ELECTRONS BY A PERIODIC POTENTIAL

Let the perturbation due to the crystal lattice be written as a Fourier series:

(A.1)
$$H' = \sum_{-\infty}^{\infty} V_n e^{-2\pi i n x/a}; \qquad (V_0 = 0).$$

For example, if the perturbation is simply $V_1 \cos (2\pi x/a)$, then

$$H' = \frac{V_1}{2} (e^{2\pi i x/a} + e^{-2\pi i x/a}).$$

The matrix elements of H' in a plane wave representation are

(A.2)
$$(k'|H'|k) = \sum_n \frac{V_n}{L} \int_0^L e^{-ik'x} e^{-2\pi i n x/a} e^{ikx} \, dx;$$

the integral is zero unless

(A.3)
$$k' = k - \frac{2\pi n}{a},$$

in which case the matrix element is equal to the appropriate V_n. The first order wave function is

(A.4)
$$\psi_k = \frac{1}{L^{1/2}} \left[e^{ikx} + \sum_{k'} \frac{(k'|H'|k)}{E_k - E_{k'}} e^{ik'x} \right]$$

$$= \frac{1}{L^{1/2}} e^{ikx} \left[1 + \sum_n \frac{V_n}{E_k - E_{k'}} e^{-2\pi i n x/a} \right],$$

subject to $k' = k - 2\pi n/a$. The solution (A.4) is of the Bloch form as required. We have $E_{k'} = \hbar^2 k'^2/2m$. The energy to the second order is

$$(A.5) \qquad E_k = \frac{\hbar^2 k^2}{2m} + \sum_n \frac{|V_n|^2}{E_k - E_{k'}}.$$

The assumption on which this calculation is based is that the denominator

$$E_k - E_{k'} = \frac{\hbar^2}{2m}\left[k^2 - \left(k - \frac{2\pi n}{a}\right)^2\right]$$

is not very small. The denominator will, however, vanish for $k = \pi n/a$. In this case we must do a more careful calculation.

When k is close to $\pi n/a$, we may take the wave function as

$$(A.6) \qquad \psi = e^{ikx}(A_0 + A_n e^{-2\pi i n x/a}),$$

because the other Fourier coefficients will be small. The coefficients A_0, A_n are determined by minimizing the energy

$$(A.7) \qquad E = \frac{E_0 A_0{}^2 + E_n A_n{}^2 + 2V_n A_0 A_n}{A_0{}^2 + A_n{}^2};$$

here
$$E_0 = \frac{\hbar^2 k^2}{2m}; \qquad E_n = \frac{\hbar^2 \left(\dfrac{k - 2\pi n}{a}\right)^2}{2m},$$

and the mean value of V is taken to be zero; we have supposed that $V^*_n = V_n$.

At the minimum we have, by taking variations δA_0 and δA_n,

$$2A_0(E - E_0) - 2V_n A_n = 0;$$

$$-2V_n A_0 + 2A_n(E - E_n) = 0.$$

These equations have solutions for A_0, A_n only if

$$(E - E_0)(E - E_n) + V_n{}^2 = 0,$$

or

$$(A.8) \qquad E = \tfrac{1}{2}\{E_0 + E_n \pm [(E_0 - E_n)^2 + 4V_n{}^2]^{1/2}\}.$$

The most interesting feature of this result is the discontinuity in energy for $k = \pi n/a$; we have at this point

$$(A.9) \qquad \Delta E = 2|V_n|,$$

so that energies lying between

$$\frac{\hbar^2}{2m}\left(\frac{n\pi}{a}\right)^2 \pm |V_n|$$

are forbidden.   We note that the Bragg condition for reflection is also $k = \pi n/a$, and this condition also marks the boundaries on the Kronig-Penney model.   At the boundary the wave functions are standing waves which do not carry current.

For k just above the first gap we find on expanding (A.8) to the first order in $(E_0 - E_n)^2$ that, letting $k' = k - \pi/a$,

$$(A.10) \qquad E \cong \frac{\hbar^2}{2m}\left[\left(\frac{\pi}{a}\right)^2 + k'^2\left(1 + \frac{4E_a}{\Delta E}\right)\right] + \frac{\Delta E}{2},$$

E_a being the energy at the gap, so that as far as dependence on k' is concerned

$$(A.11) \qquad E - E_a = \frac{\hbar^2}{2m}\,\alpha k'^2; \qquad \alpha = 1 + \frac{4E_a}{\Delta E},$$

which suggests that the electron behaves as if it had a mass

$$(A.12) \qquad m^* = \frac{m}{\alpha}.$$

THREE DIMENSIONS

In a three-dimensional simple cubic lattice

$$H' = \sum_{G} V_G e^{i\mathbf{G}\cdot\mathbf{r}},$$

and the condition for nonvanishing matrix elements is

$$\mathbf{k}' = \mathbf{k} + \mathbf{G}.$$

A forbidden zone occurs when

$$(A.13) \qquad k^2 = (\mathbf{k} + \mathbf{G})^2,$$

or

$$(A.14) \qquad 2\mathbf{k} \cdot \mathbf{G} + G^2 = 0,$$

or

$$(A.15) \qquad k_x n_1 + k_y n_2 + k_z n_3 = \frac{\pi(n_1{}^2 + n_2{}^2 + n_3{}^2)}{a},$$

where n_1, n_2, n_3 are positive or negative integers.

B. TIGHT BINDING APPROXIMATION FOR METALLIC ELECTRONS

Suppose that the ground state of an electron moving in the potential $V(r)$ of an isolated atom is $\phi(r)$ and that the energy is E_0; suppose further that ϕ is an s state.   The treatment of bands arising from degenerate $(p, d, \cdots)$ atomic levels is more complicated. If the influence of one atom on another is small, we get a zero order wave function for one electron in the whole crystal by taking

(B.1)
$$\psi_k(\mathbf{r}) = \sum_j C_{kj}\phi(\mathbf{r} - \mathbf{r}_j),$$

where the sum is over all lattice points. This function is of the Bloch form if we take $C_{kj} = e^{i(\mathbf{k}\cdot\mathbf{r}_j)}$, which gives

(B.2)
$$\psi_k(\mathbf{r}) = \sum_j e^{i(\mathbf{k}\cdot\mathbf{r}_j)}\phi(\mathbf{r} - \mathbf{r}_j).$$

We prove it is of the Bloch form by considering the effect of a translation by a vector $\mathbf{g}$ connecting two lattice points:

(B.3)
$$\psi_k(\mathbf{r} + \mathbf{g}) = \sum e^{i(\mathbf{k}\cdot\mathbf{r}_j)}\phi(\mathbf{r} + \mathbf{g} - \mathbf{r}_j)$$
$$= e^{i(\mathbf{k}\cdot\mathbf{g})}\sum e^{i\mathbf{k}\cdot(\mathbf{r}_j - \mathbf{g})}\phi[\mathbf{r} - (\mathbf{r}_j - \mathbf{g})]$$
$$= e^{i(\mathbf{k}\cdot\mathbf{g})}\psi_k(\mathbf{r})$$

and so the Bloch requirement is satisfied.

We get the first order energy by calculating the diagonal matrix elements of the perturbation $H'(r)$ expressing the difference between the potential in the crystal near an ion and the potential of an individual atom. We have

(B.4)
$$(\mathbf{k}|H'|\mathbf{k}) = \sum_j \sum_m e^{i\mathbf{k}\cdot(\mathbf{r}_j - \mathbf{r}_m)}(\phi_{r_i}|H'|\phi_j);$$

writing $\varrho_m = \mathbf{r}_m - \mathbf{r}_j$ and treating all lattice points as equivalent,

(B.5)
$$(\mathbf{k}|H'|\mathbf{k}) = N \sum_m e^{-i\mathbf{k}\cdot\varrho_m} \int \phi(\mathbf{r} - \varrho_m)H'\phi(\mathbf{r})\,dV.$$

If now we neglect all integrals except those between nearest neighbors connected by ϱ and write, for a crystal of N atoms,

(B.6)
$$\int \phi^*(\mathbf{r})H'\phi(\mathbf{r})\,dV = -\frac{\alpha}{N};$$

(B.7)
$$\int \phi^*(\mathbf{r} - \varrho)H'\phi(\mathbf{r})\,dV = -\frac{\gamma}{N};$$

we get

$$(\mathbf{k}|H'|\mathbf{k}) = -\alpha - \gamma \sum_m e^{-i\mathbf{k}\cdot\varrho_m},$$

and so the first order energy is given by

(B.8)
$$E = E_0 - \alpha - \gamma \sum e^{i(\mathbf{k}\cdot\varrho_m)}.$$

For a simple cubic lattice the nearest neighbor atoms are at the positions

(B.9) $\qquad \varrho_m = (\pm a, 0, 0); \qquad (0, \pm a, 0); \qquad (0, 0, \pm a),$

and

(B.10) $\qquad E = E_0 - \alpha - 2\gamma(\cos k_x a + \cos k_y a + \cos k_z a),$

so that the energies are confined to a band with limits $\pm 6\gamma$. For small k,

(B.11) $\qquad E \cong E_0 - \alpha - 6\gamma + \gamma k^2 a^2.$

The energy at the bottom of the band is independent of the direction of motion. The effective mass is

(B.12) $$m^* = \frac{\hbar^2}{2\gamma a^2}.$$

We see that for every state of an electron in the free atom there exists a band of energies in the crystal. We have considered here one state of the free atom and have obtained one band. The number of states in the zone which corresponds to a nondegenerate atomic level is equal to $2N$, where N is the number of atoms. We see this directly: (B.10) is periodic in $\mathbf{k}$, and thus only values of $\mathbf{k}$ lying within a certain polyhedron in $\mathbf{k}$-space will define independent wave functions. In the simple cubic case the polyhedron is defined by $-\pi/a < k_x < \pi/a$, etc. The volume of the polyhedron is $8\pi^3/a^3$; now the number of states (counting both spin orientations) per unit volume of $\mathbf{k}$-space is $1/4\pi^3$, so the number of states is $2/a^3 = 2N$.

C. IMPORTANT CONVERSION FACTORS

(Approximate—velocity of light taken as 3×10^{10} cm/sec)

To obtain result in	Multiply number of	By
gauss	webers/meter^2	10^4
webers/m^2	gauss	10^{-4}
oersteds	ampere-turns/meter	$4\pi \times 10^{-3}$
ampere-turns/meter	oersteds	$10^3/4\pi$
statvolts	volts	$1/300$
volts	statvolts	300
amps	abamps	10
amps	statamps	$1/(3 \times 10^9)$
esu resistivity	ohm-cm	$1/(9 \times 10^{11})$
ohm-cm	esu resistivity	9×10^{11}
mho/cm	esu conductivity	$1/(9 \times 10^{11})$
esu conductivity	mho/cm	9×10^{11}
mho/meter	esu conductivity	9×10^9
esu charge/cm^2	cculomb/meter^2	3×10^5
coulomb/meter^2	esu charge/cm^2	$\frac{1}{3} \times 10^{-5}$
volt-cm/amp	statvolt-cm/statamp	9×10^{11}

D. VALUES OF GENERAL PHYSICAL CONSTANTS

Source: J. W. M. Du Mond and E. R. Cohen, "A least squares adjustment of the atomic constants, as of Dec. 1950," published by the National Research Council, Washington, D.C., 1951.

Quantity	Value
Avogadro's number, L	$(6.025438 \pm 0.000107) \times 10^{23}$ g mol^{-1} (phys.)
Electronic charge, e	$-(4.802233 \pm 0.000071) \times 10^{-10}$ esu
Electron rest mass, m	$(9.107208 \pm 0.000246) \times 10^{-28}$ grams
Planck's constant, h	$(6.623773 \pm 0.000180) \times 10^{-27}$ erg sec
(h-"bar"), $\hbar$	$(1.054206 \pm 0.000028) \times 10^{-27}$ erg sec
Velocity of light, c	(299790.22 ± 0.86) km sec^{-1}
Faraday constant, $F = Ne$	$(2.893556 \pm 0.000021) \times 10^{13}$ esu g mol^{-1} (phys.)
Specific charge of the electron, e/m	$(1.758897 \pm 0.000032) \times 10^7$ emu g^{-1}
Compton radian length of the electron, $\lambda_{ce} = \hbar/mc$	$(3.8612050 \pm 0.0000516) \times 10^{-11}$ cm
First Bohr radius, $a_0 = \hbar^2/me^2$	$(5.291508 \pm 0.000035) \times 10^{-9}$ cm
Classical radius of the electron, $r_0 = e^2/mc^2$	$(2.817515 \pm 0.000056) \times 10^{-13}$ cm
Atomic weight of hydrogen	1.0081284 (phys.) ± 0.0000030
Ratio proton mass to electron mass	1836.1388 ± 0.0339
Boltzmann's constant, k	$(1.3802565 \pm 0.0000615) \times 10^{-16}$ erg deg^{-1}
Bohr magneton, $\mu_B = e\hbar/2mc$	$-(0.92712031 \pm 0.0000219) \times 10^{-20}$ erg gauss^{-1}
Wavelength associated with 1 ev, λ_0	$(12396.44 \pm 0.174) \times 10^{-8}$ cm
Frequency associated with 1 ev, ν_0	$(2.418357 \pm 0.000032) \times 10^{14}$ sec^{-1}
Wave number associated with 1 ev, k_0	(8066.832 ± 0.113) cm^{-1}
Energy associated with 1 ev	$(1.601864 \pm 0.000024) \times 10^{-12}$ erg
Energy associated with unit wave number	$(1.985742 \pm 0.000054) \times 10^{-16}$ erg
Energy associated with 1 rydberg	13.60353 ± 0.00210 ev
Speed of 1-ev electron	$(5.931099 \pm 0.000055) \times 10^7$ cm sec^{-1}
Energy associated with 1°K	$(8.616562 \pm 0.000357) \times 10^{-5}$ ev
"Temperature" associated with 1 ev	(11605.556 ± 0.480)°K
Loschmidt's number, n_0	$(2.687444 \pm 0.000067) \times 10^{19}$ cm^{-3}

Index

Acceptors, 207, 210
Adiabatic demagnetization, 260
Alloys, 182
  magnetic moments, 192
  strength, 322
Amplifier, dielectric, 105
Anisotropy energy, 282, 285
Antiferromagnetic resonance, 294
Antiferromagnetism, 291
  table, 293
Atomic scattering factor, 35

Barium titanate structure, 93
Basis, 5
Binding, crystal, 18
Bloch functions, 154
Bloch theorem, 153
Bloch wall, 287
Body-centered cubic lattice, 9
Boltzmann factor, 45
Bragg law, 29, 33
Brass, 184
Bravais lattice, 6, 8
Brillouin function, 257
Brillouin zones, 143, 146, 170
Burgers vector, 312

Calcium fluoride structure, 15, 16
Catastrophe, ferroelectric, 95
Cesium chloride structure, 14, 15
Clausius-Mossotti equation, 76
Coercive field, 94
Coercive force, ferromagnetism, 278, 283
Conductivity, electric, 107, 135, 170
  table, 112

Covalent crystals, 22
Creep, 322
Crystal axes, 4, 6, 17
Crystal growth, 326
Crystal structure, 1, 5, 17
Cubic lattices, 6
Curie constant, 273
Curie-Weiss law, 273
Cyclotron resonance, 223

Debye length, 136
Debye relaxation time, 85
Debye temperature, 55
  table, 58
Debye unit, dipole moment, 84
Demagnetization factor, 71
Density of states, electronic, 123
Density, table, 17
Depolarization factor, 71
Diamagnetism, 251
Diamond structure, 12, 13
Dielectric constant, 75
Dielectric losses, 84
Diffusion equation, 220
Diffusion length, 221
Dislocation loops, 319
Dislocations, 309
Domains, ferroelectric, 101
  ferromagnetic, 276, 281, 290
Donors, 207, 209
Drift velocity, 107

Effective magneton number, 258, 276
Effective mass, 157, 180
Einstein oscillator, 50
Einstein relation, 239

Elastic limit, 307
Electrets, 90
Electrical conductivity, 107, 133, 170
    table, 112
Electronegativity scale, 23
Electronic polarizability, 79
Energy bands, 144
Energy gap, 144, 152
    table, 204
Entropy, spins, 261
Esaki diode, 240
Etch pits, 314
Ewald construction, 35
Exchange interaction, 273
Exclusion principle, 120
Extrinsic conductivity, 205

Face-centered cubic lattice, 9
Fatigue, 322
Fermi-Dirac distribution law, 124, 127,
    135
Fermi level, table for metals, 122
Fermi surface, aluminum, 181
    copper, 180
Ferrites, 295
Ferroelectrics, table, 91
Ferromagnetic resonance, 270
Ferromagnetism, 271
Fluorite structure, 15, 16
Frank-Read mechanism, 321

Grain boundary, 313
Growth, crystal, 326

Hagen-Rubens relation, 142
Hall angle, 167
Hall constant, table, 168
Hall effect, 166
Heat capacity, 47
    conduction electrons, 114, 128
        table, 130
    Debye model, 52
    Einstein model, 48
    electronic, 60
Hexagonal close-packed structure,
    11
Hole injection, 222
Holes, 102
Hume-Rothery rules, 183
Hydrogen-bonded crystals, 24

Hysteresis, 283
    ferroelectric, 94

Impurity states, 208
Interfacial polarization, 104
Intrinsic conductivity, 199
Ionic crystals, 19
Ionic polarizability, 80
Ionic radii, 24, 25, 26
Iron group ions, magnetic properties,
    259

Langevin-Debye equation, 83
Langevin diamagnetism, 252
Langevin function, 83
Langevin paramagnetism, 255
Larmor theorem, 253
Lattice, Bravais, 6, 8
    space, 5, 8
Lattice constants, 17
Laue diffraction, 30, 32, 39
Lifetime, carrier, 217
Lorentz field, 72, 75
Lorenz-Lorentz equation, 76
Lorenz number, 113
Loss angle, 89

Magnetic resonance, 263
Magnetic susceptibility, conduction
    electrons, 115, 131
        table, 162
Magnetite, 297
Magnetostriction, 286
Magnons, 300
Masers, 302
Matthiessen's rule, 170
Maxwell-Wagner relaxation, 104
Mean free path, electron, 111
Metals, free electron model, 106, 116
Miller indices, 10
Mobility, intrinsic, 204
    table, 205
Molar polarizability, 76
Molecular crystals, 23
Molecular field, 272

Néel temperature, 293
Nickel, band structure, 188, 190
n-p-n transistor, 247
Nuclear induction, 269

Ohm's law, 107
Optical properties of metals, 137, 141
Order-disorder transformation, 192
Orientational polarizability, 80

Packing of spheres, 27
Palladium, susceptibility, 191
Paramagnetic susceptibility, conduc-
    tion electrons, 115, 131
    table, 162
Paramagnetism, 254
Pauli principle, 120
Periodic table, 21
Permeability, 284
Perovskite structure, 93
    local field, 98
Phase transition, ferroelectric, 100
Phonons, 61
    mean free path, 64
Photoelectric effect, 140
Plasma frequency, 136
p-n junction, 234
Polarizability, electric, 75
    electronic, table, 79
    ionic, 80
    orientational, 80
Polarization, interfacial, 104
    spontaneous, 91
Polarization catastrophe, 95
Powder method, 39, 42
Power factor, 89
Primitive cell, 6
Primitive translation vector, 4
Pyroelectricity, 90

Q factor, 89

Radiation damage, 228
Rare earth ions, magnetic properties,
    258
Reciprocal lattice, 33
    vector, 174
Recombination, 217, 219
Rectification, 230
Reduced zone scheme, 172
Reflecting plane, 31
Relaxation, dipole, 84
    spin-lattice, 267
Relaxation time, 85

Relaxation time, electronic, 107, 170
Remanence, 279
Resistivity, electrical, 109
Richardson-Dushman equation, 139
Rotating crystal method, 40, 42

Scattering factor, 35
Schrödinger equation, 117
Semiconductors, 199
Slip, 308
Sodium chloride structure, 14
Space lattice, 5, 8
Specific heat, see Heat capacity
Spectroscopic splitting factor, 255
Spin entropy, 261
Spin waves, 300
Spinel structure, 299
Strain-hardening, 322
Strength, 305
Structure, amplitude, 37
Structure factor, 37, 38

Thermal conductivity, 61
Thermal expansion, 65
Thermionic emission, 138
Transition, ferroelectric, 100
Transition elements, 186
Transistors, point contact, 244
    junction, 246
Translation group, 5
Translation operation, 4
Tunnel diodes, 240

Ultraviolet transparency, 137
Unit cell, 6

Valence band, Ge and Si, 226

Wave equation, Schrödinger, 117
Weiss field, 272
Whiskers, 328
Wiedemann-Franz ratio, 113
Wigner-Seitz wave function, 156
Work function, 138
Work-hardening, 323

X-ray diffraction, 29

Zinc blende structure, 12